CONTENTS

GRADE 1

CHAPTER 1 • Understanding Numbers to 10

CHAPTER 2 • Adding Facts to 5

CHAPTER 3 • Subtracting Facts to 5

CHAPTER 4 • Adding Facts to 10

CHAPTER 5 • Subtracting Facts to 10

CHAPTER 6 • Understanding Numbers to 99

CHAPTER 7 • Money

CHAPTER 8 • Measurement

CHAPTER 9 • Adding and Subtracting Facts to 12

CHAPTER 10 • Time

CHAPTER 11 • Geometry and Fractions

CHAPTER 12 • Adding and Subtracting Facts to 18

CHAPTER 13 • Adding and Subtracting 2-Digit Numbers

Name

ONE AND TWO

Study

Check

Write the number.

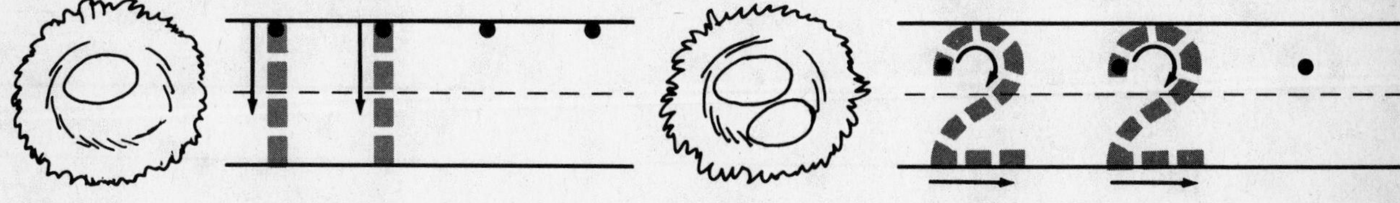

Write how many.

Macmillan/McGraw-Hill, MATHEMATICS IN ACTION
Grade 1, Chapter 1, Lesson 2, pages 11–12

Name

THREE AND FOUR

Study

3 three

4 four

Check

Write the number.

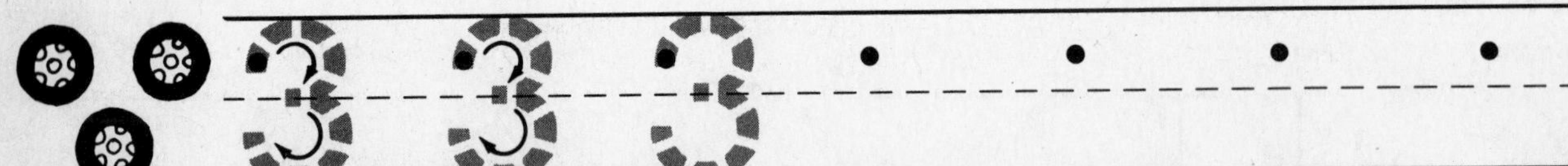

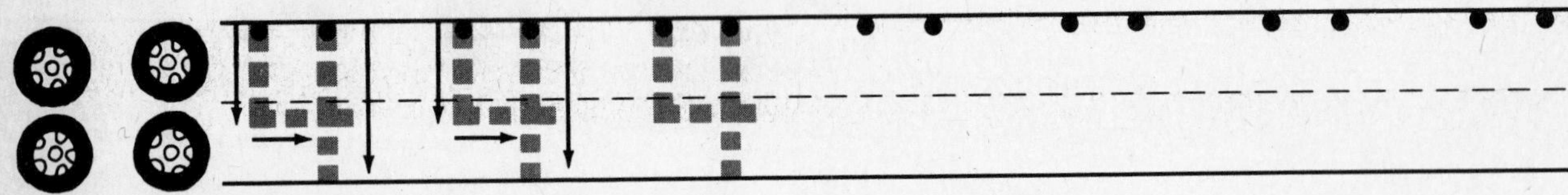

Write how many.

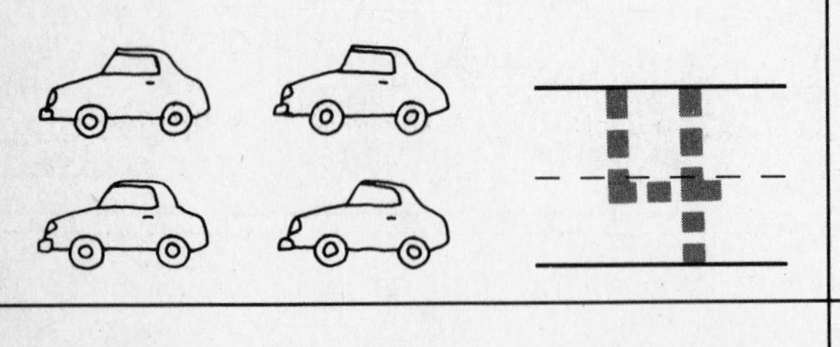

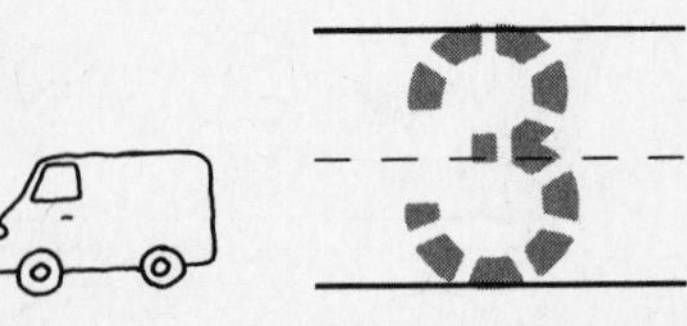

Name

FIVE AND ZERO

Study

5 five

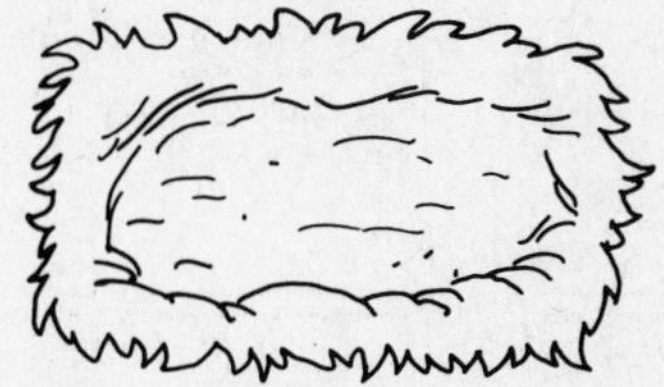

0 zero

Check

Write the number.

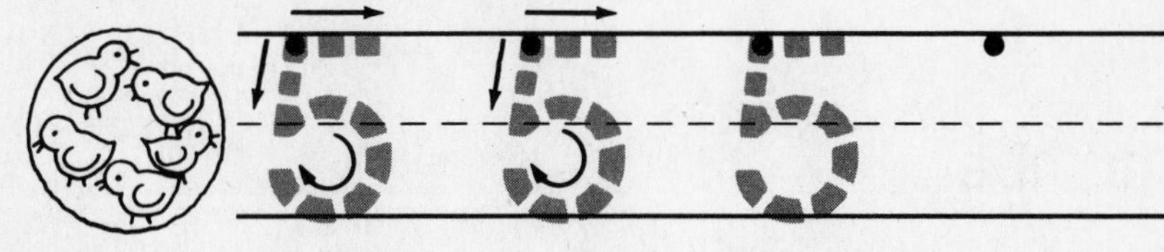

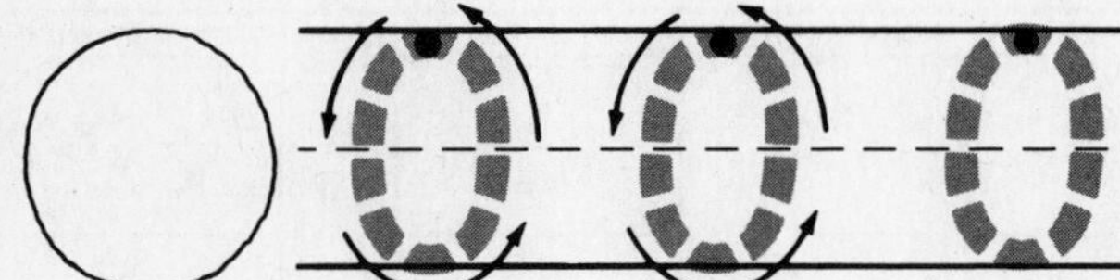

Match.

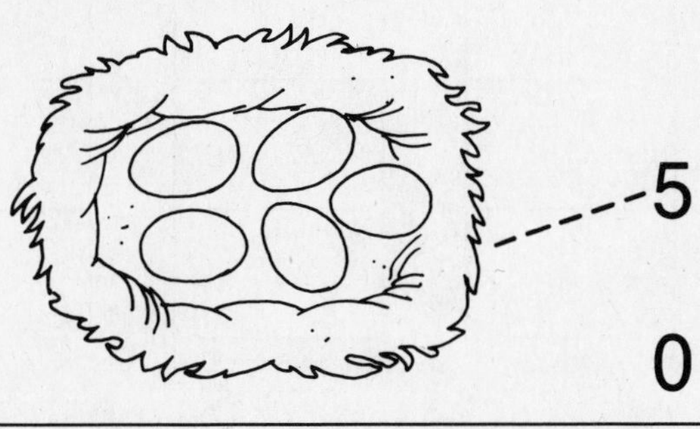

5

0

3

5

0

5

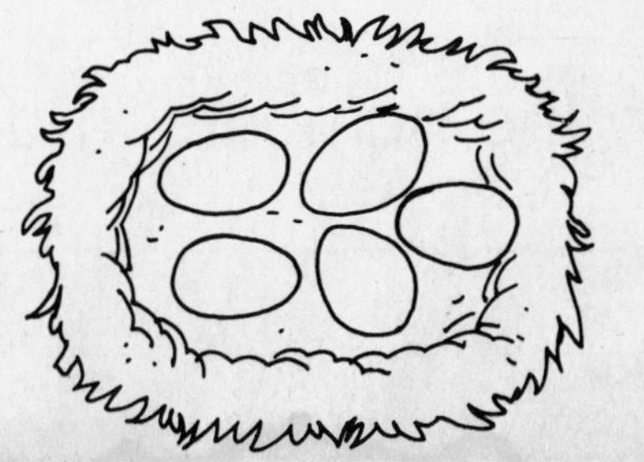

0

5

MACMILLAN/McGRAW-HILL

Macmillan/McGraw-Hill, MATHEMATICS IN ACTION
Grade 1, Chapter 1, Lesson 4, pages 15–16

Name

ORDER 0–5

Study

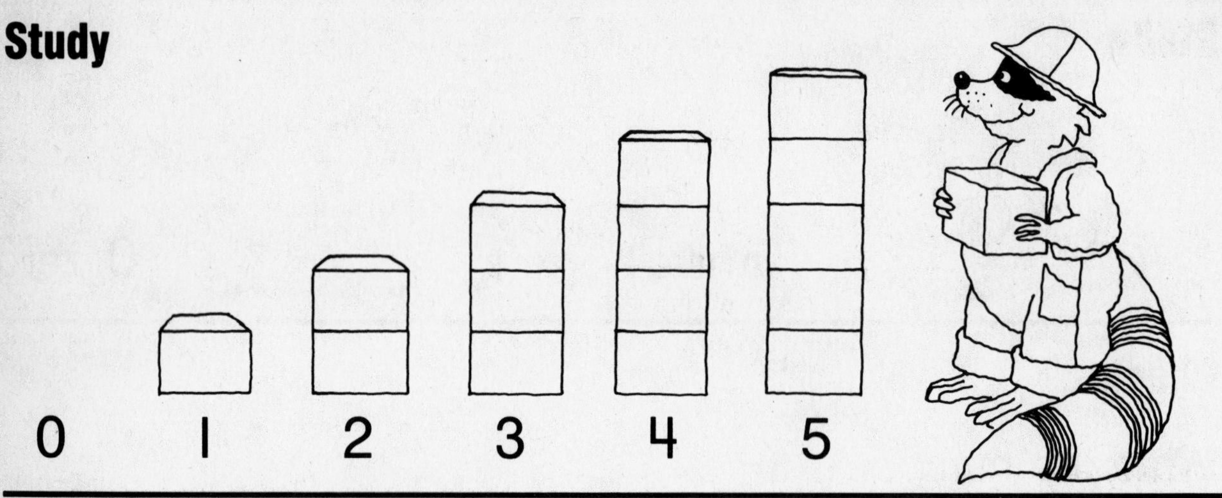

Check

Color to show each number.

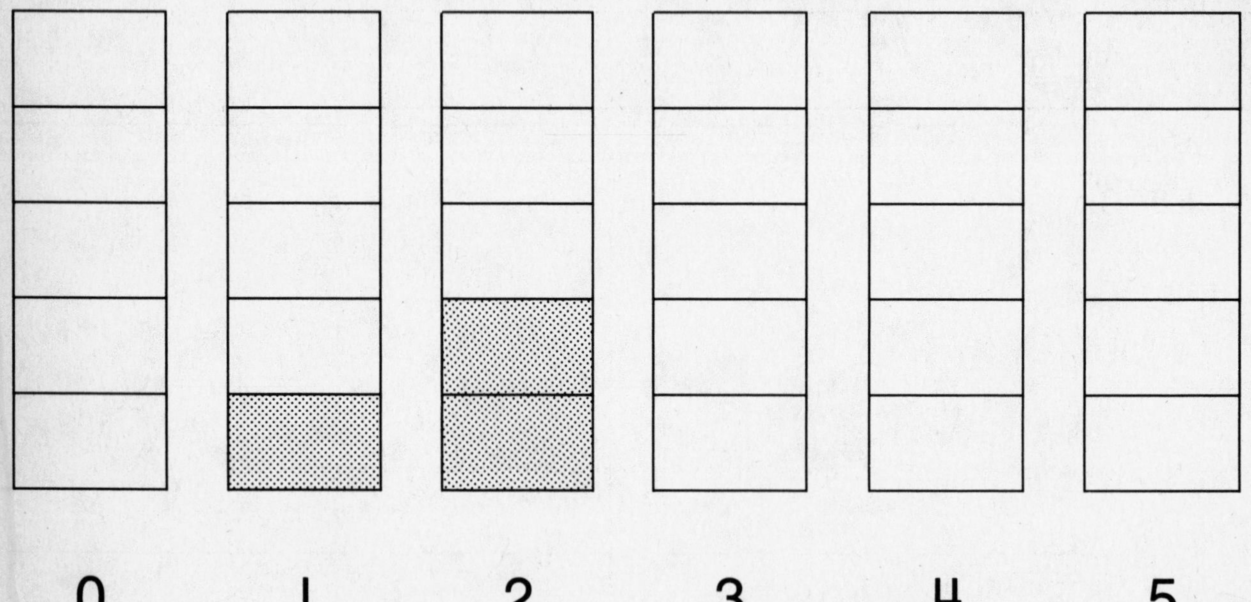

Write the numbers in order.

Name

PROBLEM SOLVING: USING INFORMATION FROM A PICTURE

Study

Count.

3

Check

Write how many.

1. 2

2.

3.

4.

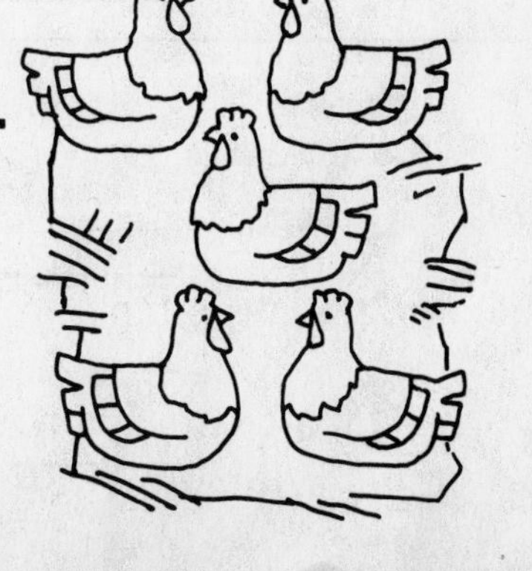

MACMILLAN/McGRAW-HILL

Name

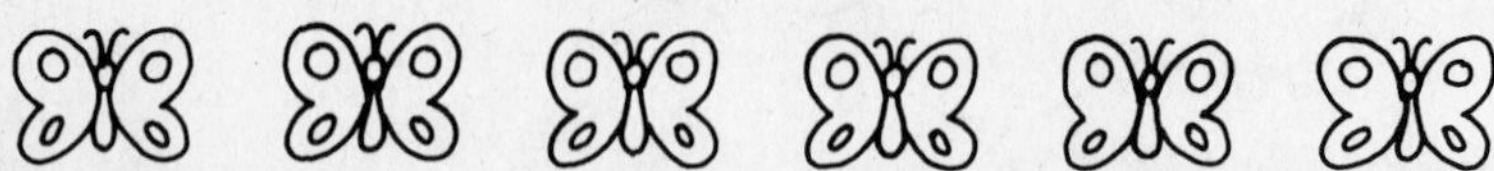

SIX AND SEVEN

Study

6 six

7 seven

Write the number.

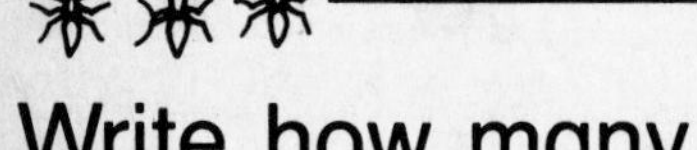

Write how many.

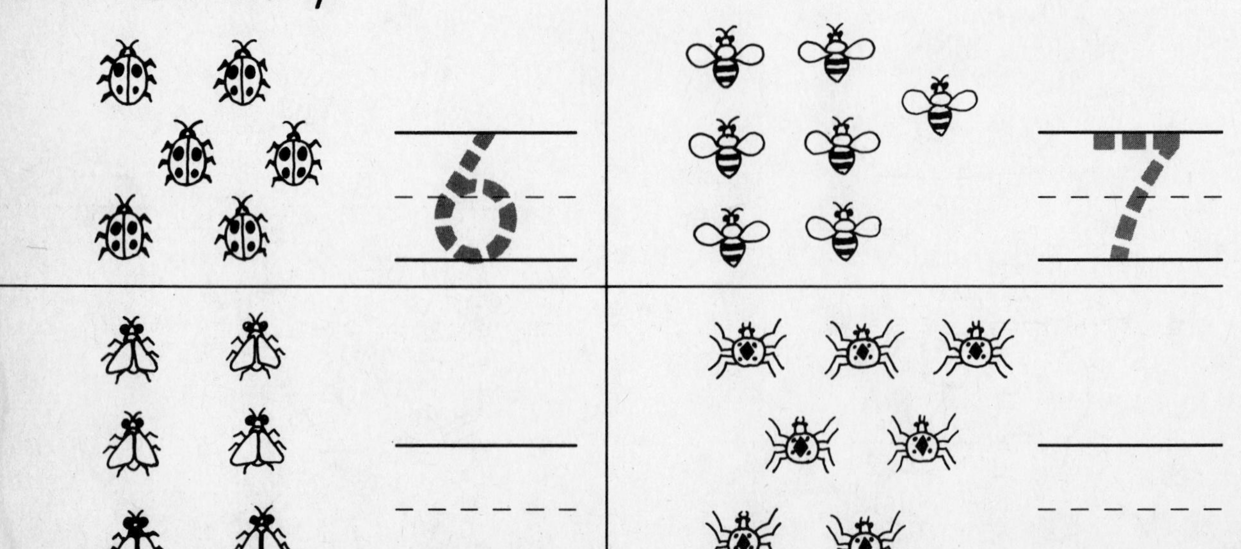

MACMILLAN/McGRAW-HILL

Name

EIGHT AND NINE

Study

8

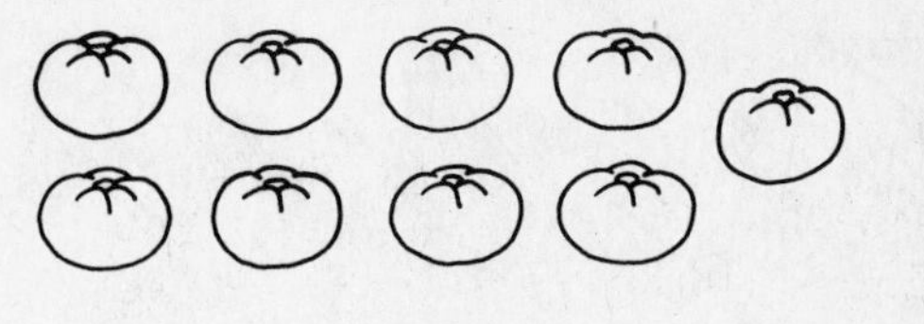

9

eight

nine

Check

Write the number.

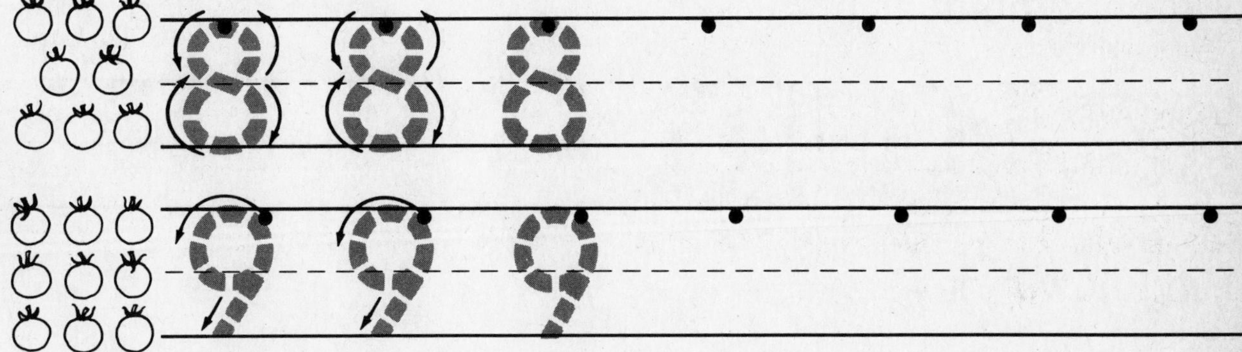

How many? Ring the number.

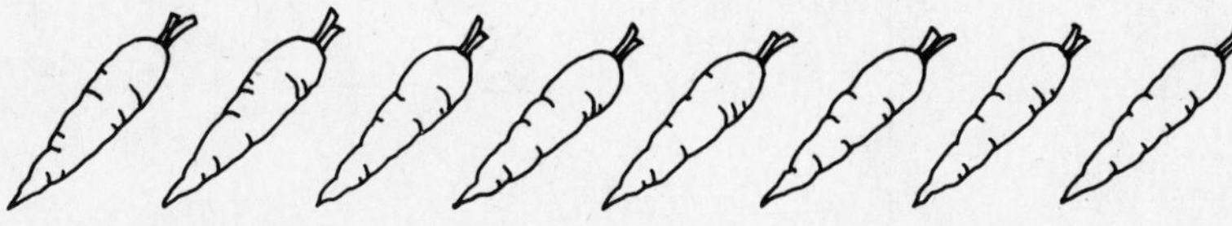

8 9

8 9

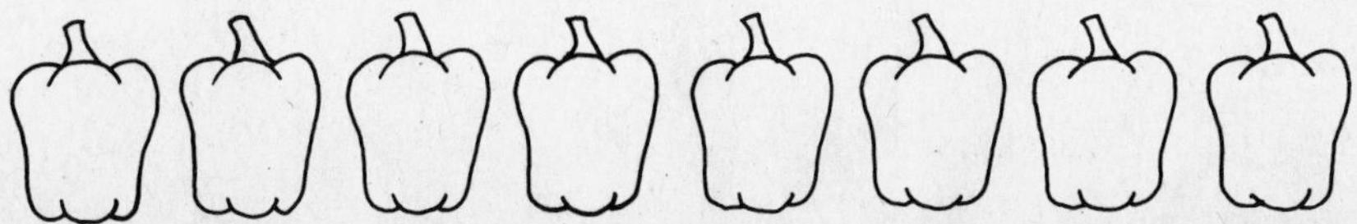

8 9

Name

Ten

Study

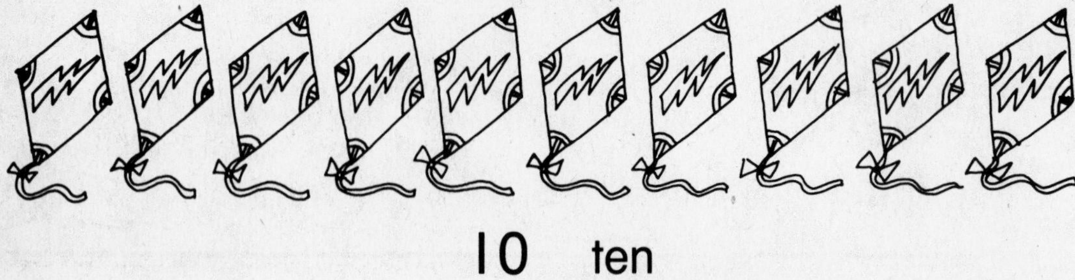

10 ten

Check

Write the number.

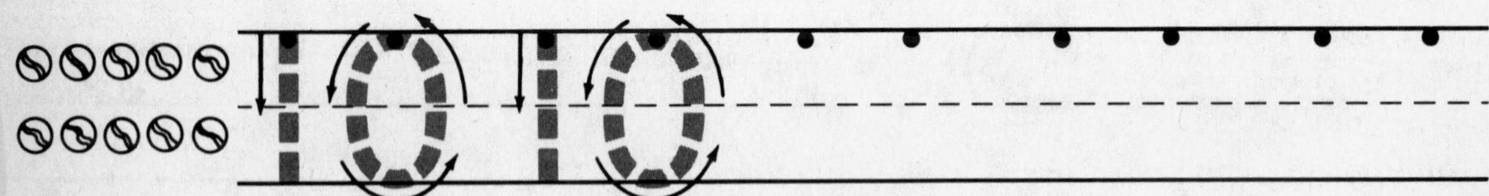

Ring how many.

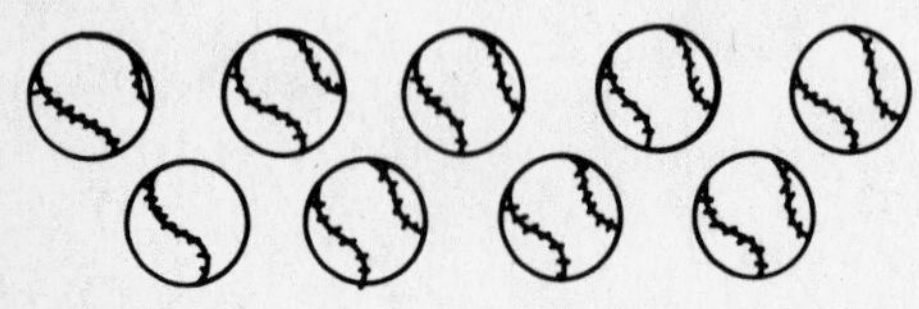

9 10

9 10

9 10

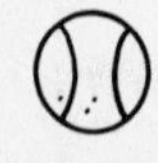 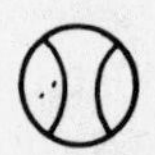 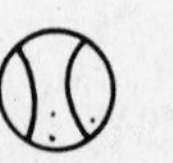 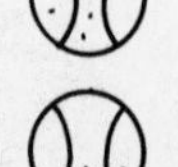 

9 10

Name

ORDER 0–10

Study

0 1 2 3 4 5 6 7 8 9 10

Check

Write the numbers in order.

Connect the dots in order.

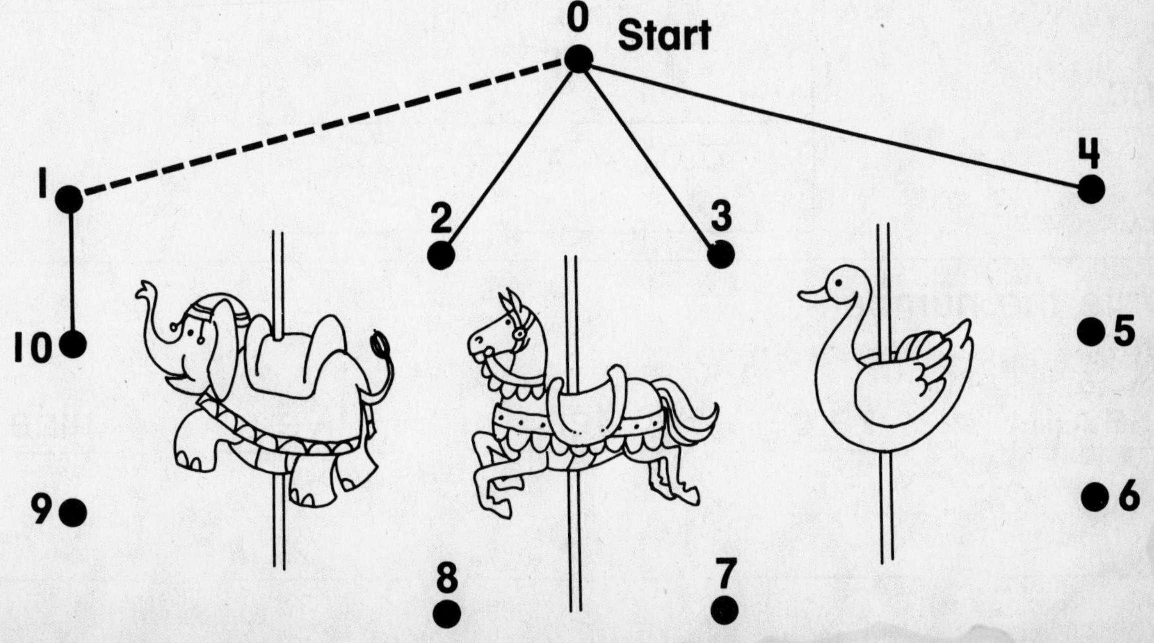

MACMILLAN/McGRAW-HILL

Name

NUMBER WORDS TO TEN

Study

0 zero

1 one

2 two

3 three

4 four

5 five

6 six

7 seven

8 eight

9 nine

10 ten

Check

Match.

two

four

one

six

4

2

6

1

Write the numbers.

seven zero ten five nine

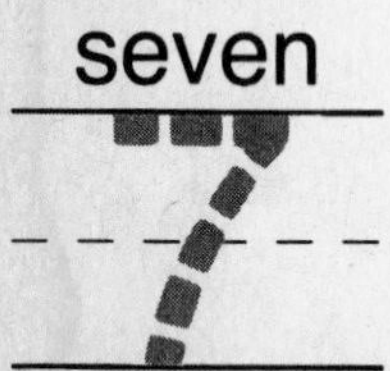

MACMILLAN/McGRAW-HILL

Name

GREATER AND LESS

Study

4 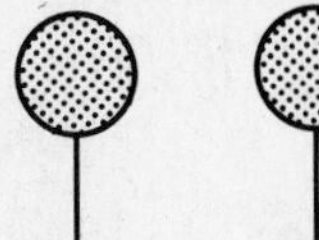 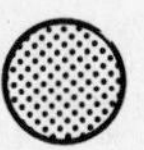

2

2 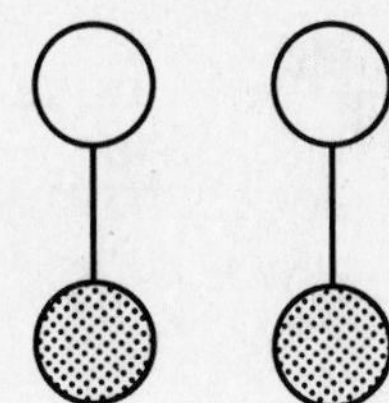 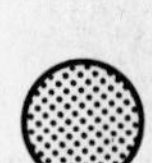

4

4 is greater than 2

2 is less than 4

Check

Write how many.
Ring the number that is greater.

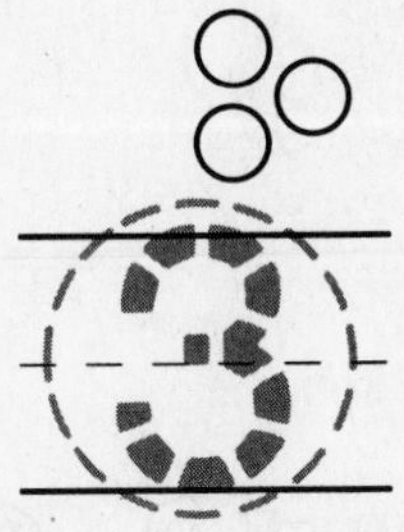
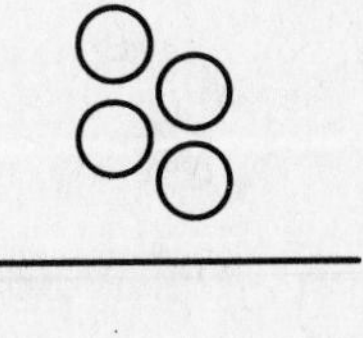
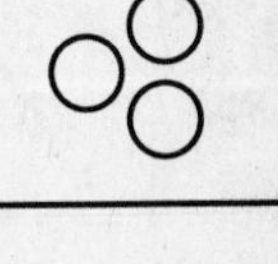

Write how many.
Ring the number that is less.

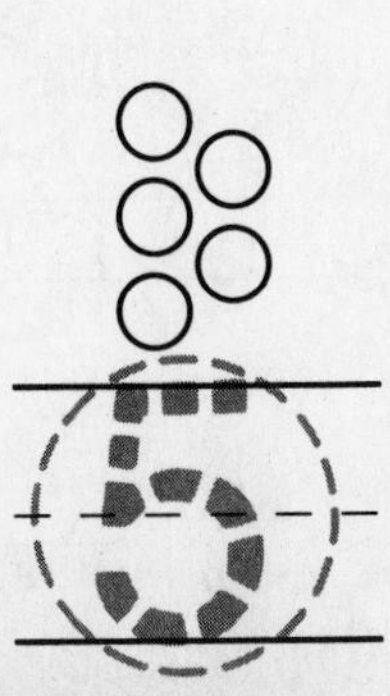
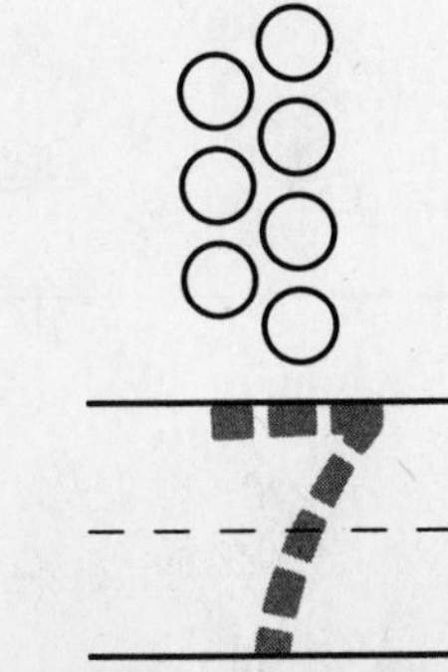
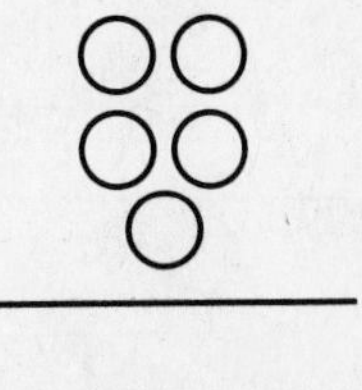
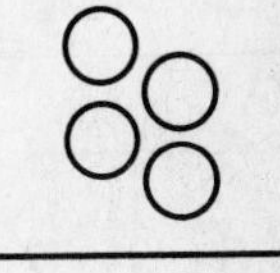

Macmillan/McGraw-Hill, MATHEMATICS IN ACTION
Grade 1, Chapter 1, Lesson 13, pages 31–32

Name

ORDINAL NUMBERS

Study

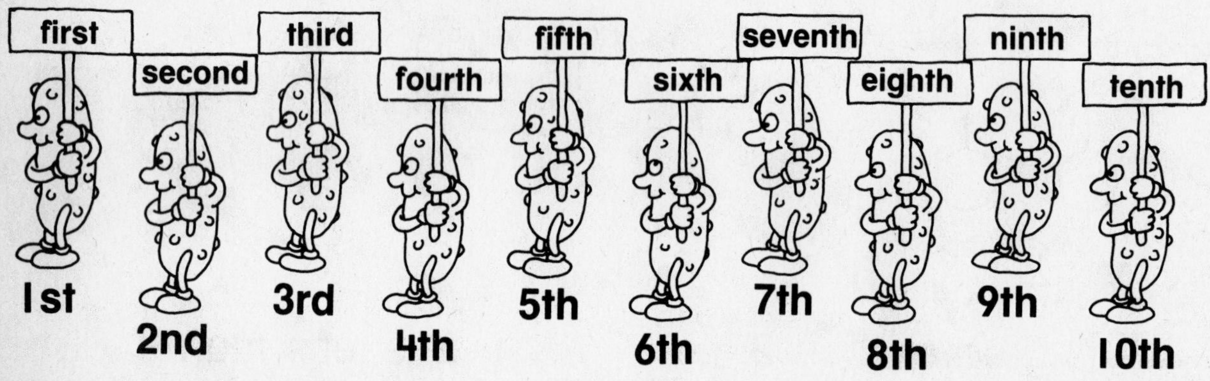

Check

Start at the left.
Ring the fifth.

Ring the seventh.

Ring the fourth.

Ring the tenth.

Name

PROBLEM SOLVING STRATEGY: USING A PHYSICAL MODEL

Study

You can show a counter for each item.

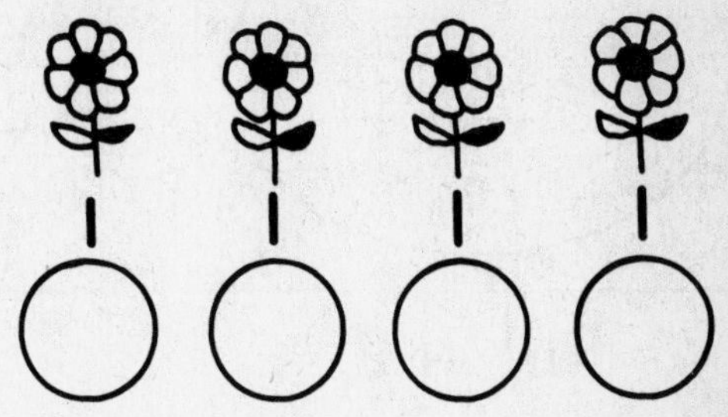

Check

Show a red counter for each  .

Show a yellow counter for each .

Which group has one more?
Ring.

Macmillan/McGraw-Hill, MATHEMATICS IN ACTION
Grade 1, Chapter 1, Lesson 15, pages 35–36

Name

ADDITION READINESS

Study

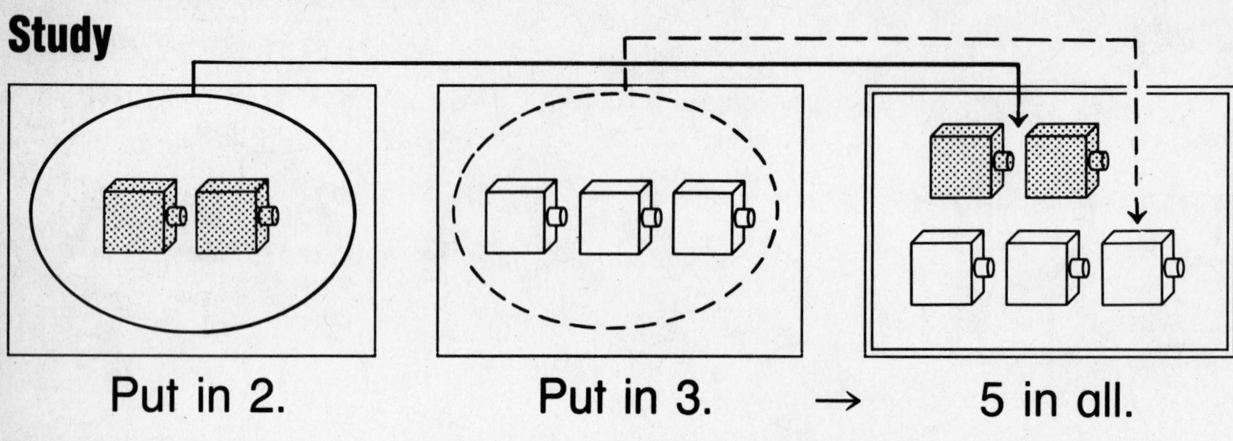

Put in 2. Put in 3. → 5 in all.

Check

Use 5 .

1. Put in 2. Put in 1. How many in all? ______

2. Put in 2. Put in 2. How many in all? ______

3. Put in 1. Put in 1. How many in all? ______

4. Put in 1. Put in 3. How many in all? ______

5. Put in 3. Put in 2. How many in all? ______

Name

BEGINNING ADDITION

Study

3 + 2 = 5

Check

Write how many in all.

1. 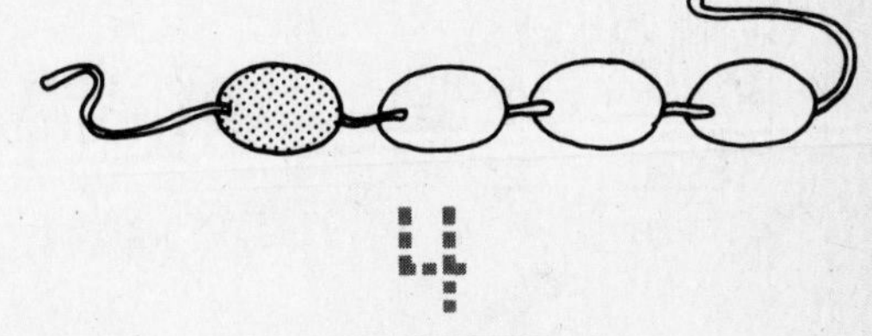

1 + 3 = 4

2. 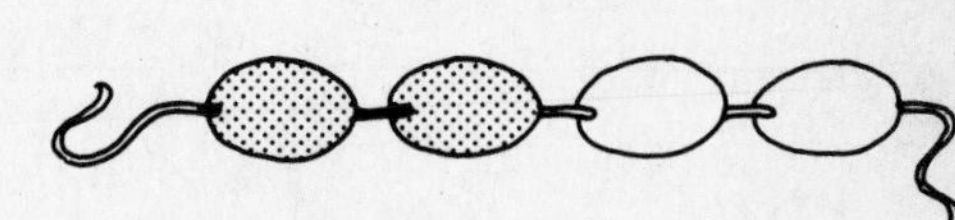

2 + 2 = ____

3. 3 + 2 = ____

4. 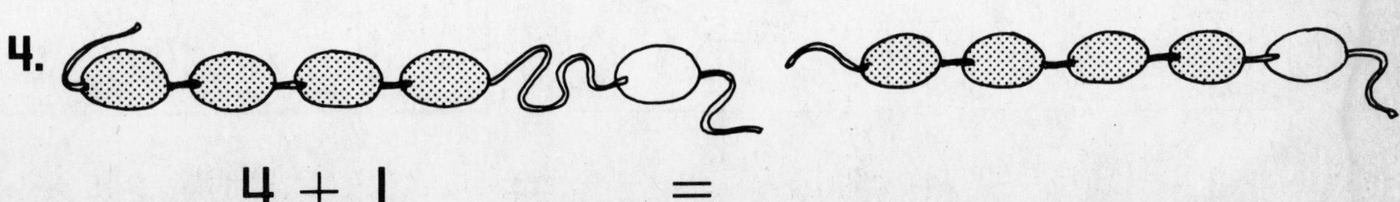

4 + 1 = ____

Name

ADDITION SENTENCES

Study

2 + 1 = 3

Check

Write how many in all.

1.

3 + 2 = 5

2.

1 + 3 = ____

3.

1 + 1 = ____

Name ______________________

MORE ADDITION SENTENCES

Study

2 + 1 = 3   1 + 2 = 3

Check

Add. Match related facts.

1\. 1 + 3 = 4

3 + 2 = ____

2\. 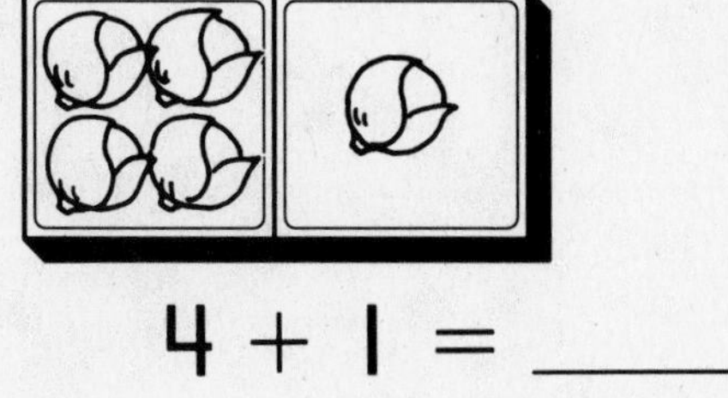

4 + 1 = ____

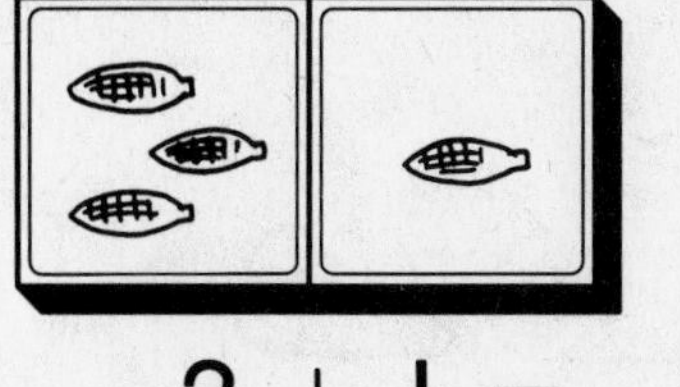

3 + 1 = 4

3\. 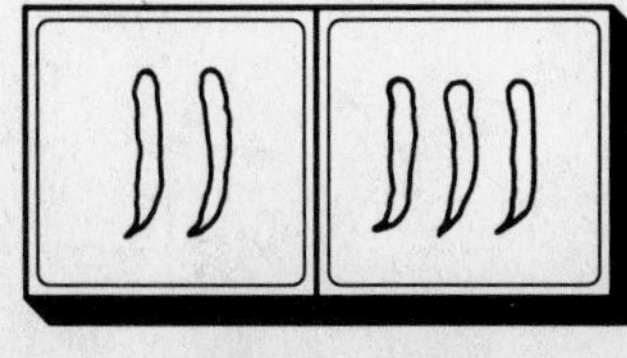

2 + 3 = ____

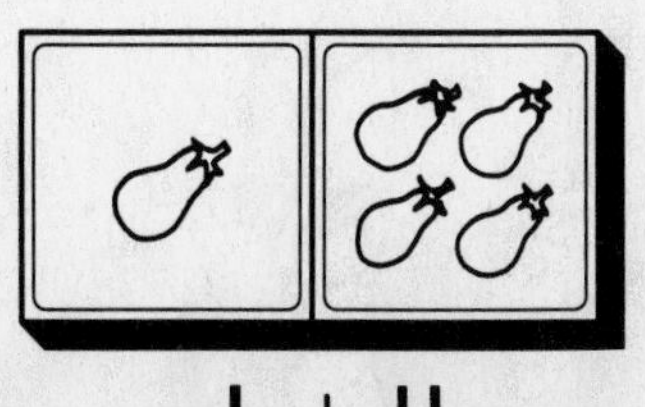

1 + 4 = ____

Macmillan/McGraw-Hill, MATHEMATICS IN ACTION
Grade 1, Chapter 2, Lesson 6, pages 55–56

Name

PROBLEM SOLVING: USING INFORMATION FROM A PICTURE

Study

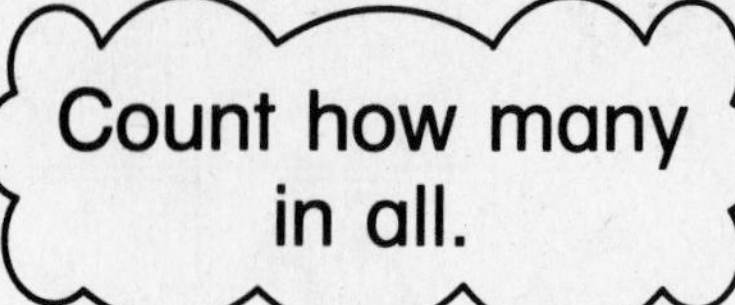

1 2 3 in all

Check

Write how many.

1.  

2 ___ 1 ___ 3 ___ in all

2. 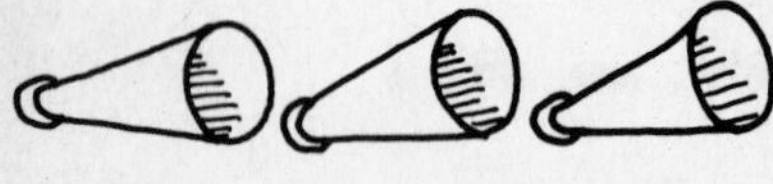 

___ ___ ___ in all

3.  

___ ___ ___ in all

Name

Counting on to add

Study

4 + 1 = 5

3 + 2 = 5

Check

Count on to add.

1. 

4

3 + 1 = 4

2. 

2 + 2 = ____

3. 

____

4 + 1 = ____

4. 

____

2 + 1 = ____

5. 

____ 1 + 1 = ____

Macmillan/McGraw-Hill, MATHEMATICS IN ACTION
Grade 1, Chapter 2, Lesson 9, pages 61–62

Name

VERTICAL ADDITION

Study

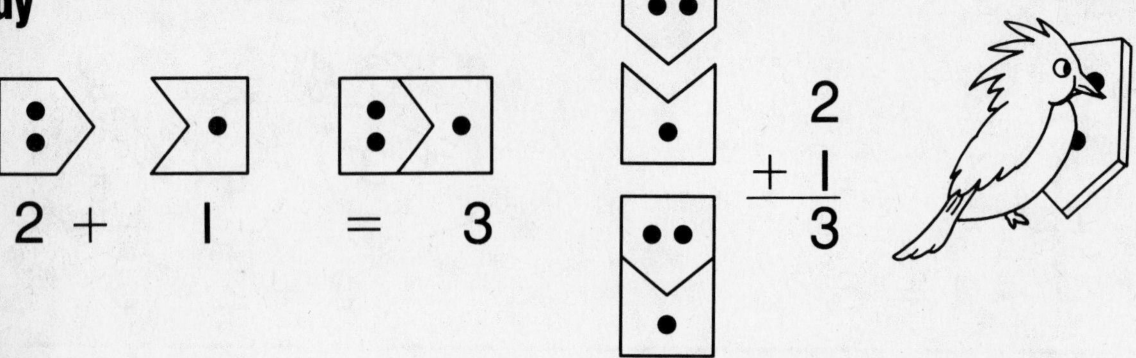

2 + 1 = 3

$$\begin{array}{r} 2 \\ +\ 1 \\ \hline 3 \end{array}$$

Check

Draw dots. Find the sum.

1. 1 + 4 = 5

$$\begin{array}{r} 1 \\ +\ 4 \\ \hline 5 \end{array}$$

2. $\begin{array}{r} 2 \\ +\ 2 \\ \hline \end{array}$ $\begin{array}{r} 3 \\ +\ 2 \\ \hline \end{array}$ $\begin{array}{r} 2 \\ +\ 0 \\ \hline \end{array}$ $\begin{array}{r} 1 \\ +\ 1 \\ \hline \end{array}$

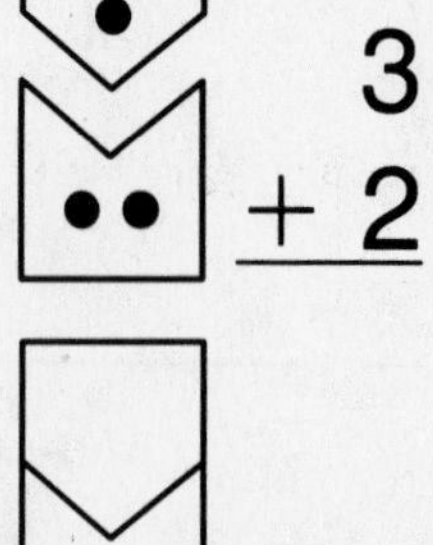

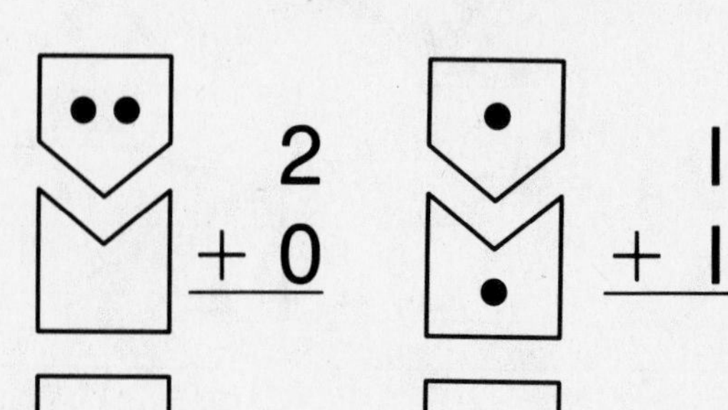

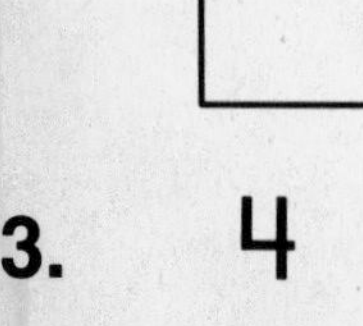

3. $\begin{array}{r} 4 \\ +\ 1 \\ \hline \end{array}$ $\begin{array}{r} 0 \\ +\ 3 \\ \hline \end{array}$ $\begin{array}{r} 2 \\ +\ 2 \\ \hline \end{array}$ $\begin{array}{r} 1 \\ +\ 3 \\ \hline \end{array}$ $\begin{array}{r} 4 \\ +\ 0 \\ \hline \end{array}$ $\begin{array}{r} 1 \\ +\ 2 \\ \hline \end{array}$

Name

PROBLEM SOLVING STRATEGY: COMPLETING AN ADDITION SENTENCE

Study

2 + 1 = 3

Check

How many in all?

1.

2 + 2 = 4

2.

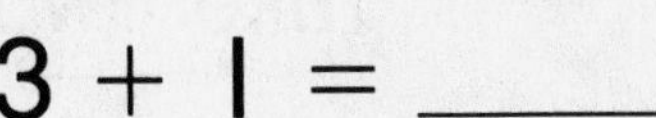

3 + 1 = ____

3.

3 + 2 = ____

4.

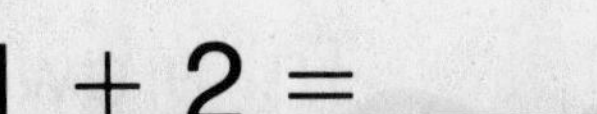

1 + 2 = ____

Macmillan/McGraw-Hill, MATHEMATICS IN ACTION
Grade 1, Chapter 2, Lesson 11, pages 65–66

Name

SUBTRACTION READINESS

Study

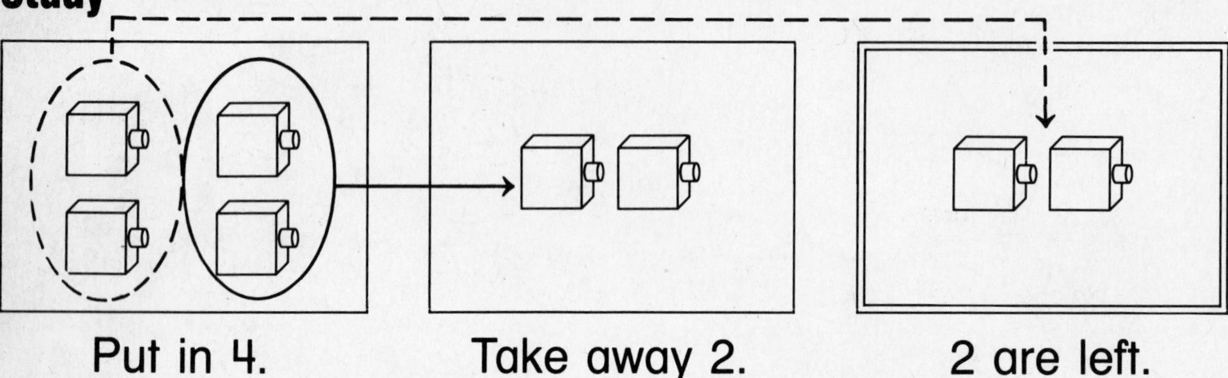

Put in 4. Take away 2. 2 are left.

Check

Use 5 .

1. Put in 4. Take away 4. How many are left?  ______
2. Put in 3. Take away 1. How many are left? ______
3. Put in 2. Take away 1. How many are left? ______
4. Put in 4. Take away 1. How many are left? ______
5. Put in 5. Take away 2. How many are left? ______

Name

BEGINNING SUBTRACTION

Study

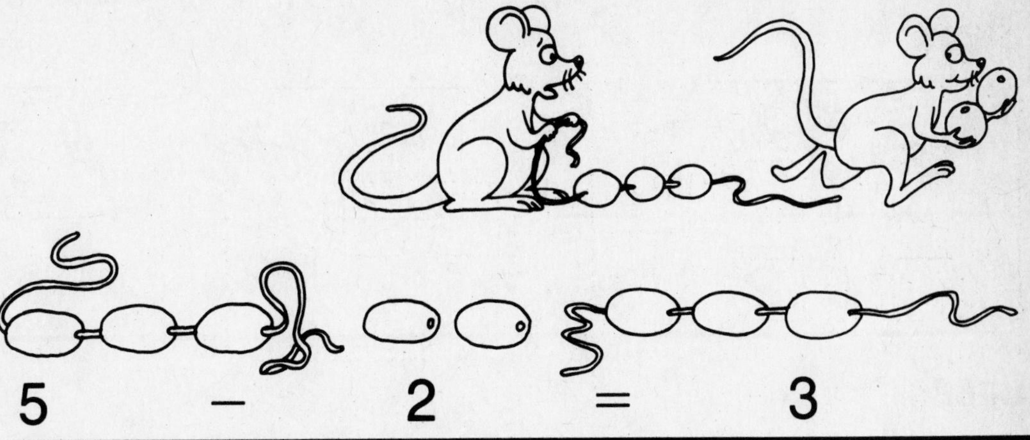

5 − 2 = 3

Check

Write how many are left.

1. 4 − 1 = 3

2. 3 − 2 = ____

3. 5 − 3 = ____

4. 4 − 2 = ____

MACMILLAN/McGRAW-HILL

Name

Subtraction Sentences

Study

5 − 2 = 3

Check

Write how many are left.

1. 

3 − 1 = 2

2. 
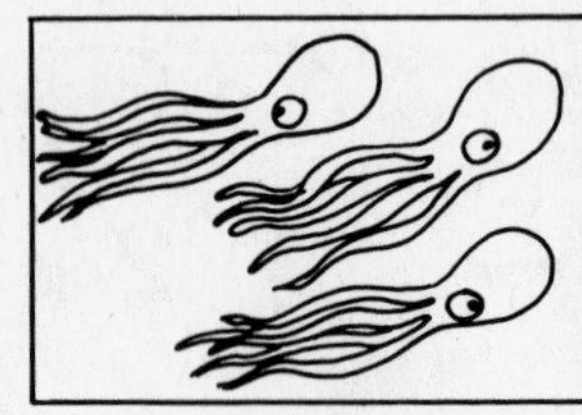

4 − 3 = ____

3. 

5 − 1 = ____

Name

MORE SUBTRACTION SENTENCES

Study

5 − 1 = 4

5 − 4 = 1

Check

Subtract. Match related facts.

1. 

4 − 3 = 1

5 − 3 = ____

2. 

5 − 2 = ____

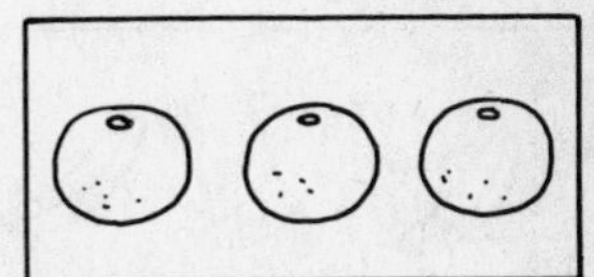

3 − 0 = ____

3. 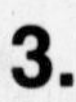 

3 − 3 = ____

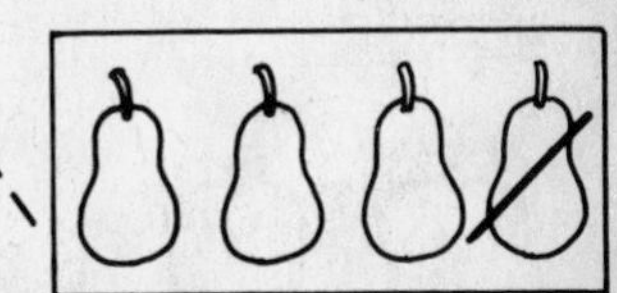

4 − 1 = 3

Macmillan/McGraw-Hill, MATHEMATICS IN ACTION
Grade 1, Chapter 3, Lesson 6, pages 85–86

Name

PROBLEM SOLVING STRATEGY: USING NUMBER SENSE

Study

There are more apples than pears.

Check

Ring.

1.     

Are there more  or ?  

2. 

Are there more  or  ?  

3.    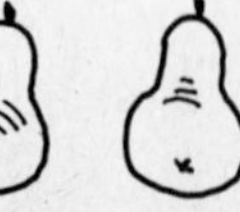 

Are there more  or ?  

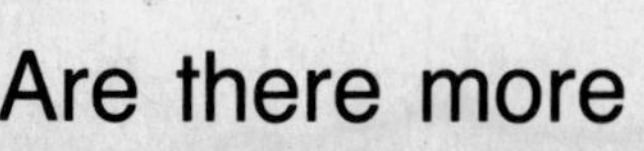

Name

COUNTING BACK TO SUBTRACT

Study

5 − 2 = 3

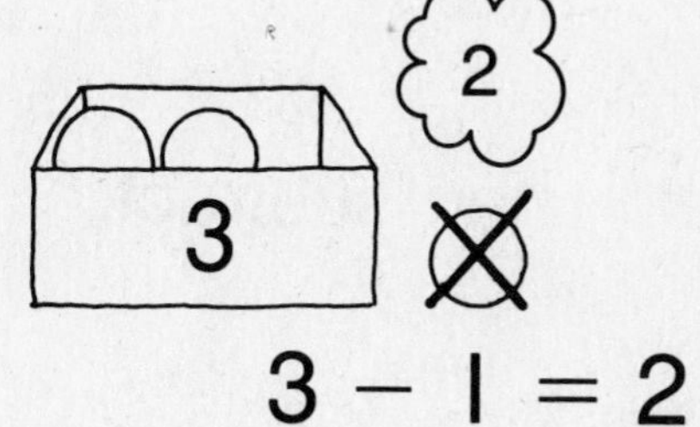

3 − 1 = 2

Check

Count back to subtract.

1.

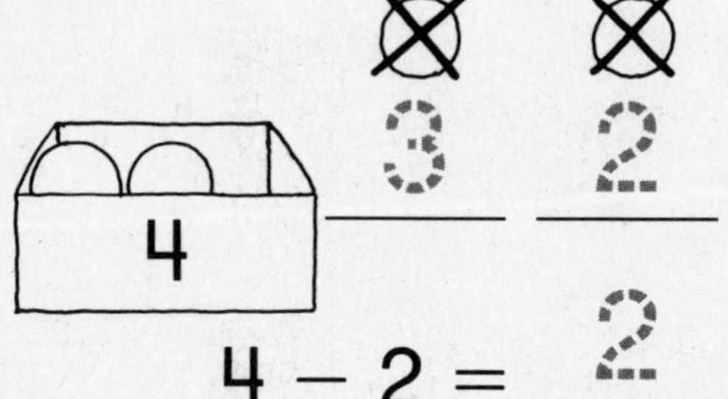

4 − 2 = 2

2.

5 − 1 = ____

3.

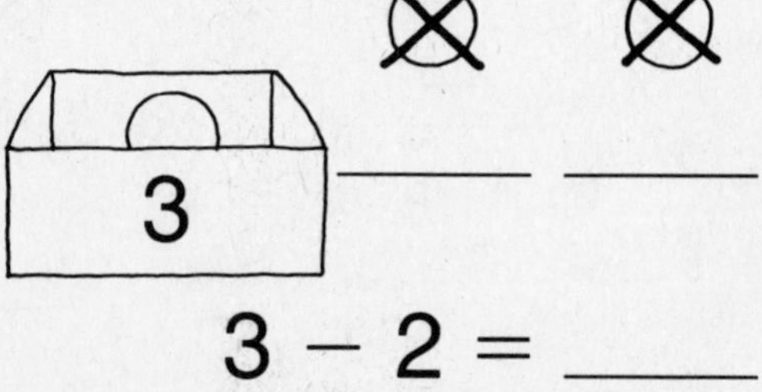

3 − 2 = ____

4.

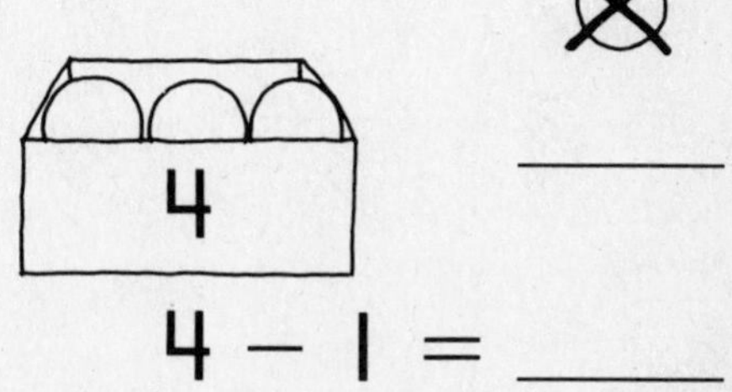

4 − 1 = ____

5.

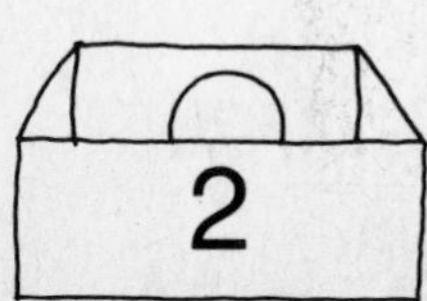

____ 2 − 1 = ____

Name

VERTICAL SUBTRACTION

Study

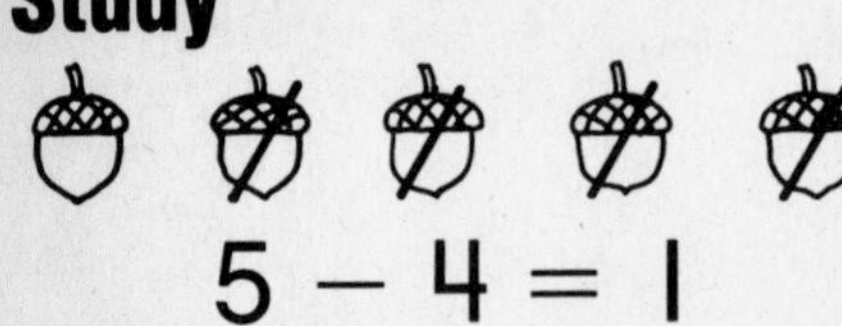

$5 - 4 = 1$

$$\begin{array}{r} 5 \\ -\ 4 \\ \hline 1 \end{array}$$

Check

Cross out. Then subtract.

1. $4 - 1 = 3$

$$\begin{array}{r} 4 \\ -\ 1 \\ \hline 3 \end{array}$$

2. $3 - 2 =$ ___

$$\begin{array}{r} 3 \\ -\ 2 \\ \hline \end{array}$$

3. $\begin{array}{r} 2 \\ -\ 2 \\ \hline \end{array}$ $\begin{array}{r} 4 \\ -\ 3 \\ \hline \end{array}$ $\begin{array}{r} 3 \\ -\ 1 \\ \hline \end{array}$ $\begin{array}{r} 5 \\ -\ 3 \\ \hline \end{array}$

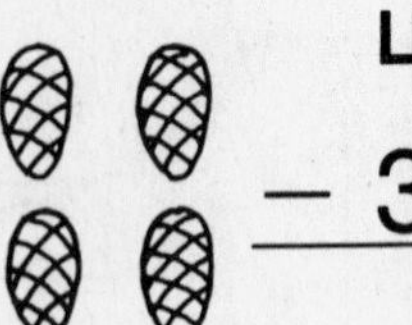

4. $\begin{array}{r} 4 \\ -\ 4 \\ \hline \end{array}$ $\begin{array}{r} 2 \\ -\ 0 \\ \hline \end{array}$ $\begin{array}{r} 5 \\ -\ 2 \\ \hline \end{array}$ $\begin{array}{r} 3 \\ -\ 0 \\ \hline \end{array}$ $\begin{array}{r} 1 \\ -\ 1 \\ \hline \end{array}$ $\begin{array}{r} 4 \\ -\ 0 \\ \hline \end{array}$

Name

FACT FAMILIES

Study

1 + 3 = 4   3 + 1 = 4   4 − 3 = 1   4 − 1 = 3

Check

Complete each fact family.

1. 2 + 3 = 5
3 + 2 = 5
5 − 3 = 2
5 − 2 = 3

2. 2 + 1 = ____
1 + 2 = ____
3 − 1 = ____
3 − 2 = ____

3. 4 + 1 = ____
1 + 4 = ____
5 − 1 = ____
5 − 4 = ____

4. 5 + 0 = ____
0 + 5 = ____
5 − 0 = ____
5 − 5 = ____

Macmillan/McGraw-Hill, MATHEMATICS IN ACTION
Grade 1, Chapter 3, Lesson 11, pages 95–96

Name

PROBLEM SOLVING STRATEGY: COMPLETING A SUBTRACTION SENTENCE

Study

  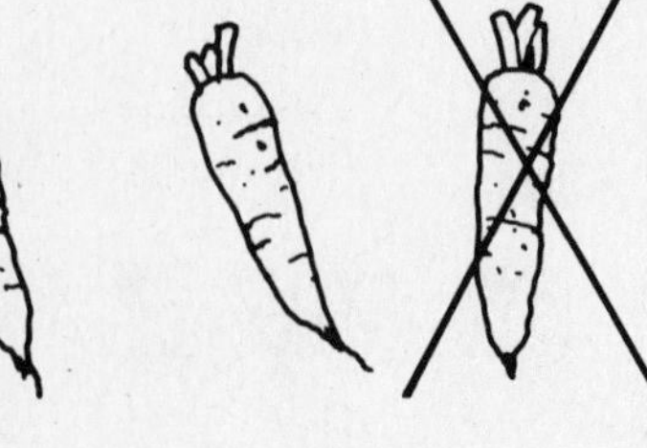

5 − 2 = 3

Check

How many are left?

1.

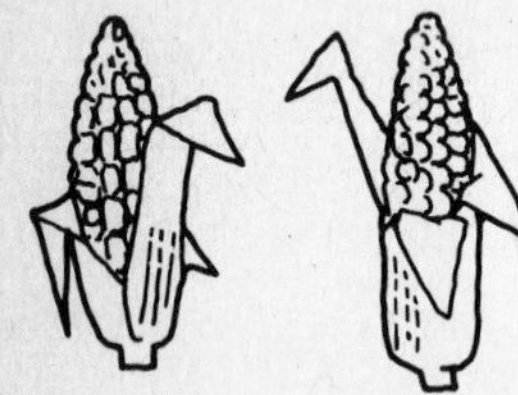  

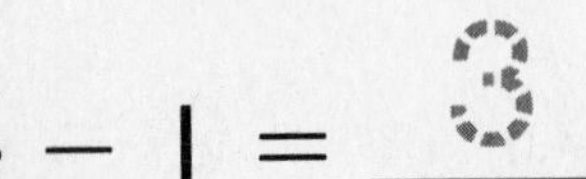

4 − 1 = 3

2.

4 − 2 = ____

3.

 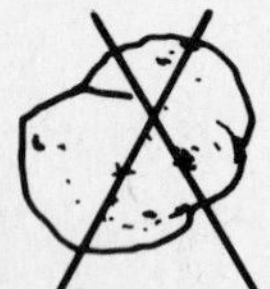 

3 − 2 = ____

4.

5 − 3 = ____

Name

COUNTING ON

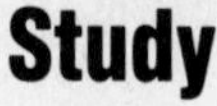

Study

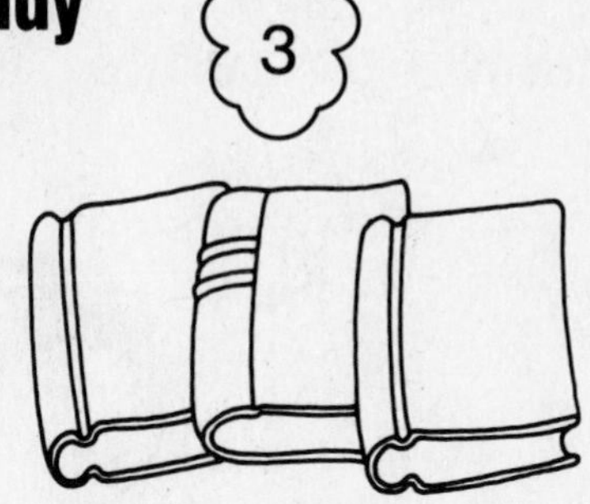

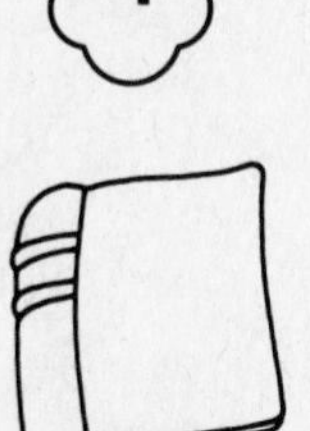

3 + 1 = 4

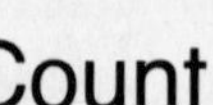

Check

Count on to add.

1. 

5 + 1 = 6

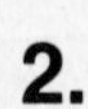

2. 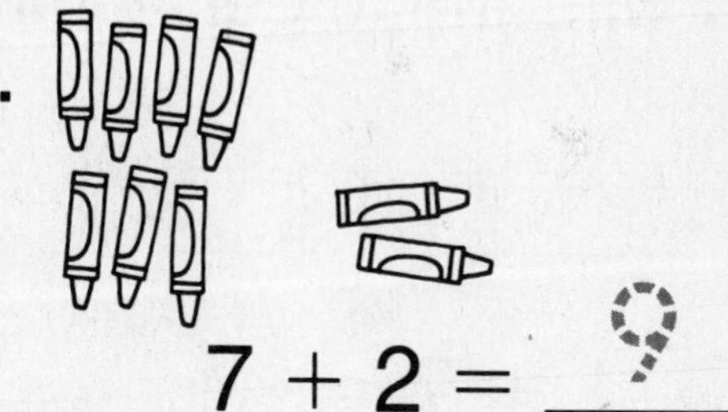

7 + 2 = 9

3. 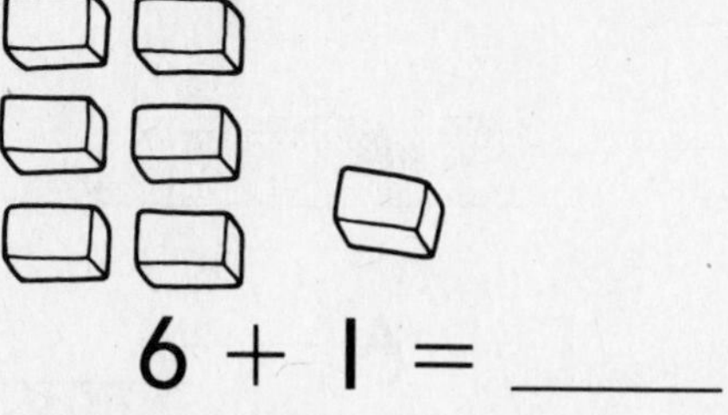

6 + 1 = ____

4. 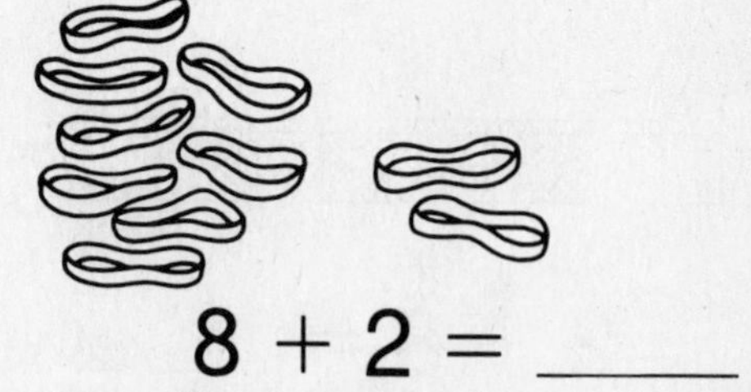

8 + 2 = ____

5. 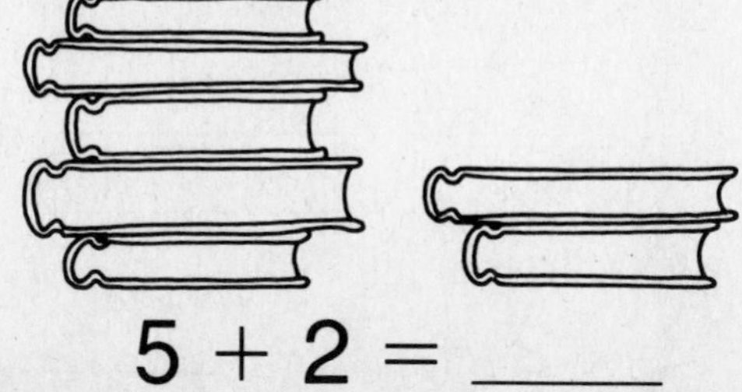

5 + 2 = ____

6. 

9 + 1 = ____

Name

USING THE LARGER NUMBER FIRST

Study

I counted on from 2.
2, **3**, **4**, **5**, **6**, **7**, **8**

I counted on from 6.
6, **7**, **8**

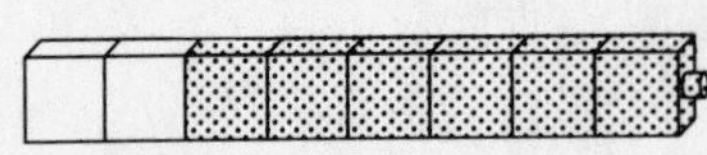

2 + 6 = 8

Check

Count on to add.
Begin with the larger number.

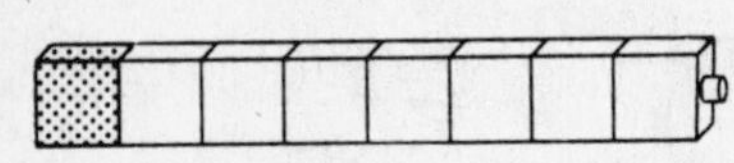

1 + 7 = 8

2.

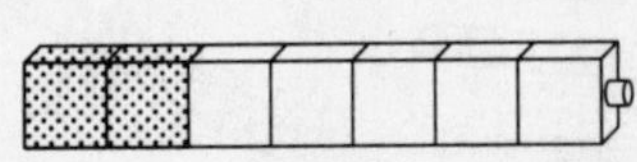

2 + 5 = 7

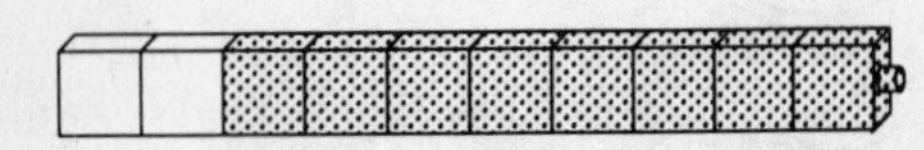

2 + 8 = ____

4.

1 + 6 = ____

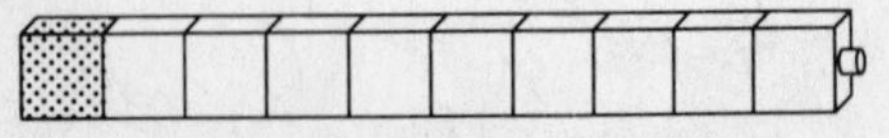

1 + 9 = ____

6.

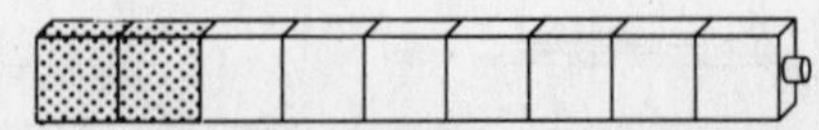

2 + 7 = ____

Name

PATTERNS

Study

2	3	4	5	6
+ 1	+ 1	+ 1	+ 1	+ 1
3	4	5	6	7

Check

Add. Look for patterns.

1.	1	2	3	4	5	6
	+ 2	+ 2	+ 2	+ 2	+ 2	+ 2
	3	4	5	6	7	8
2.	3	3	3	3	3	3
	+ 0	+ 1	+ 2	+ 3	+ 4	+ 5
3.	4	4	4	4	4	4
	+ 6	+ 5	+ 4	+ 3	+ 2	+ 1
4.	8	7	6	5	4	3
	+ 2	+ 2	+ 2	+ 2	+ 2	+ 2

Name

USING DOUBLES

Study

$$\begin{array}{r} 1 \\ +\ 1 \\ \hline 2 \end{array} \quad \begin{array}{r} 1 \\ +\ 2 \\ \hline 3 \end{array} \quad \begin{array}{r} 2 \\ +\ 2 \\ \hline 4 \end{array} \quad \begin{array}{r} 2 \\ +\ 3 \\ \hline 5 \end{array}$$

1 more

1 more

1 more

1 more

Check

Add.

1. $\begin{array}{r} 3 \\ +\ 3 \\ \hline 6 \end{array}$ $\begin{array}{r} 3 \\ +\ 4 \\ \hline 7 \end{array}$ $\begin{array}{r} 4 \\ +\ 4 \\ \hline \end{array}$ $\begin{array}{r} 4 \\ +\ 5 \\ \hline \end{array}$

2. $\begin{array}{r} 2 \\ +\ 2 \\ \hline 4 \end{array}$ $\begin{array}{r} 3 \\ +\ 2 \\ \hline \end{array}$ $\begin{array}{r} 1 \\ +\ 1 \\ \hline \end{array}$ $\begin{array}{r} 2 \\ +\ 1 \\ \hline \end{array}$ $\begin{array}{r} 3 \\ +\ 3 \\ \hline \end{array}$ $\begin{array}{r} 4 \\ +\ 3 \\ \hline \end{array}$

3. $\begin{array}{r} 5 \\ +\ 5 \\ \hline \end{array}$ $\begin{array}{r} 5 \\ +\ 3 \\ \hline \end{array}$ $\begin{array}{r} 2 \\ +\ 4 \\ \hline \end{array}$ $\begin{array}{r} 5 \\ +\ 4 \\ \hline \end{array}$ $\begin{array}{r} 3 \\ +\ 6 \\ \hline \end{array}$ $\begin{array}{r} 8 \\ +\ 1 \\ \hline \end{array}$

4. $\begin{array}{r} 7 \\ +\ 0 \\ \hline \end{array}$ $\begin{array}{r} 6 \\ +\ 1 \\ \hline \end{array}$ $\begin{array}{r} 9 \\ +\ 1 \\ \hline \end{array}$ $\begin{array}{r} 8 \\ +\ 2 \\ \hline \end{array}$ $\begin{array}{r} 7 \\ +\ 3 \\ \hline \end{array}$ $\begin{array}{r} 2 \\ +\ 6 \\ \hline \end{array}$

Name

PROBLEM SOLVING STRATEGY: WRITING AN ADDITION SENTENCE

Study

4 + 2 = 6

Check

Write an addition sentence.

1. How many in all?

6 + 3 = 9

2. How many altogether?

4 + 3 = ____

3. How many in all?

3 + 2 = ____

4. How many altogether?

7 + 3 = ____

Macmillan/McGraw-Hill, MATHEMATICS IN ACTION
Grade 1, Chapter 4, Lesson 8, pages 121–122

ADDING THREE NUMBERS

Study

4

4 + 1

Check

Add.

1.

2	3	1
3	4	2
+ 4	+ 1	+ 4
9	8	

Clouds: 5, 7, 3

2.

5	2	2
2	2	1
+ 3	+ 3	+ 3

Use ◯ if you need help.

3.

1	2	1	3	2
4	1	2	1	2
+ 5	+ 2	+ 5	+ 4	+ 2

MACMILLAN/McGRAW-HILL

Name

PROBLEM SOLVING STRATEGY: LOOKING FOR A PATTERN

Study

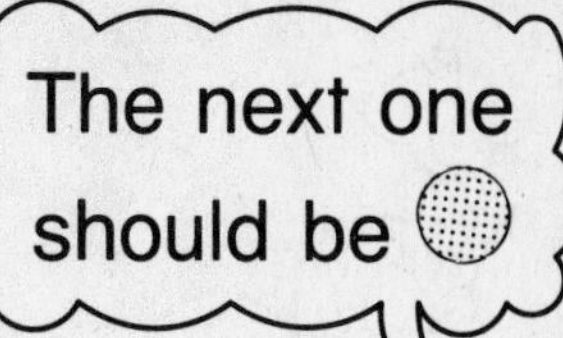

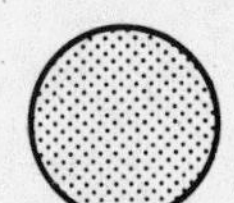  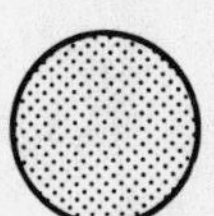      

Check

Color. Next.

1.
 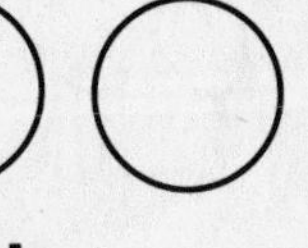 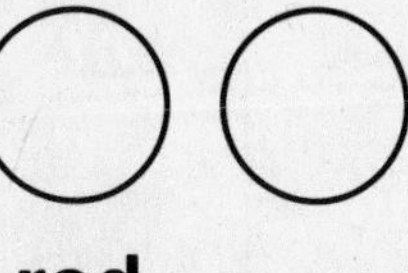 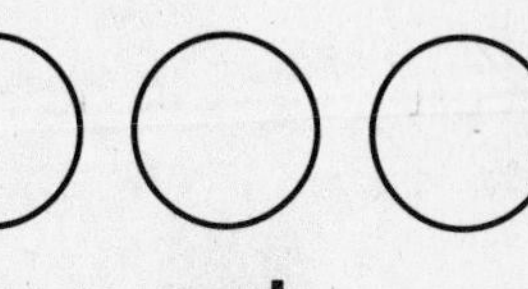 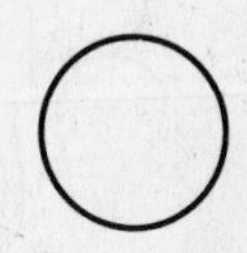

red red red red

2.
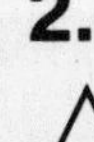 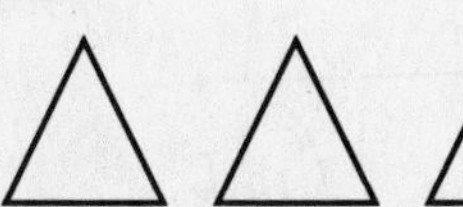 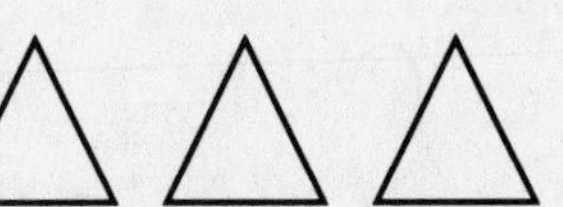 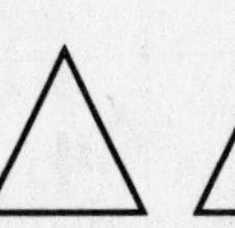 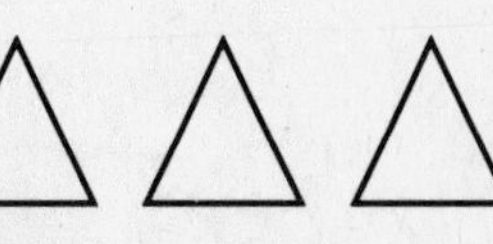 

blue blue blue blue blue blue

3.
 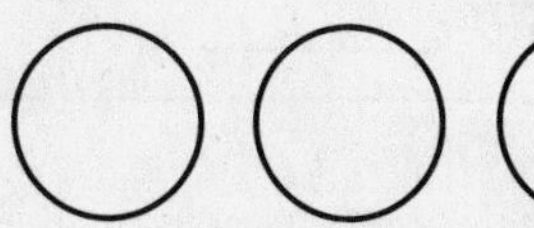 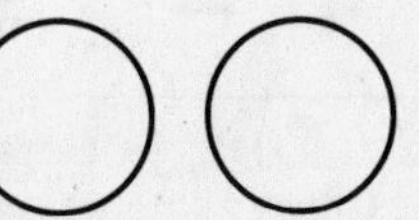  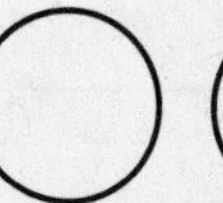 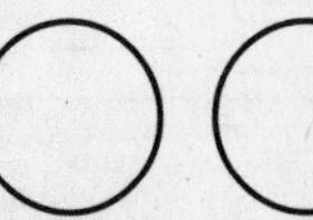 

green blue green blue green blue green blue

4.
 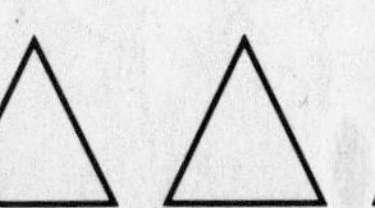  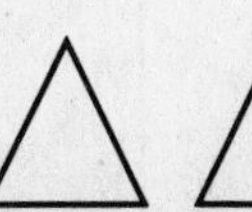 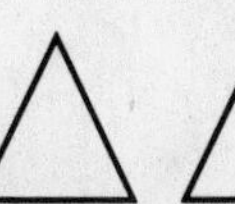 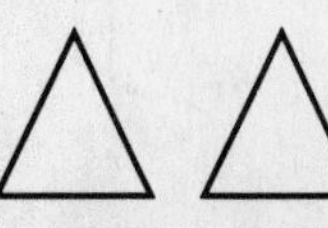 

red blue blue red blue blue red blue blue

Name

COUNTING BACK TO SUBTRACT

Study

5 4

$5 - 1 = 4$

Check

Count back to subtract.

1. 

$7 - 1 =$ 6

2. 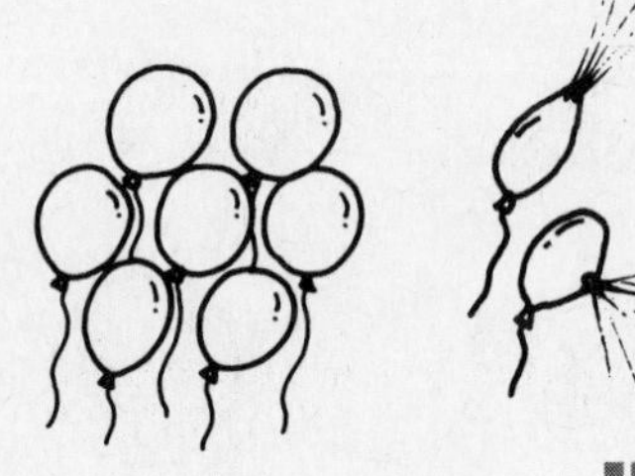

$9 - 2 =$ 7

3. 

$4 - 1 =$ ____

4. 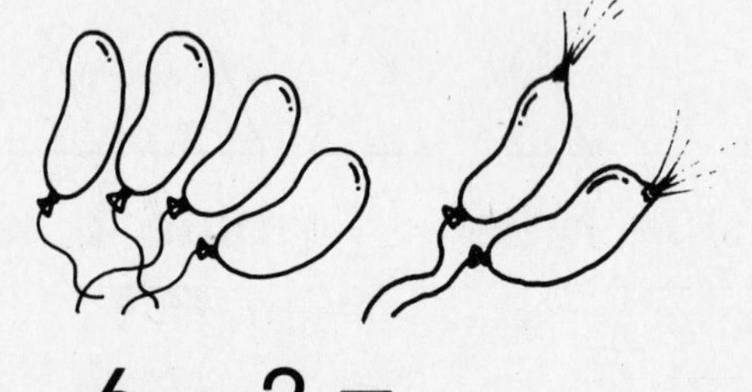

$6 - 2 =$ ____

5. 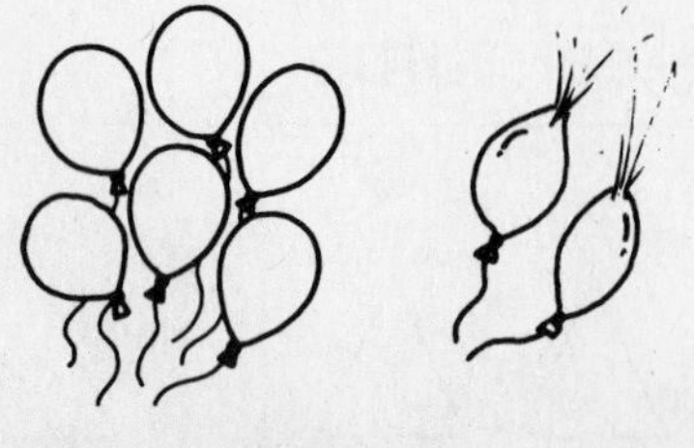

$8 - 2 =$ ____

6. 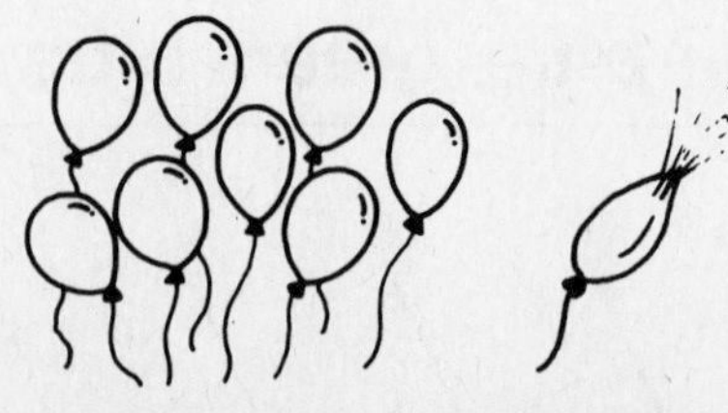

$9 - 1 =$ ____

Name ______________________________

USING RELATED SUBTRACTION FACTS

Study

This shows 7 − 3 = 4.

This shows 7 − 4 = 3.

These are related facts.

Check

Complete each pair of facts.

1. 

   9 − 5 = 4

   9 − 4 = 5

2. 10 − 6 = ___

   10 − 4 = ___

3. 8 − 3 = 5   7 − 5 = ___   9 − 6 = ___

   8 − 5 = 3   7 − 2 = ___   9 − 3 = ___

4. 6 − 1 = ___   10 − 8 = ___   8 − 2 = ___

   6 − 5 = ___   10 − 2 = ___   8 − 6 = ___

Name

SUBTRACTION PATTERNS

Study

5	5	5	5	5	5
− 0	− 1	− 2	− 3	− 4	− 5
5	4	3	2	1	0

Check

Subtract. Look for patterns.

1.

9	8	7	6	5	4
− 3	− 3	− 3	− 3	− 3	− 3
6	5	4	3	2	1

2.

7	7	7	7	7	7
− 7	− 6	− 5	− 4	− 3	− 2

3.

10	10	10	10	10	10
− 1	− 2	− 3	− 4	− 5	− 6

4.

8	7	6	5	4	3
− 2	− 2	− 2	− 2	− 2	− 2

Name ____________________

PROBLEM SOLVING STRATEGY: WRITING A SUBTRACTION SENTENCE

Study

$9 - 4 = 5$

Check

How many are left?

1.

9 — 3 = 6

2.

7 — 3 = ______

3.

10 — 5 = ______

4.

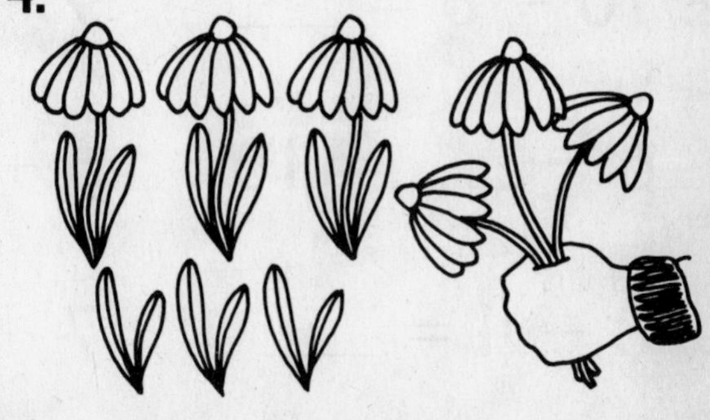

6 — 3 = ______

Name

SUBTRACTION AND ADDITION

Study

7 ◯
How many ◯ in the box?

Outside the box.

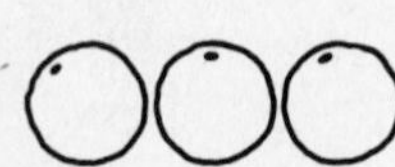

7 − 3 = 4

Inside the box.

3 + 4 = 7

Check

Write the missing numbers.
Use ◯ if you need help.

1.  9 − 4 = 5  8 − 2 = 6

 4 + 5 = 9 2 + ___ = 8

2. 10 − 6 = 4 9 − 6 = ___ 8 − 5 = ___

6 + ___ = 10 6 + ___ = 9 5 + ___ = 8

3. 8 − 4 = ___ 7 − 2 = ___ 6 − 2 = ___

4 + ___ = 8 2 + ___ = 7 2 + ___ = 6

Name

FACT FAMILIES

Study

5 + 3 = 8 8 − 3 = 5 3 + 5 = 8 8 − 5 = 3

fact family

Check

Complete each fact family.

1.

2 + 6 = 8 8 − 6 = 2

6 + 2 = 8 8 − 2 = 6

2.

7 + 3 = ____ 10 − 3 = ____

3 + 7 = ____ 10 − 7 = ____

3.

4 + 5 = ____ 9 − 5 = ____

5 + 4 = ____ 9 − 4 = ____

4.

8 + 1 = ____ 9 − 1 = ____

1 + 8 = ____ 9 − 8 = ____

Name ______________________________

PROBLEM SOLVING STRATEGY: USING A PHYSICAL MODEL

Study

Ted had 7 .

He lost 2 .

How many were left?

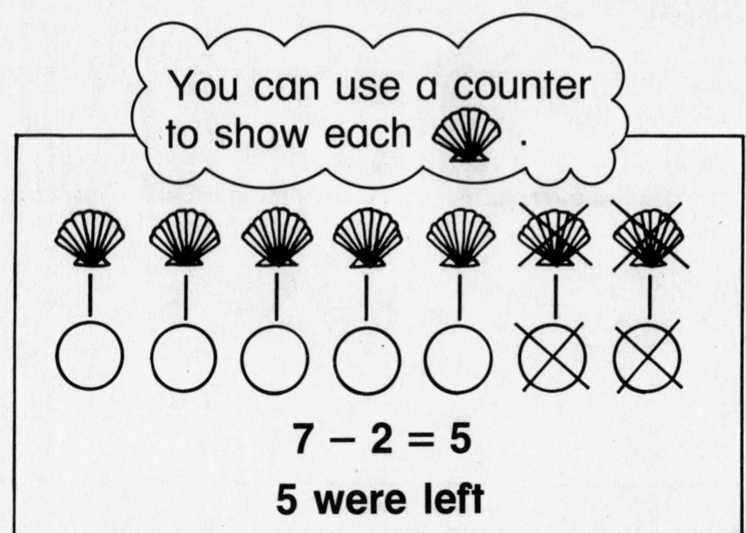

Check

Solve. Use counters.

1. Lisa had 6 .

   She gave 3 away.

   How many were left?

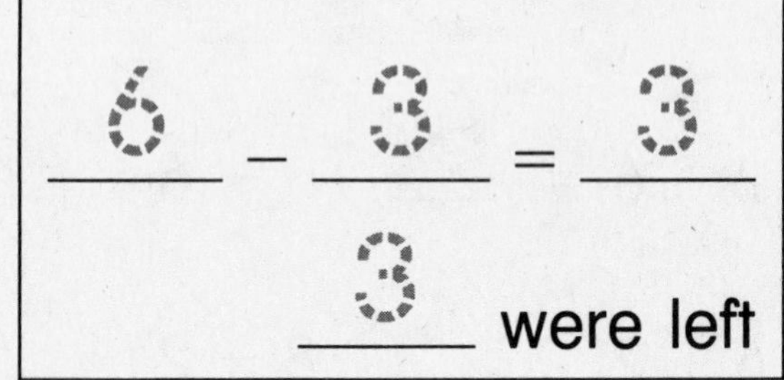

2. Pat had 8 .

   She broke 4 .

   How many were left?

_____ – _____ = _____

_____ were left

Name ______________________________

NUMBERS TO 19

Study

I ten 0 ones
10

I ten 5 ones
15

Check

Color each ten.
Write how many tens and ones. Write the number.

<u>I</u> ten <u>I</u> ones

<u>II</u>

___ ten ___ ones

___

<u>I</u> ten <u>2</u> ones

<u>I2</u>

___ ten ___ ones

___

___ ten ___ ones

___

___ ten ___ ones

___

___ ten ___ ones

___

___ ten ___ ones

___

Macmillan/McGraw-Hill, MATHEMATICS IN ACTION
Grade 1, Chapter 6, Lesson 3, pages 169–170

Name

Counting by tens

Study

10

1 ten

ten

2 tens

twenty

3 tens

thirty

Check

Write how many tens. Write the number.

1.  4 tens 40 forty

2.  5 tens 50 fifty

3. 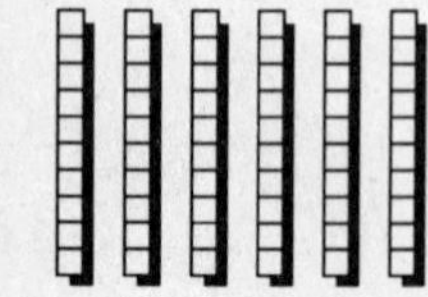 _____ tens _____ sixty

4. 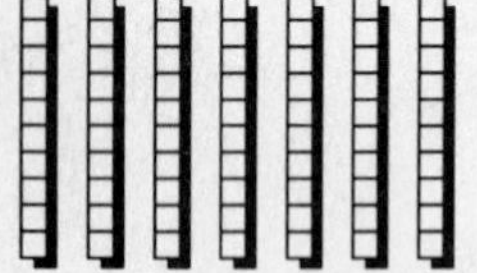 _____ tens _____ seventy

5. 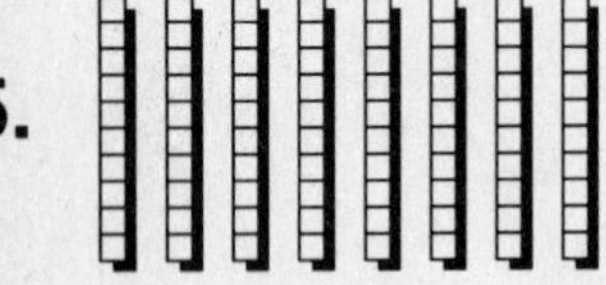 _____ tens _____ eighty

6. 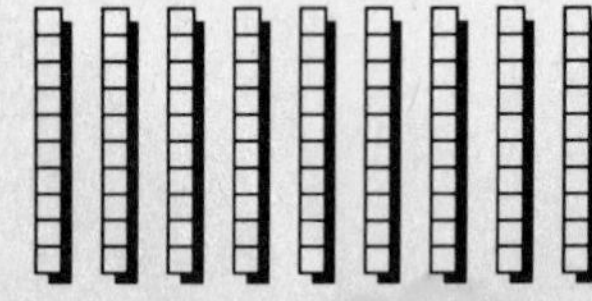 _____ tens _____ ninety

Name

NUMBERS TO 39

Study

tens	ones
2	3

23

Check

Write how many tens and ones.
Then write the number.

1.

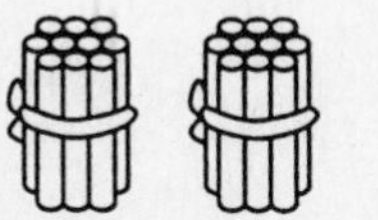

tens	ones
2	5

25

2.

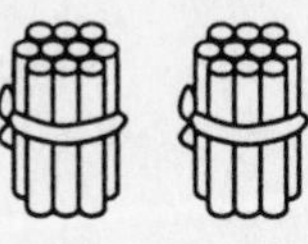

tens	ones
2	8

28

3.

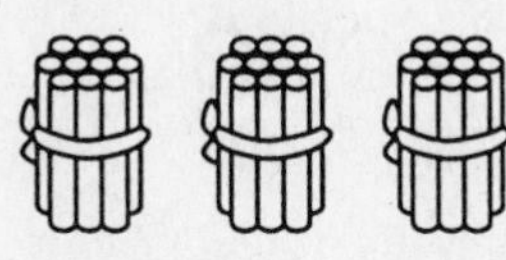

tens	ones

4.

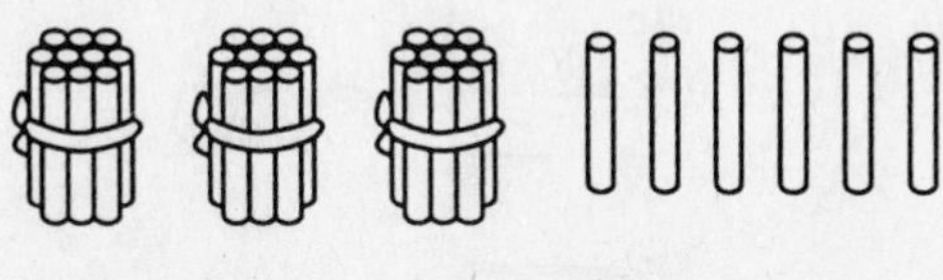

tens	ones

5.

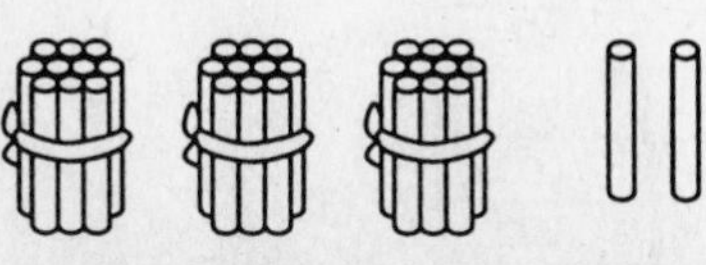

tens	ones

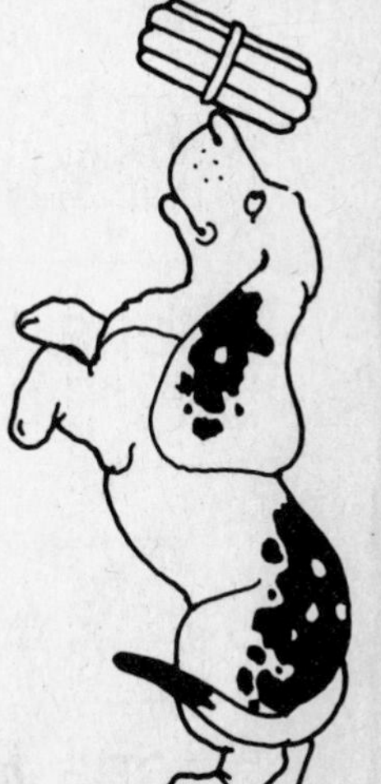

Name

NUMBERS TO 59

Study

5  2 ○

5 tens 2 ones 52

Check.

Match. Then write the number.

1. 4  7 ○
   4 tens 7 ones

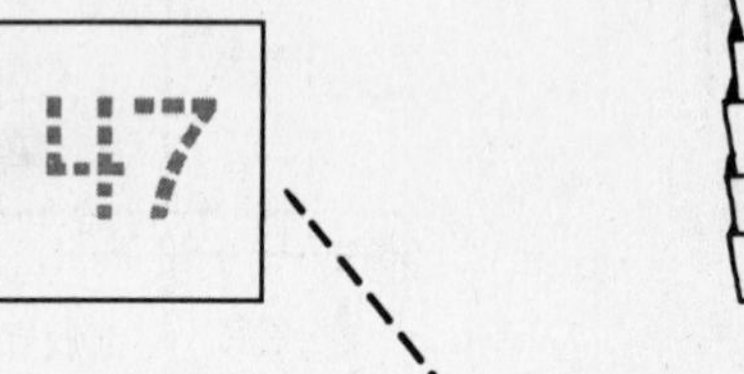

2. 5  4 ○
   5 tens 4 ones

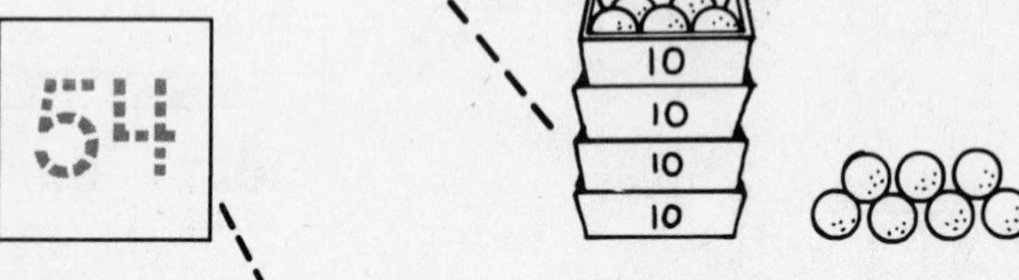

3. 3  5 ○
   3 tens 5 ones

4. 5  8 ○
   5 tens 8 ones

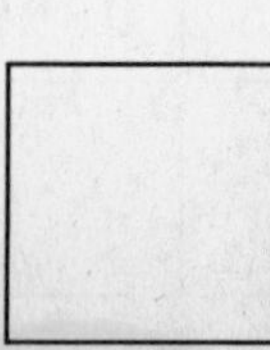

Name ______________________________

PROBLEM SOLVING STRATEGY: CHOOSING THE OPERATION

Study

Bob had 5  .

He got 3 more  .

How many fish in all?

5 + 3 = 8

8 fish in all

Sue had 7 turtles.

She gave away 4 turtles.

How many turtles were left?

Subtract to take away some from a group.

7 − 4 = 3

3  were left

Check

Ring the number sentence that solves the problem.

Andy had 4  .

He got 3 more  .

How many rabbits in all?

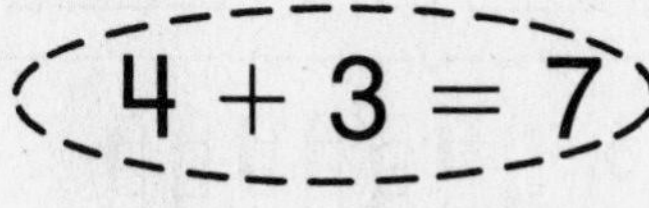

4 − 3 = 1

in all

Lien had 8 hamsters.

She gave away 2 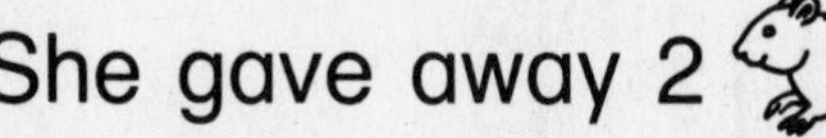 .

How many hamsters were left?

8 + 2 = 10

8 − 2 = 6

______  were left

Name ______

NUMBERS TO 79

Study

3 tens is not the same as 3 ones.

3 tens 7 ones 37

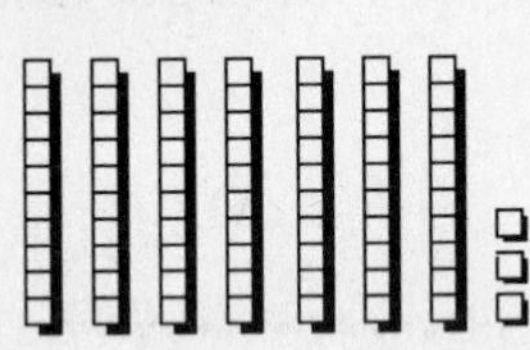

7 tens 3 ones 73

Check

Write the numbers.

1. 5 tens 6 ones 56

2. 6 tens 5 ones 65

3. 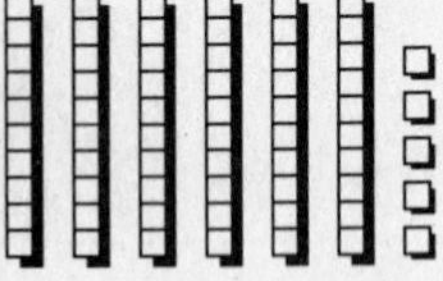

______ tens ______ ones ______

4. 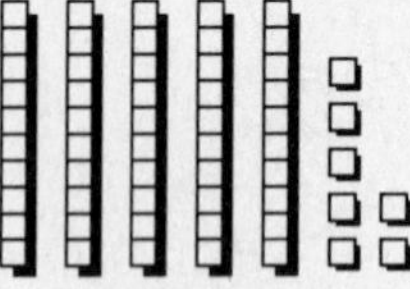

______ tens ______ ones ______

5. 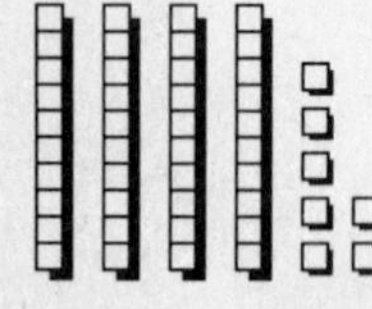

______ tens ______ ones ______

6. 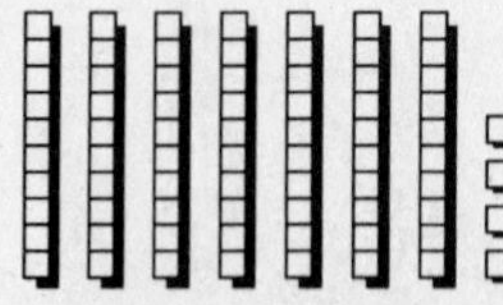

______ tens ______ ones ______

Name ______________________________

NUMBERS TO 100

Study

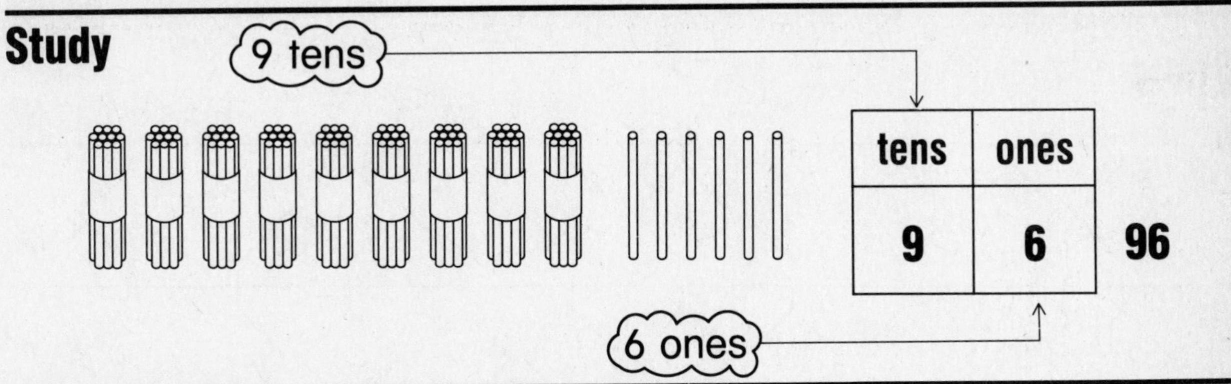

tens	ones	
9	6	96

Check

Write how many tens and ones.
Write the number.

1. 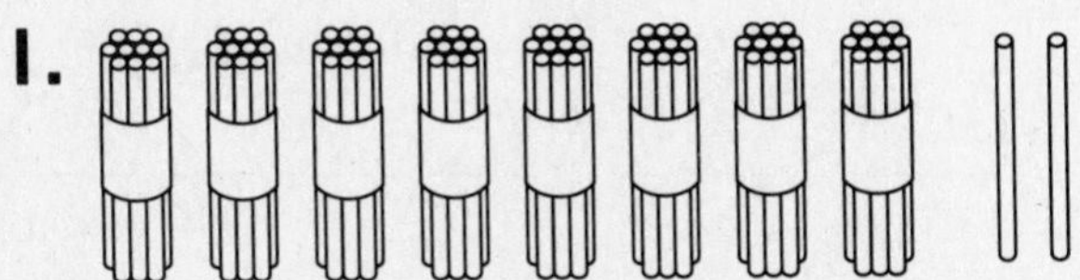

tens	ones	
8	2	82

2. 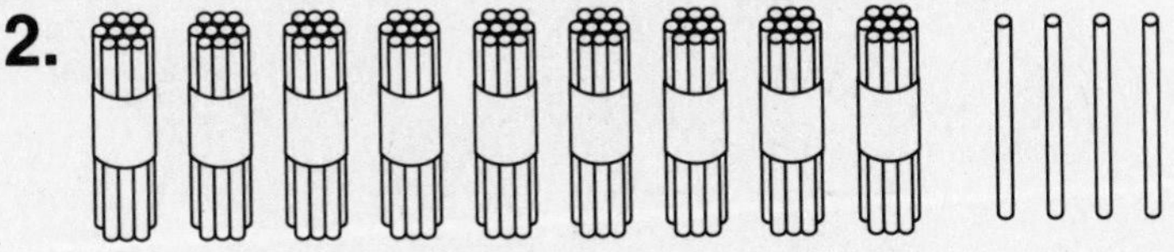

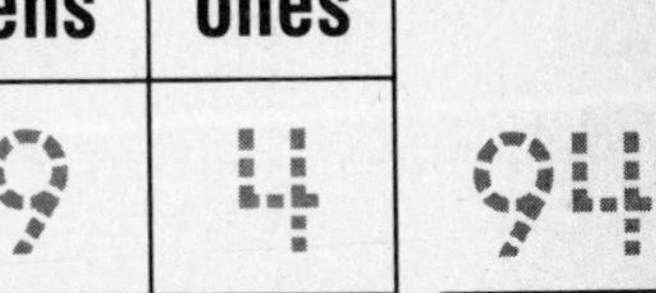

tens	ones	
9	4	94

3. 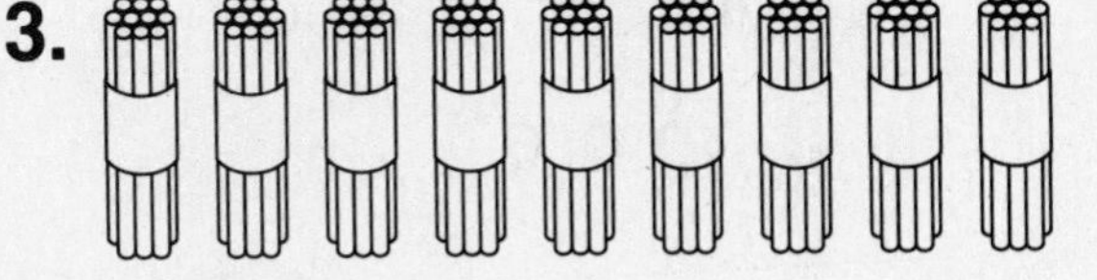

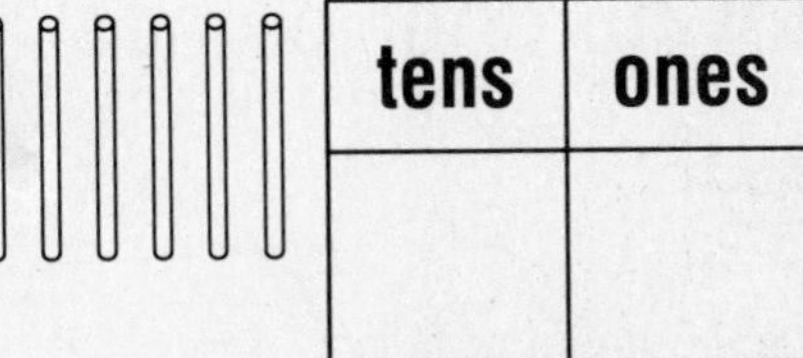

tens	ones	
		____

4. 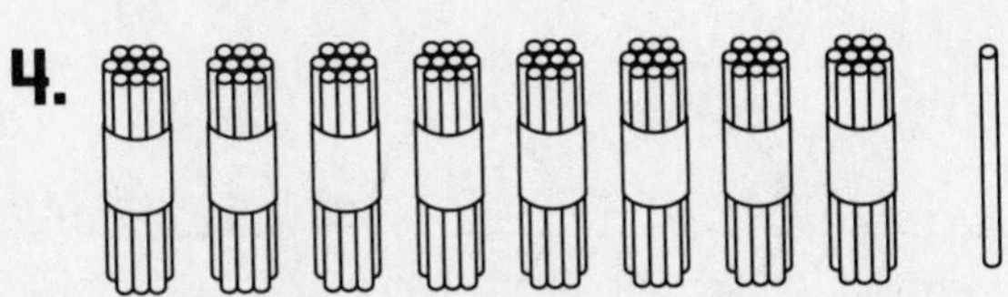

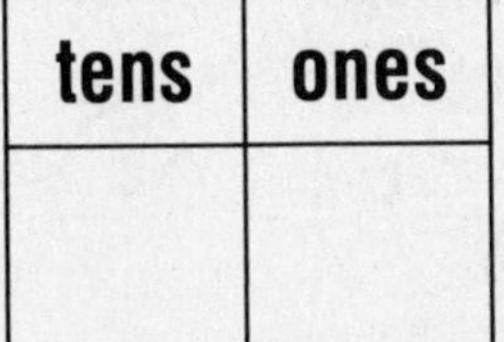

tens	ones	
		____

5. 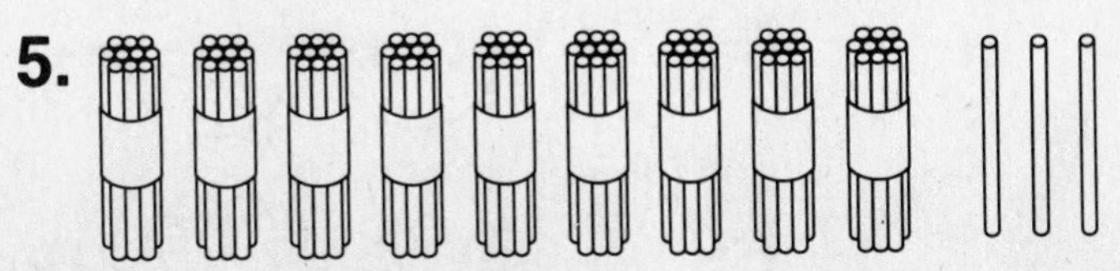

tens	ones	
		____

Macmillan/McGraw-Hill, MATHEMATICS IN ACTION
Grade 1, Chapter 6, Lesson 9, pages 181–182

Name

ORDER

Study

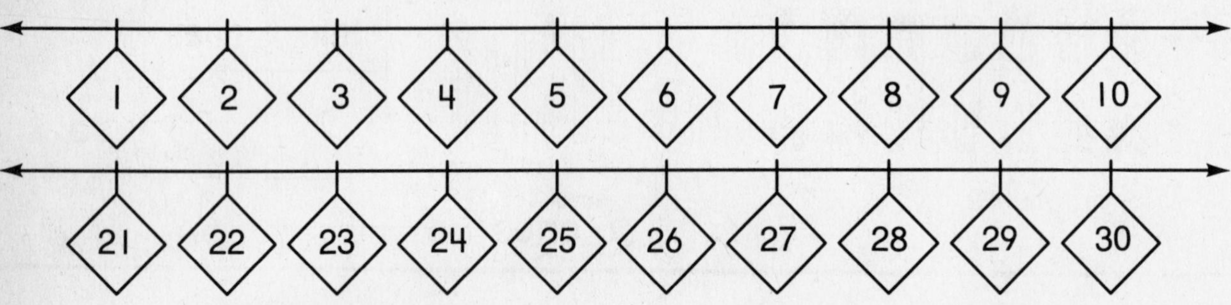

Check

Count by ones. Write the numbers.

1. 31 32 33 ___ 35 ___ 37 ___ ___ 40

2. 61 62 ___ 64 ___ ___ ___ 68 ___ 70

3. 81 ___ ___ ___ 85 ___ ___ ___ 89 ___

4. What number comes just after?

5. What number comes just before?

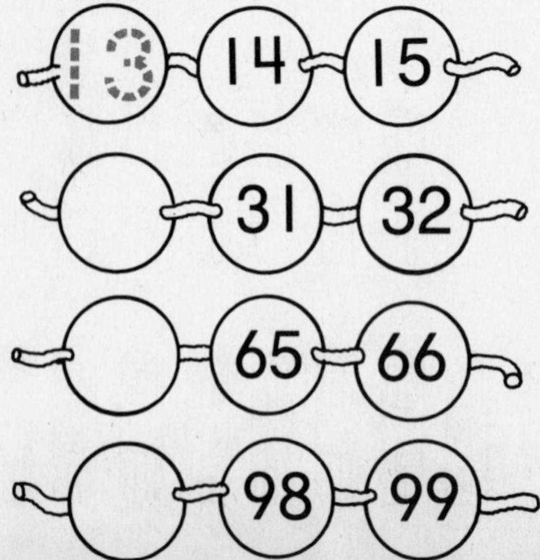

MACMILLAN/McGRAW-HILL

Name ______

SKIP-COUNTING

Study

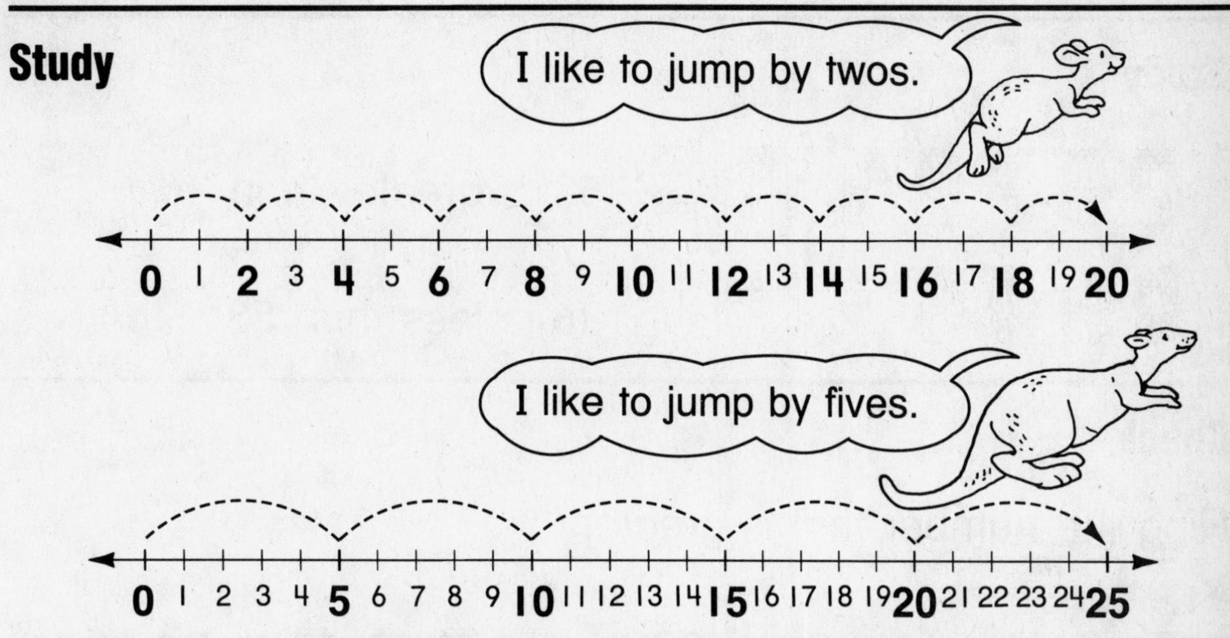

Check

Count by twos.

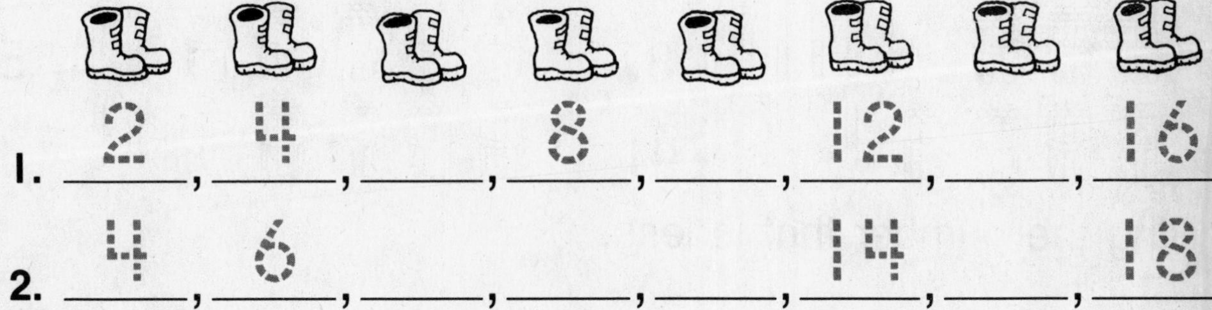

1. 2, 4, ___, 8, ___, 12, ___, 16
2. 4, 6, ___, ___, ___, 14, ___, 18

Count by fives.

3. 5, 10, ___, 20, ___, ___, ___, 40
4. 10, 15, ___, ___, ___, ___, ___, 45

Macmillan/McGraw-Hill, MATHEMATICS IN ACTION
Grade 1, Chapter 6, Lesson 12, pages 187–188

Name

GREATER AND LESS

Study

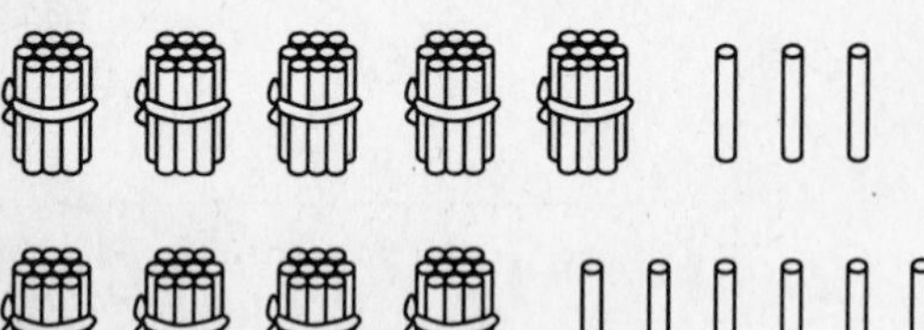

53 is greater than 46

46 is less than 53

Check

Ring the number that is greater.

1.
(34)
22

2.
43
45

3.
37
41

4.
52
44

Ring the number that is less.

5.
52
(42)

6.
25
27

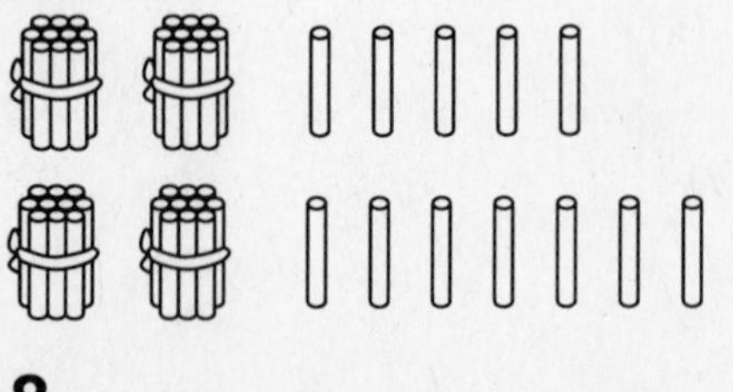

7.
34
37

8.
43
34

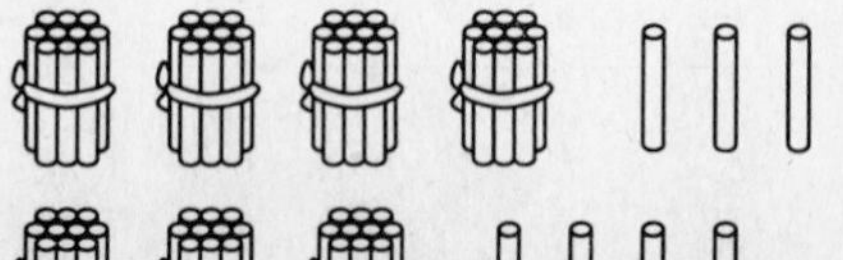

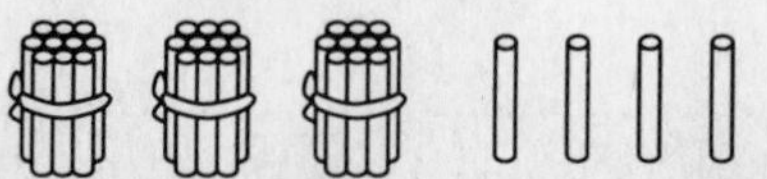

Name

GRAPHING

Study

Gold Stars

Luke	☆	☆	☆		
Bess	☆	☆			
Kim	☆	☆	☆	☆	☆

Luke has 3 ☆.

Bess has 2 ☆.

Kim has 5 ☆.

Check

Blue Ribbons

Champ	🎖	🎖	🎖	🎖	🎖
Spot	🎖	🎖	🎖		
Rex	🎖	🎖	🎖	🎖	

1. How many 🎖 did Spot win? 3

2. How many 🎖 did Champ win? ______

Ring.

3. Who won the most 🎖 ? Champ Spot Rex

4. Who won more? Spot Rex

Macmillan/McGraw-Hill, MATHEMATICS IN ACTION
Grade 1, Chapter 6, Lesson 14, pages 191–192

Name

PROBLEM SOLVING: USING INFORMATION FROM A GRAPH

Study

Mark 1 box for each item.
Go left to right.

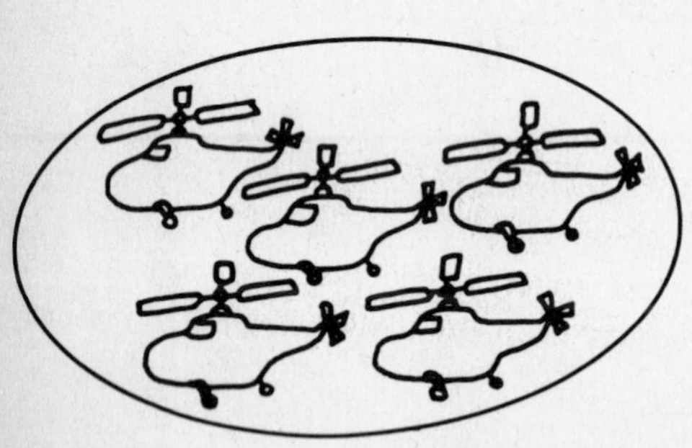

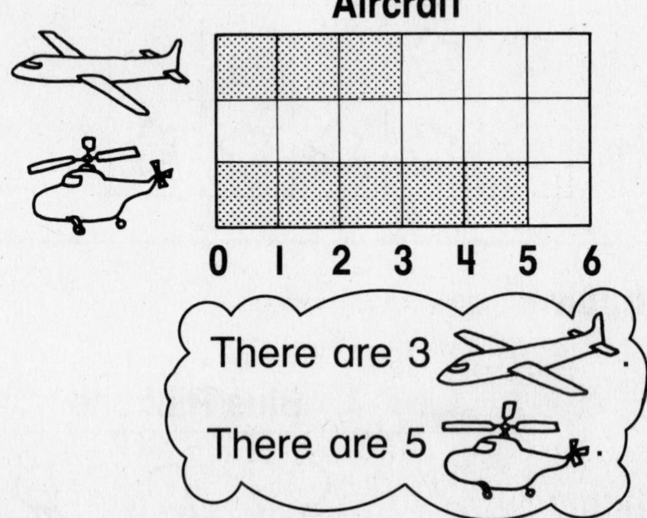

There are 3 .

There are 5 .

Color 1 box for each .

Color 1 box for each .

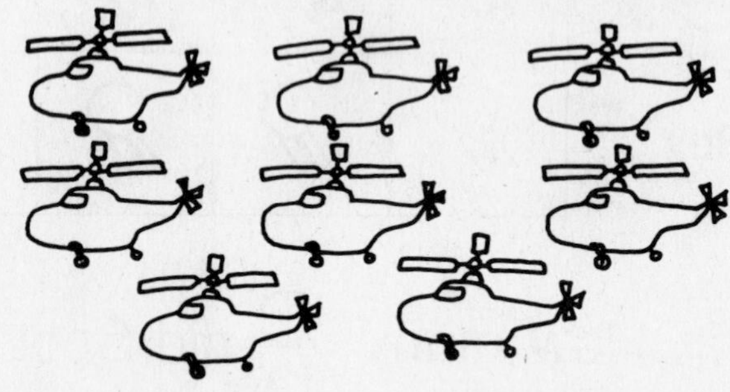

6 ____

____

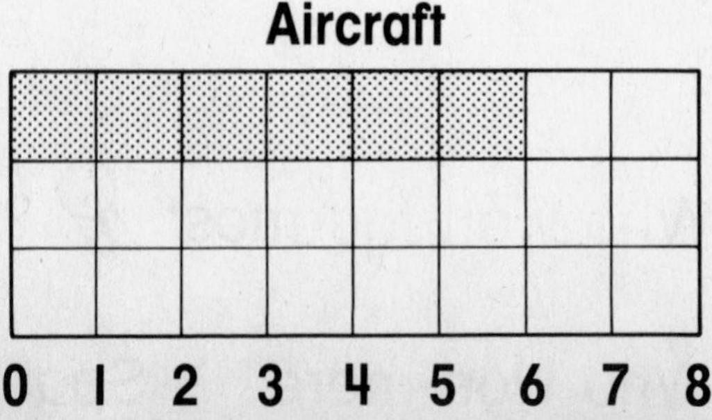

Name

PENNIES AND NICKELS

Study

1¢ | 1¢ 2¢

5¢

5¢ 10¢ 15¢

Check

Count. Write how much.

1.

1 ¢ 2 ¢ 3 ¢ 4 ¢ 5 ¢

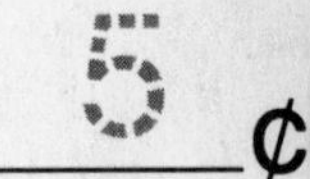

5 ¢

2.

5 ¢ ____¢ ____¢ ____¢

____¢

3.

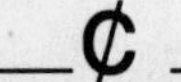

____¢ ____¢ ____¢ ____¢ ____¢ ____¢

Macmillan/McGraw-Hill, MATHEMATICS IN ACTION
Grade 1, Chapter 7, Lesson 2, pages 207–208

Name

PENNIES, NICKELS, AND DIMES

Study

10¢ 10¢ **20¢** 10¢ 20¢ 30¢ 35¢ **40¢**

Check

Count. Write how much.

1.

10 ¢ 20 ¢ 30 ¢ 40 ¢ 40 ¢

2.

____¢ ____¢ ____¢ ____¢ ____¢ ____¢

3.

____¢ ____¢ ____¢ ____¢ ____¢ ____¢

Name

COUNTING SETS OF COINS

Study

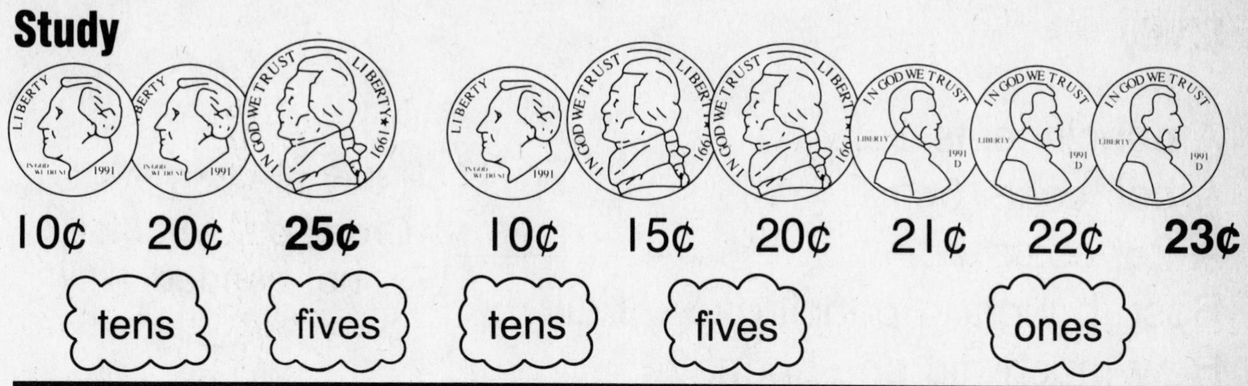

Check

Count. Write the amount.

1.

2.

____¢ ____¢ ____¢ ____¢ ____¢ ____¢

3.

____¢ ____¢ ____¢ ____¢ ____¢ ____¢ ____¢

Name

PROBLEM SOLVING: IDENTIFYING EXTRA INFORMATION

Study

A pencil costs 3¢.
A ball costs 5¢.
~~A top costs 7¢.~~
Rosa bought a pencil and a ball.
How much did she spend?

Cross out what is not needed.

Think:
pencil 3¢
ball 5¢
Add to join groups.

  3¢
+ 5¢
  8¢ Rosa spent 8¢.

Check

Cross out the fact you do not need.
Solve.

1. A pen costs 5¢.
~~A yoyo costs 7¢.~~
A ruler costs 4¢.
Neal bought a pen and a ruler.
How much did he spend?

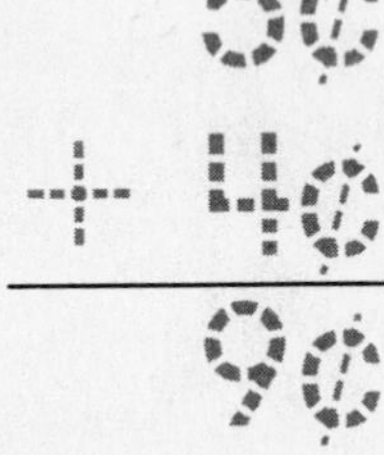

Neal spent 9 ¢

2. A hat costs 5¢.
A tie costs 5¢.
A belt costs 2¢.
Jeff bought a tie and a belt.
How much did Jeff spend?

Jeff spent ____ ¢

Name

QUARTERS

Study

25¢ 30¢ 35¢ **40¢**

25¢ 35¢ **36¢**

Check

Count. Then match.

1.

25 ¢

35 ¢

45 ¢

46 ¢

2.

_____¢

_____¢

_____¢

3.

_____¢

_____¢

_____¢

_____¢

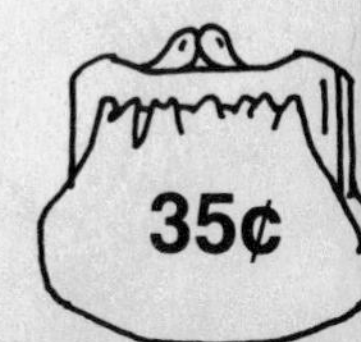

Name

Coins

Study

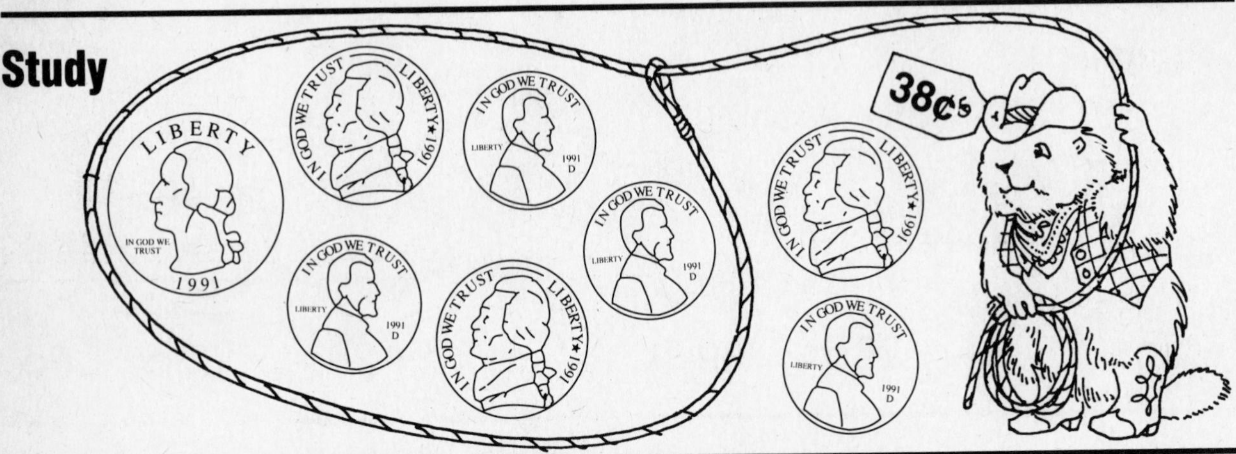

Check

Ring the coins that match the price.

1. 32¢

2. 26¢

3. 18¢

Name

PROBLEM SOLVING STRATEGY: GUESS AND TEST

Study

Tony bought 2 plants.
He spent 9¢.
Which 2 plants did he buy?

Pick 2 plants.
Test the prices to see
if they add to 9¢.

I guess 5¢ and 3¢.
8¢ is too small.
I guess 5¢ and 4¢.
9¢ is right.

Check

Ring 2 plants you can buy. Guess and test.

1. You spend 10¢.

2. You spend 8¢.

Ring 3 plants you can buy. Guess and test.

3. You spend 9¢.

4. You spend 7¢.

Macmillan/McGraw-Hill, MATHEMATICS IN ACTION
Grade 1, Chapter 7, Lesson 9, pages 221–222

Name

Centimeters and Decimeters

Study

□ 1 centimeter
1 cm

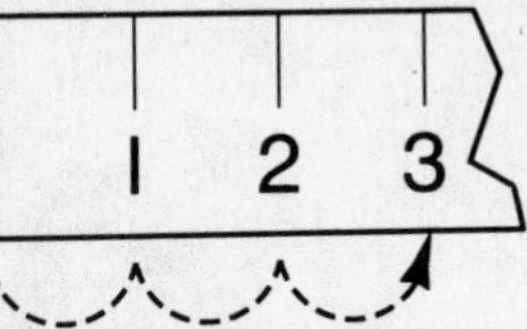

3 centimeters

3 cm

Check

Use your [ruler: 0–16 centimeters] to measure.

1. 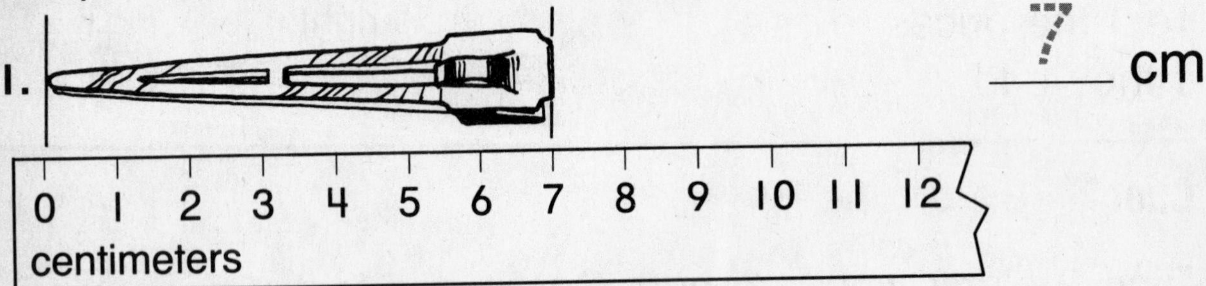

7 cm

2. 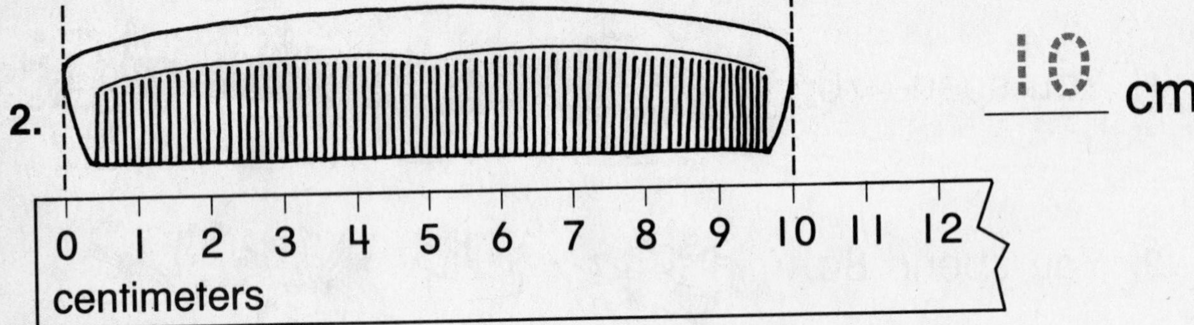

10 cm

3. 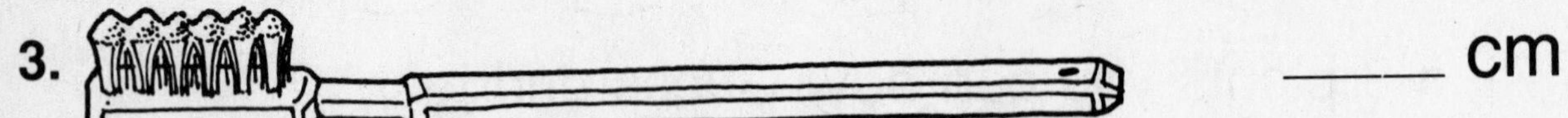

_____ cm

4. 

_____ cm

5. 

_____ cm

Name

LITER

Study

I liter

It holds less than I liter.

It holds more than I liter.

Ring the containers that hold about I liter.

1. 

 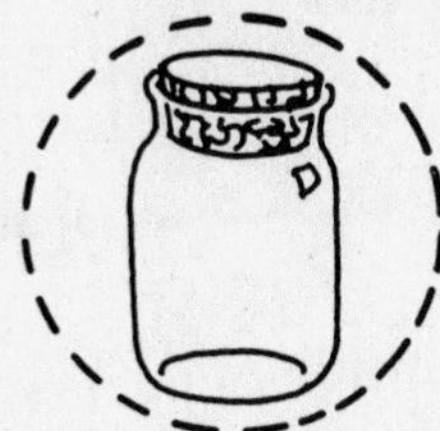  

2. 

  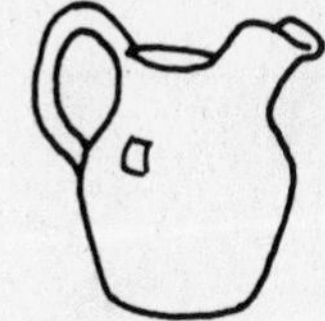 

Color the containers that hold more than I liter.

3. 

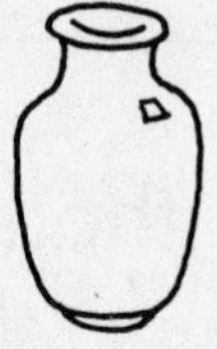   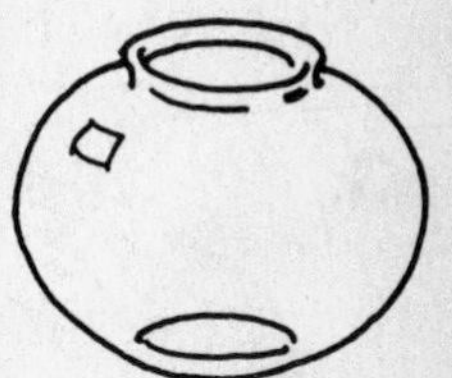

Put an X on containers that hold less than I liter.

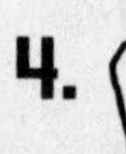

4. 

Name

KILOGRAM

Study

less than I kilogram

more than I kilogram

Check

Ring the better estimate.

I. 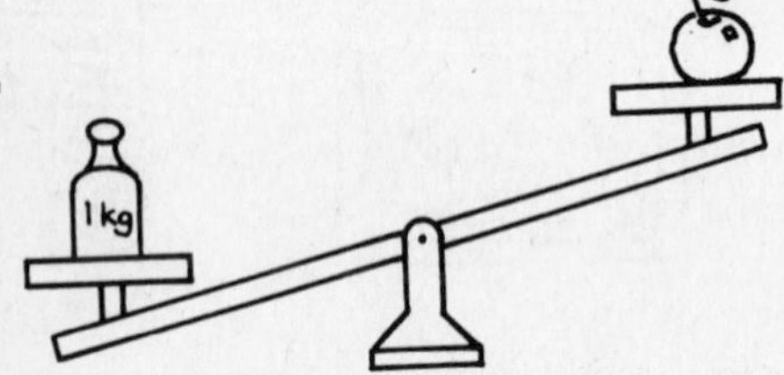

less than I kilogram

more than I kilogram

2. 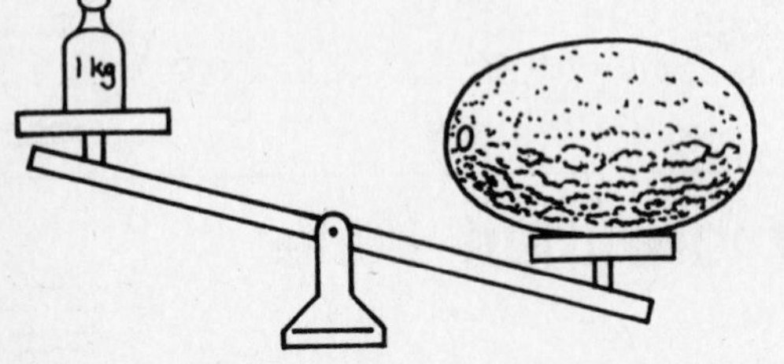

less than I kilogram

more than I kilogram

3. 

less than I kilogram

more than I kilogram

4. 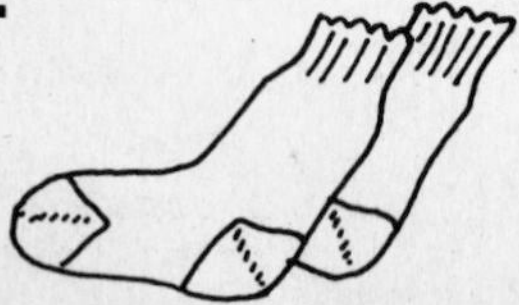

less than I kilogram

more than I kilogram

Name

PROBLEM SOLVING STRATEGY: USING ESTIMATION

Study

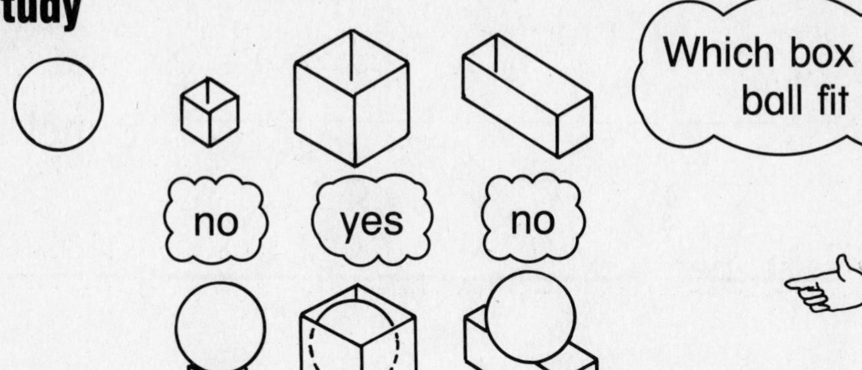

Which box will the ball fit in?

Check

Color the box that best fits the toy.

1.  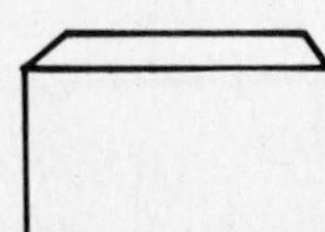  

2.  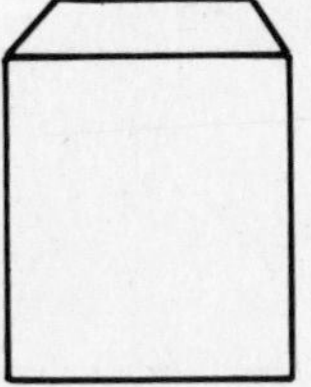 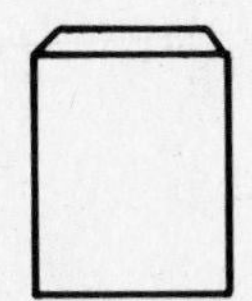 

3.    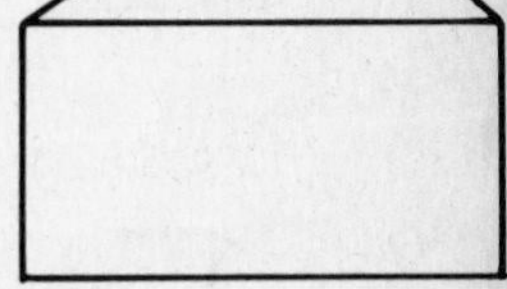

4.    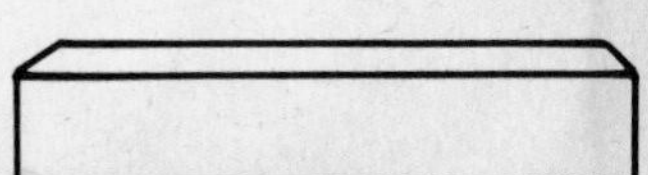

Name

INCH AND FOOT

Study

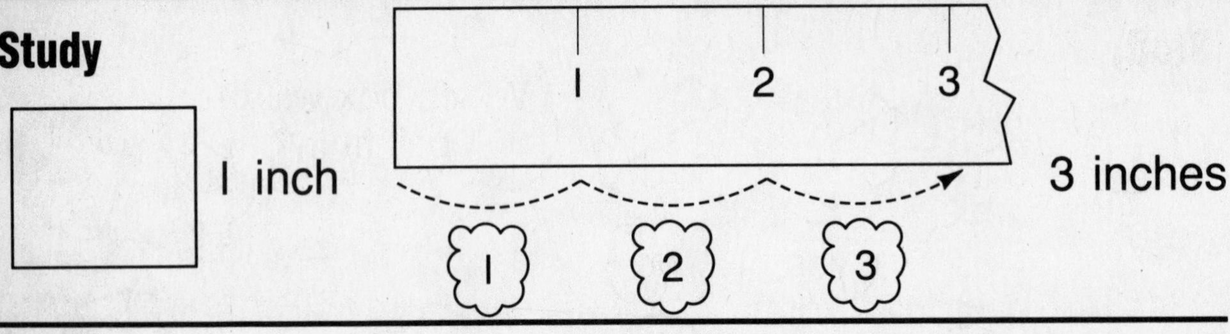

1 inch

3 inches

Check

Use your [ruler] to measure.

1. 4 inches

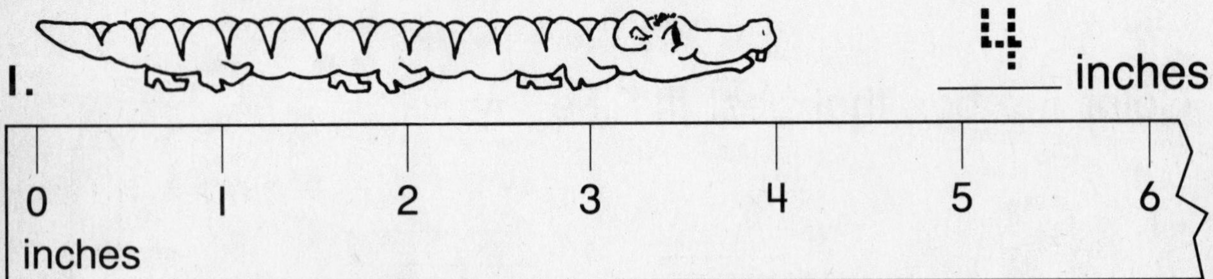

2. 2 inches

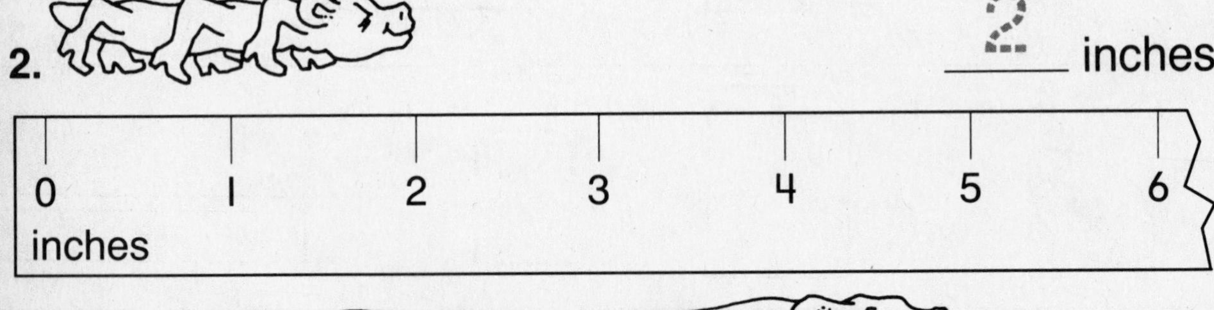

3. 

_____ inches

4. 

_____ inch

5. 

_____ inches

Name

Cup, Pint, and Quart

Study

I cup

2 cups = I pint

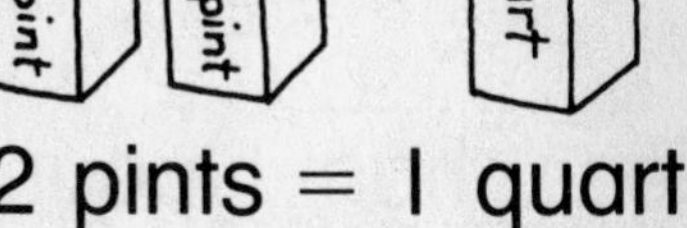
2 pints = I quart

Check

Ring how much it can hold.

1.  more than I quart | less than I quart
2.  more than I quart | less than I quart
3.  more than I quart | less than I quart
4. 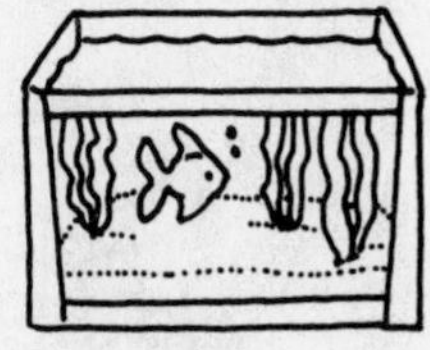 more than I quart | less than I quart
5.  more than I quart | less than I quart
6.  more than I quart | less than I quart

Name

POUND

Study

less than 1 pound

more than 1 pound

Check

Ring each object that weighs *less* than 1 pound.

1.

Ring each object that weighs *more* than 1 pound.

2.

Name

TEMPERATURE

Study

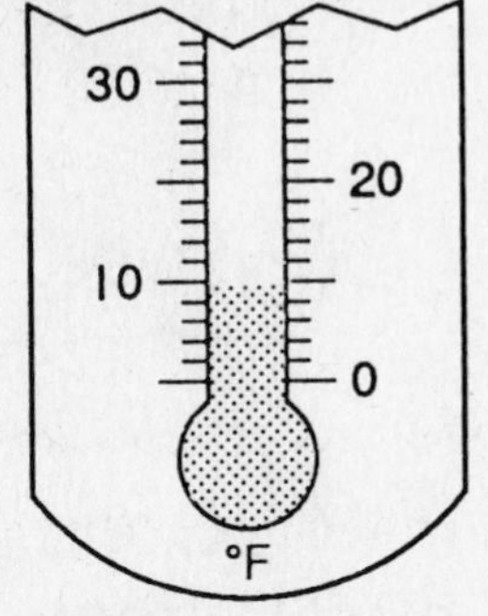

10 degrees

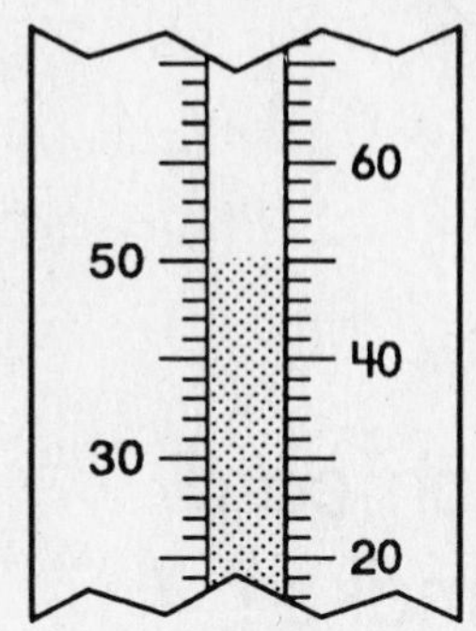

50 degrees

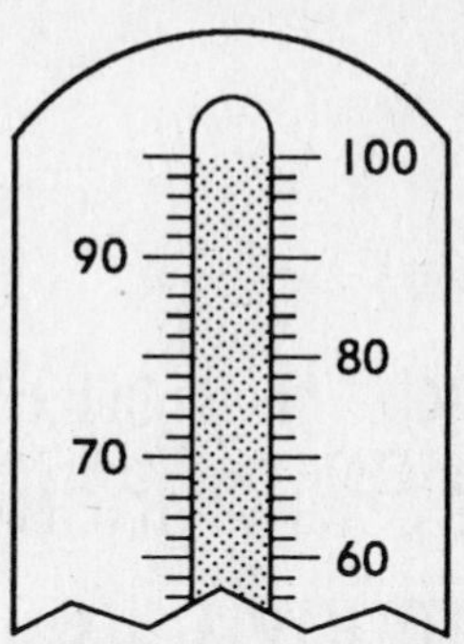

100 degrees

Check

Write the temperature.

1.

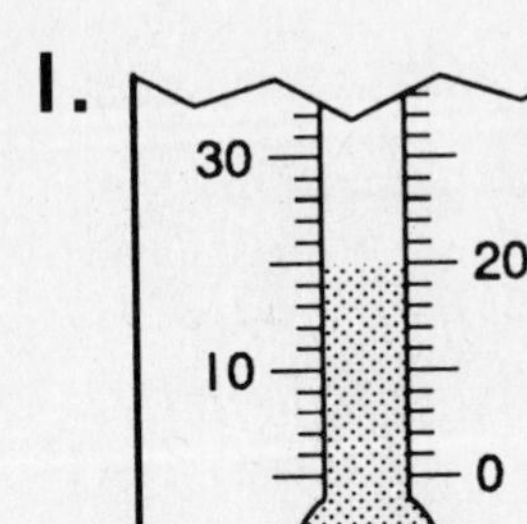

20 degrees

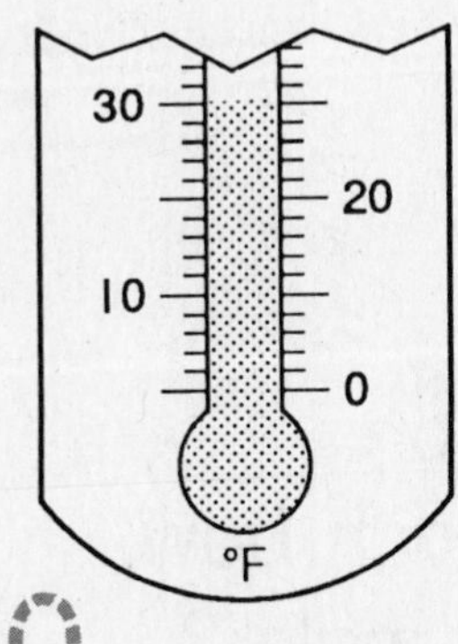

30 degrees

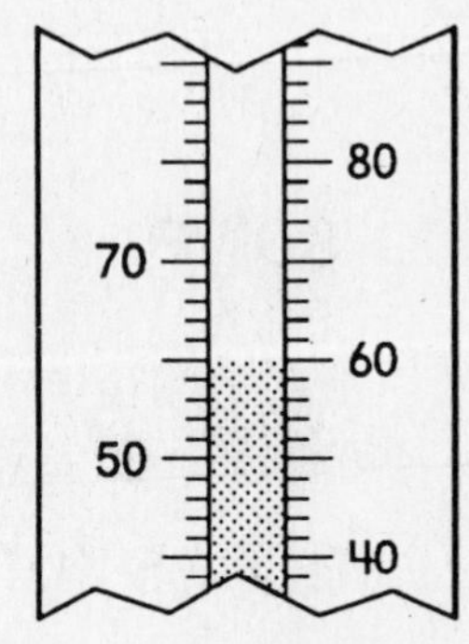

____ degrees

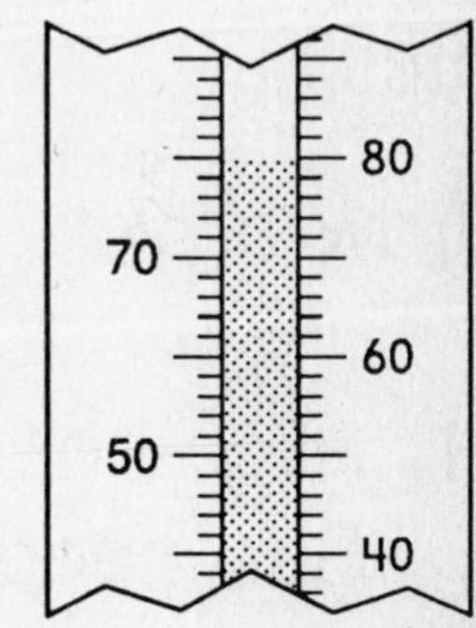

____ degrees

2.

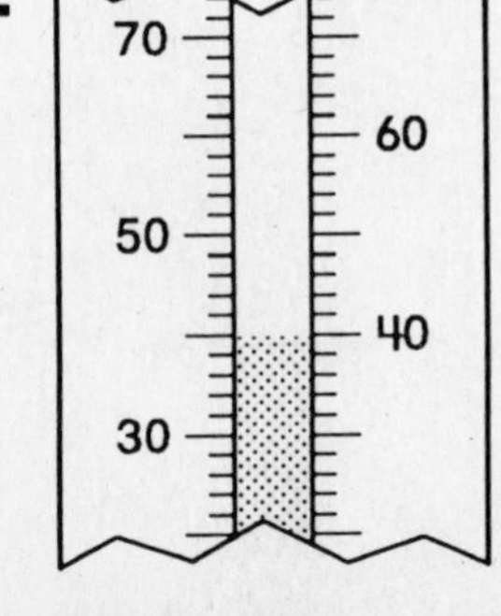

____ degrees

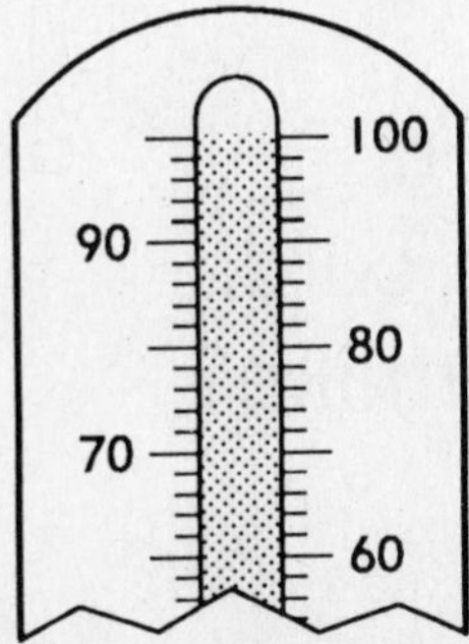

____ degrees

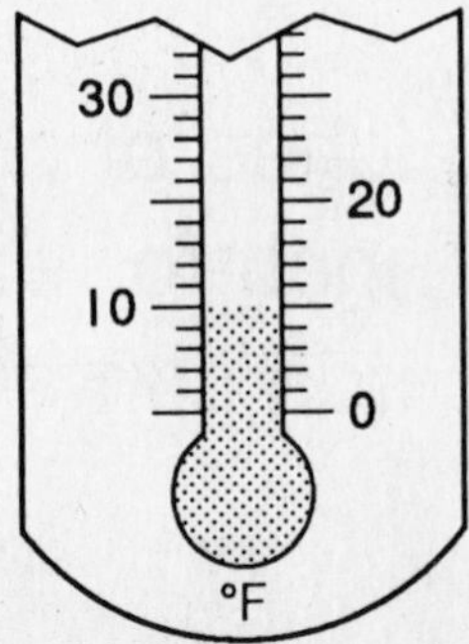

____ degrees

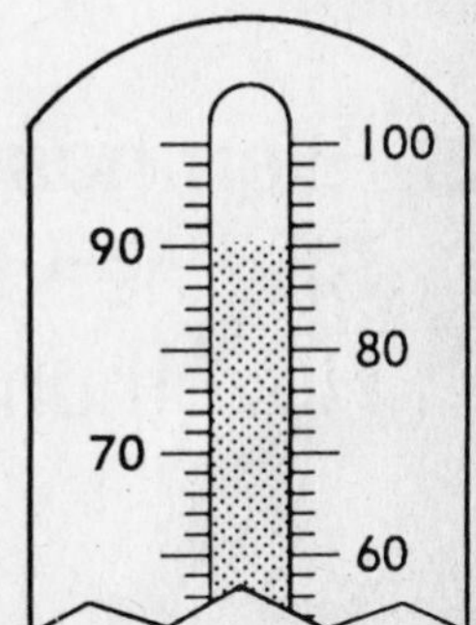

____ degrees

Macmillan/McGraw-Hill, MATHEMATICS IN ACTION
Grade 1, Chapter 8, Lesson 11, pages 249–250

Name

PROBLEM SOLVING STRATEGY: DRAWING A PICTURE

Study

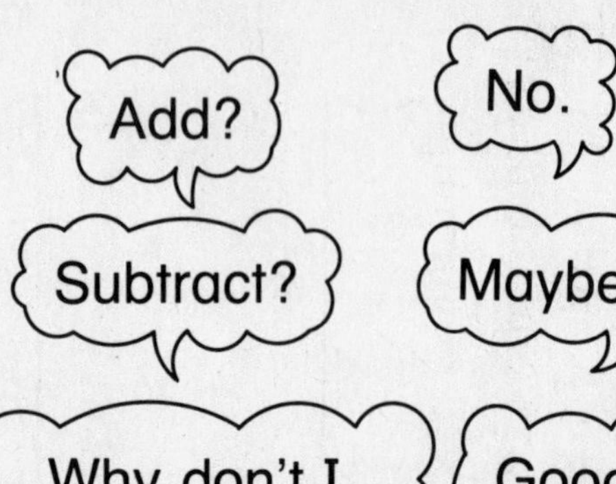

Ted has 4 inches of tape.
He needs 2 inches for each card.
How many cards can he make?

← 2 inches → ← 2 inches →

Ted can make 2 cards.

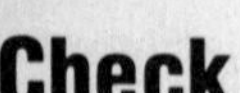

Check

Draw a picture to solve.

1. Alice has 6 inches of ribbon.
   She needs 3 inches for each bow.
   How many bows can she make?  ______ bows

   ← 3 inches → ← 3 inches →

2. Ellen has 5 inches of paper.
   She needs 1 inch for each card.
   How many cards can she make? ______ cards

Name

SUMS AND DIFFERENCES TO 11

Study

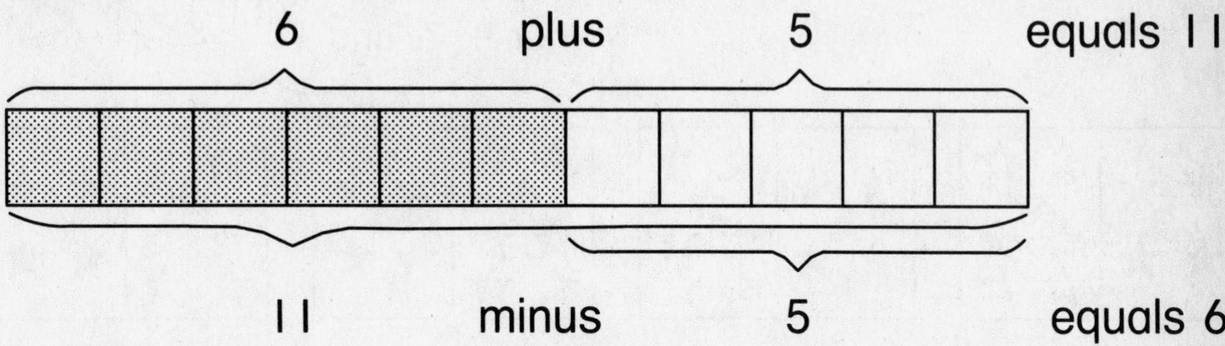

Check

Look at the addition fact.
Write a subtraction fact.

1. 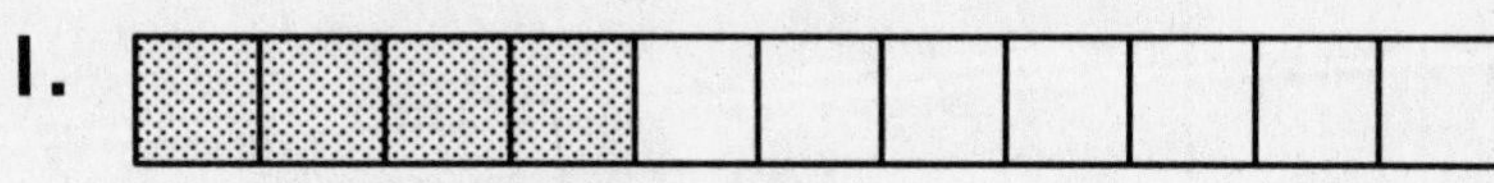

4 + 7 = 11

11 – 7 = 4

2.

8 + 3 = 11

____ – ____ = ____

3.

2 + 9 = 11

____ – ____ = ____

Macmillan/McGraw-Hill, MATHEMATICS IN ACTION
Grade 1, Chapter 9, Lesson 2, pages 265–266

Name

MORE SUMS AND DIFFERENCES TO 11

Study

This is a fact family for 4, 7, and 11.

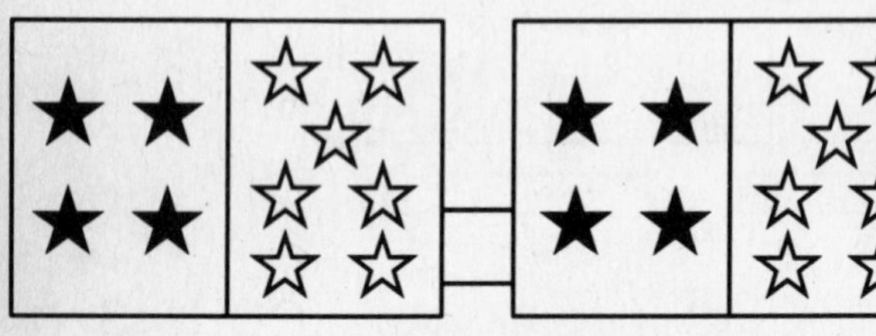

4 + 7 = 11 11 − 7 = 4 7 + 4 = 11 11 − 4 = 7

Check

Write the fact family

1\. 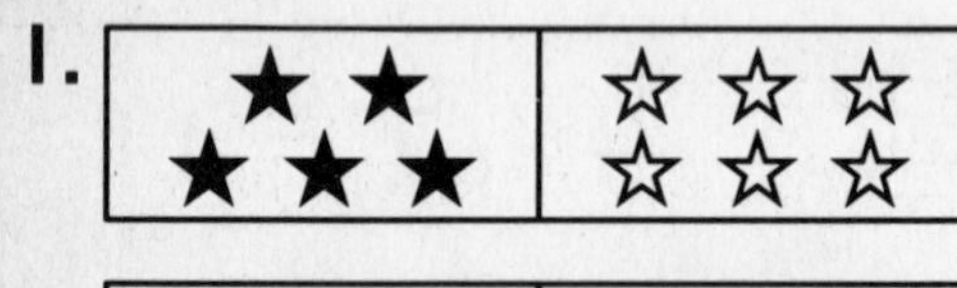

5 + 6 = 11 11 − 6 = 5

6 + 5 = 11 11 − 5 = 6

2\. 

3 + 8 = 11

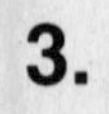

3\. 

4 + 6 = 10

Name

PROBLEM SOLVING STRATEGY: CHOOSING THE OPERATION

Study

Joe had 8 balloons.
He gave 3 balloons away.
How many does he have left?

$8 - 3 = 5$ 5 balloons

Subtract to find the part that is left.

Jill had 4 balloons.
She got 3 more from Joe.
How many does she have in all?

$4 + 3 = 7$ 7 balloons

Add to combine two parts and find the whole.

Check

Ring the number sentence that solves the problem.

1. The team had 9 baseballs.
They lost 3 baseballs.
How many do they have left?

$9 + 3 = 11$

$9 - 3 = 6$

2. JoAnn had 8 beach balls.
She gave 2 to Michael.
How many does she have left?

$8 + 2 = 10$

$8 - 2 = 6$

3. Kevin had 7 tennis balls.
He found 4 more balls.
How many does he have in all?

$7 + 4 = 11$

$7 - 4 = 3$

Macmillan/McGraw-Hill, MATHEMATICS IN ACTION
Grade 1, Chapter 9, Lesson 4, pages 269–270

Name

PROBLEM SOLVING STRATEGY: USING SUBTRACTION TO COMPARE

Study

Jan saw 5 ducks.
She saw 7 chickens.
How many more ducks than chickens did she see?

You can compare.

d d d d d
| | | | |
c c c c c [c c]

2 more chickens.

You can subtract.

$7 - 5 = 2$

2 more chickens.

Jan saw 2 more chickens than ducks.

Check

Solve.

1. Bev found 9 white eggs.
   She found 6 brown eggs.
   How many more white eggs than brown eggs did she find?

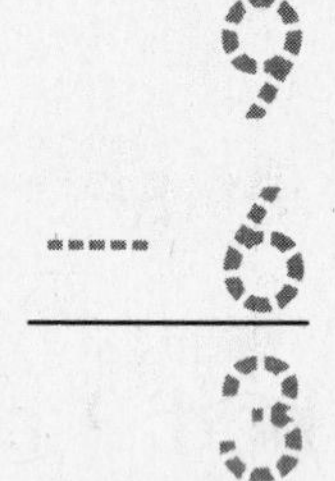

3 more

2. Jon saw 10 cows.
   He saw 5 horses.
   How many fewer horses than cows did he see?

_____ fewer

3. Sonny picked 9 tomatoes.
   He picked 11 ears of corn.
   How many more ears of corn than tomatoes did he pick?

_____ more

MACMILLAN/McGRAW-HILL

Name

SUMS AND DIFFERENCES TO 12

Study

7 dogs

5 dogs

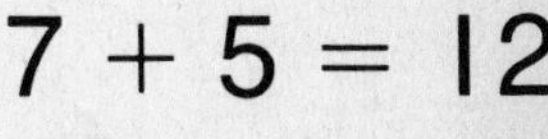

$7 + 5 = 12$

12 dogs in all

12 dogs in all

5 dogs go home

$12 - 5 = 7$

7 dogs are left

Check

Look at the addition fact.
Write a subtraction fact.

1.  

$3 + 9 = 12$

12 – 9 = 3

2.  

$7 + 5 = 12$

____ – ____ = ____

3.  

$6 + 6 = 12$

____ – ____ = ____

Name

MORE SUMS AND DIFFERENCES TO 12

Study 

4 + 8 = 12 12 − 8 = 4

8 + 4 = 12 12 − 4 = 8

I use the numbers 4, 8, and 12.

Check

Write the fact family.

1.

3 + 9 = 12  12 − 9 = 3

9 + 3 = 12 12 − 3 = 9

2.

5 + 7 = 12 

3.

6 + 5 = 11 

4.

6 + 6 = 12

MACMILLAN/McGRAW-HILL

Name

ADDING AND SUBTRACTING MONEY

Study

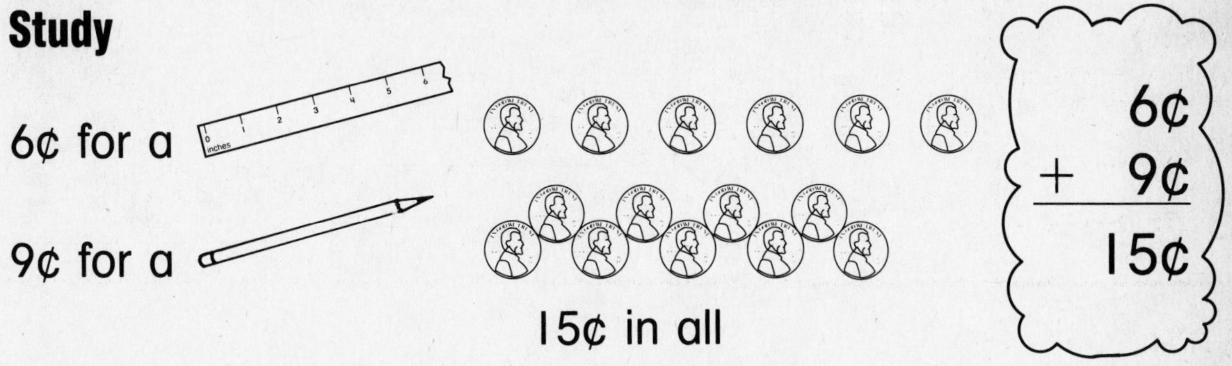

Check

Add or subtract.

1. $5¢ + 6¢ = 11¢$

2. $10¢ - 5¢ =$

3. $3¢ + 9¢ =$

4. $4¢ + 8¢ =$

5. $11¢ - 8¢ =$

6. $12¢ - 5¢ =$

Name

THREE ADDENDS

Study

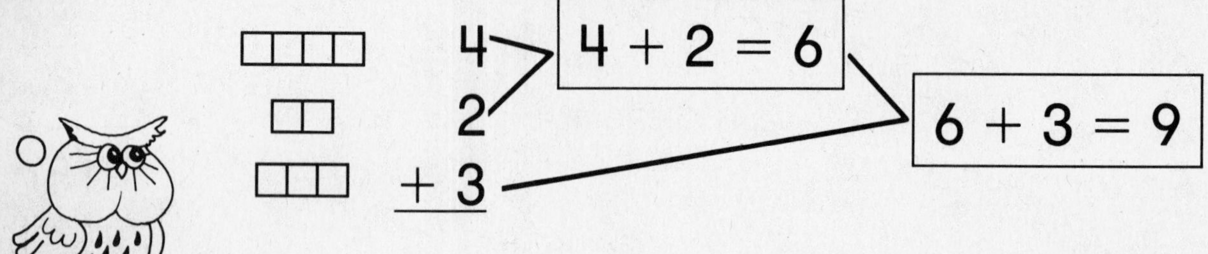

The sum is 9.

Check

Add. Use cubes to help.

1.

2, 5 → 7	6, 3 → 9	3, 3 →
2	6	3
5	3	3
+ 5	+ 2	+ 4
12	11	

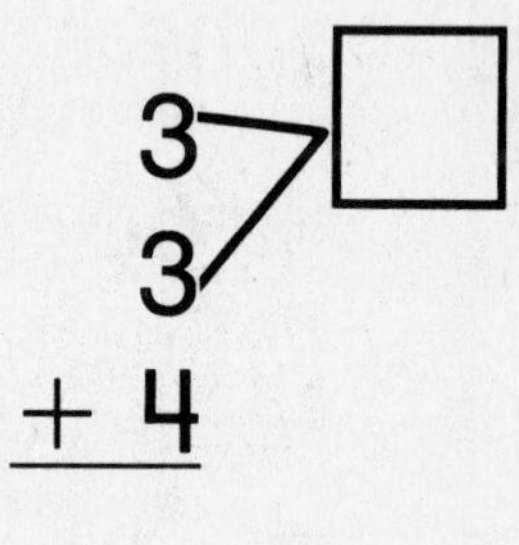

2.

5	8	1	3	4
2	1	2	4	2
+ 3	+ 3	+ 7	+ 3	+ 5

3.

2	1	5	2	3
2	4	4	4	3
+ 7	+ 6	+ 3	+ 2	+ 3

Name

Hour

Study

Check

Ring the clocks that show the same time.

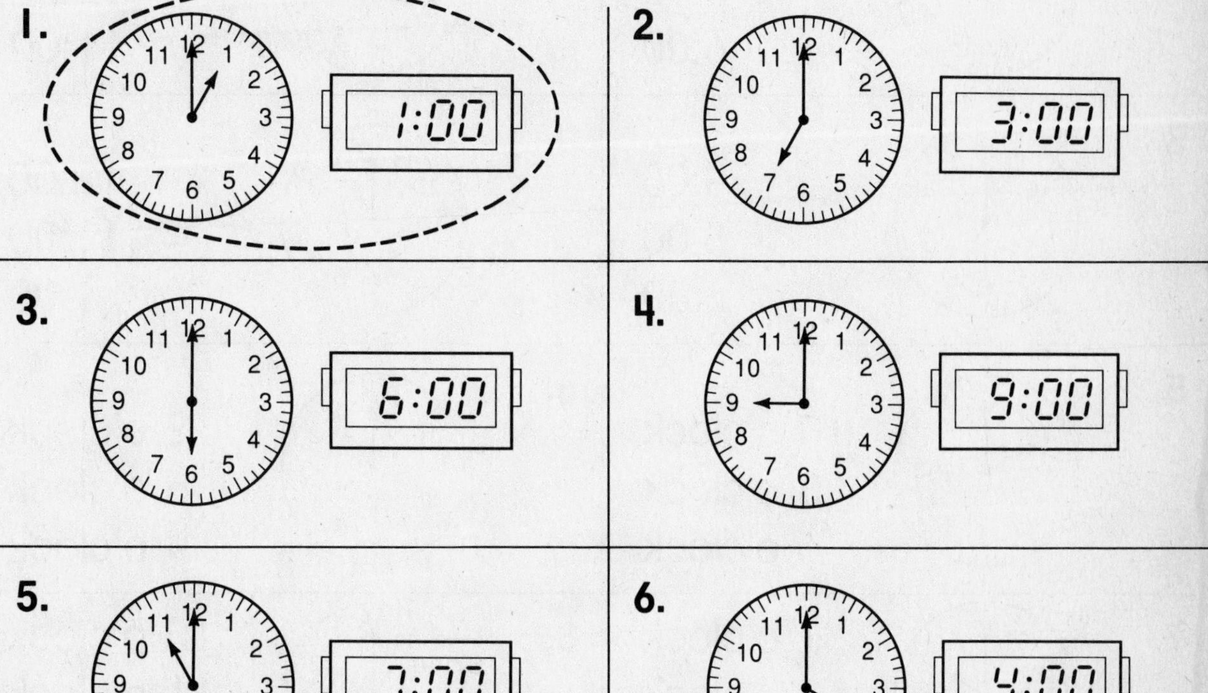

Macmillan/McGraw-Hill, MATHEMATICS IN ACTION
Grade 1, Chapter 10, Lesson 4, pages 295–296

Name

MORE ABOUT TIME TO THE HOUR

Study

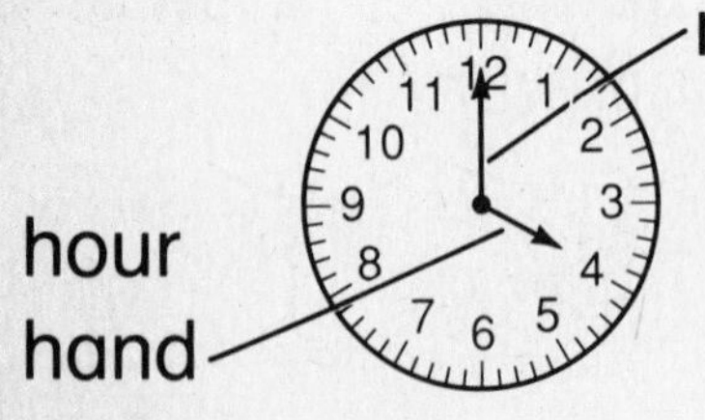

4:00 or 4 o'clock

minute hand
hour hand

8:00 or 8 o'clock

Check

Ring the time.

1. 
10:00
3:00
6:00

2. 
8:00
2:00
11:00

3. 
4:00
5:00
6:00

4. 
12:00
11:00
1:00

5. 
10 o'clock
3 o'clock
6 o'clock

6. 
2 o'clock
6 o'clock
4 o'clock

7. 
1 o'clock
2 o'clock
3 o'clock

8. 
10 o'clock
11 o'clock
12 o'clock

Name

PROBLEM SOLVING STRATEGY: MAKING A LIST

Study

Phil has these clothes.

He can make 4 different outfits.

Check

Color.

Color to show the different outfits.

Macmillan/McGraw-Hill, MATHEMATICS IN ACTION
Grade 1, Chapter 10, Lesson 6, pages 299–300

Name

HALF HOUR

Study

Check

Ring the time.

Clock	(2:00) 2:30	Clock	8:00 8:30
Clock	10:00 10:30	Clock	7:00 7:30
Clock	1 o'clock / 30 minutes after 1 o'clock	Clock	3 o'clock / 30 minutes after 3 o'clock
Clock	9 o'clock / 30 minutes after 9 o'clock	Clock	5 o'clock / 30 minutes after 5 o'clock

Name

MORE ABOUT TIME TO THE HALF HOUR

Study

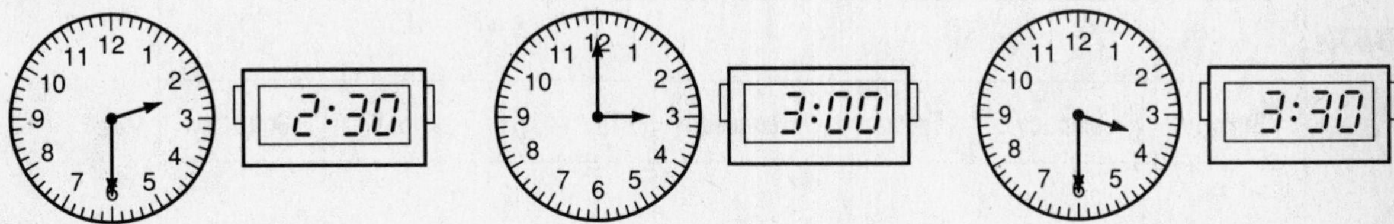

30 minutes after 2 o'clock

3 o'clock

30 minutes after 3 o'clock

Check

Write the time.

MACMILLAN/McGRAW-HILL

Macmillan/McGraw-Hill, MATHEMATICS IN ACTION
Grade 1, Chapter 10, Lesson 9, pages 305–306

Name

DAYS OF THE WEEK

Study

MONTH	JUNE							
	Sunday	Monday	Tuesday	Wednesday	Thursday	Friday	Saturday	Days
					1	2	3	
1 week	4	5	6	7	8	9	10	
	11	12	13	14	15	16	17	
	18	19	20	21	22	23	24	
	25	26	27	28	29	30		

Check

1. Write the name of the month. June

2. Write the days of the week. Sunday

______ ______ ______

______ ______ ______

3. How many days are in a week? ____

4. How many days are in June? ____

5. How many Mondays? ____

6. How many Fridays? ____

Name

PROBLEM SOLVING STRATEGIES REVIEW

Study

Jean saw 10 birds.
Then 4 birds flew away.
How many birds are left?

6 birds are left.

Check

Solve.

1. There were 12 ducks in the pond.
   4 ducks flew away.
   How many ducks are left? 8 ducks

2. Tad saw 7 hens.
   Bart saw 4 hens.
   How many hens did they see in all? ______ hens

3. Tonia makes signs for the garden.
   She has 6 inches of paper.
   She needs 3 inches of paper for each sign.
   How many signs can she make? ______ signs

Macmillan/McGraw-Hill, MATHEMATICS IN ACTION
Grade 1, Chapter 10, Lesson 11, pages 309–310

Name

THREE-DIMENSIONAL FIGURES

Study

cube cone sphere cylinder box

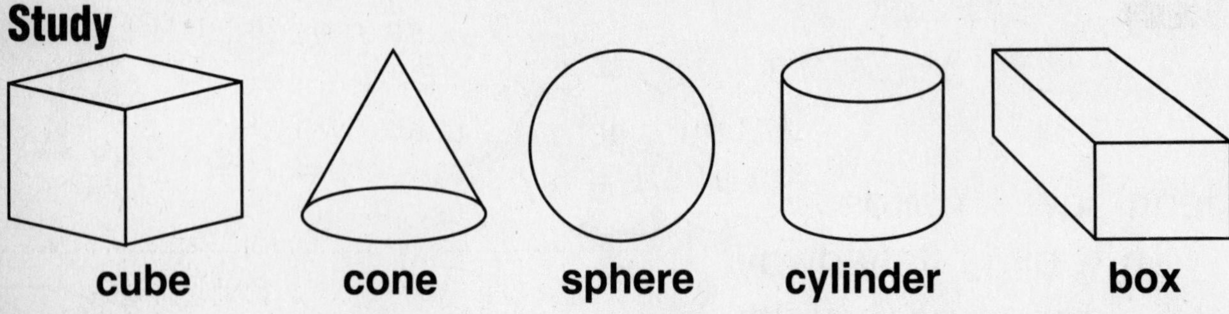

Check

Draw lines to match.
Color to match.

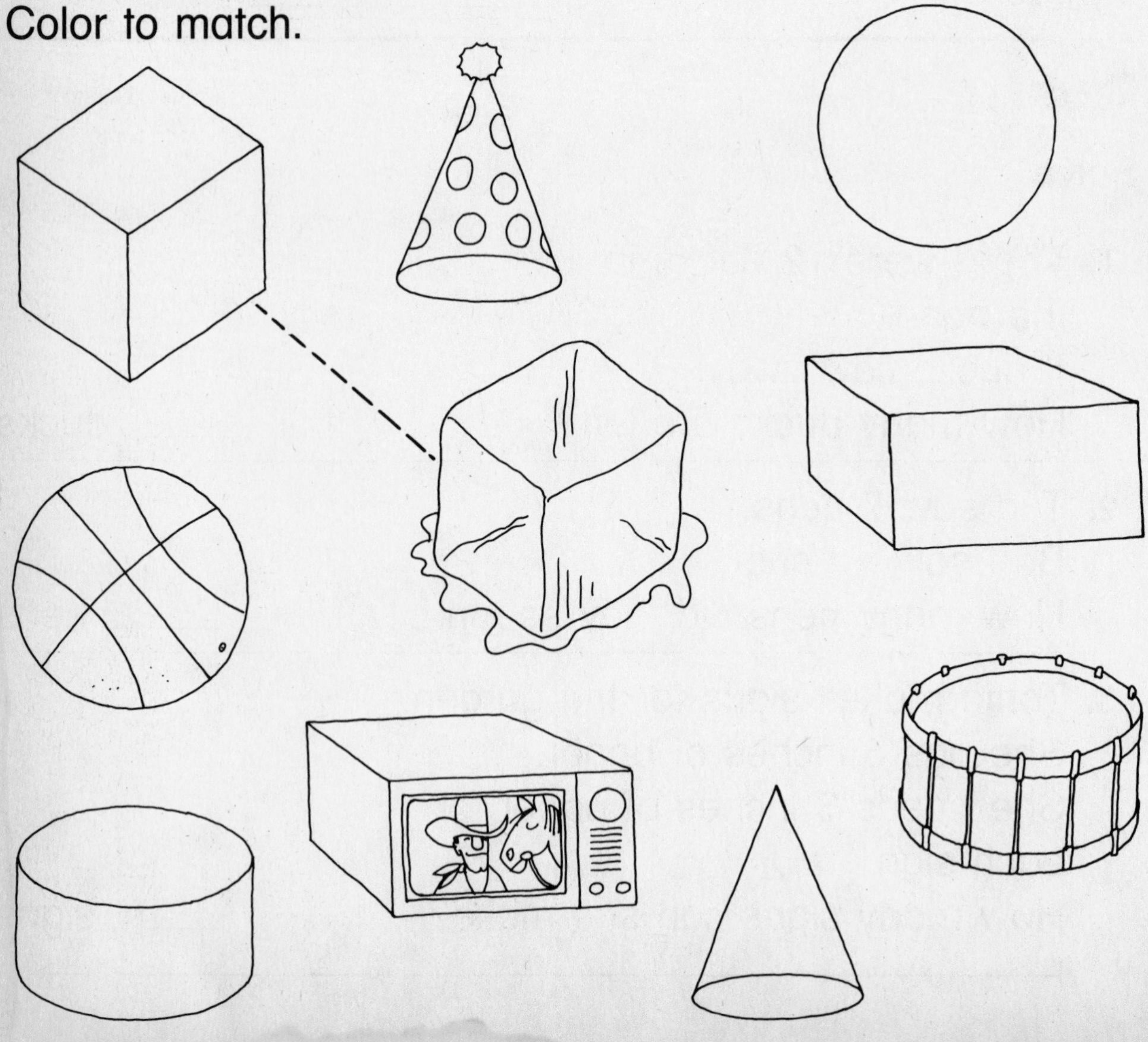

Name

TWO-DIMENSIONAL FIGURES

Study

   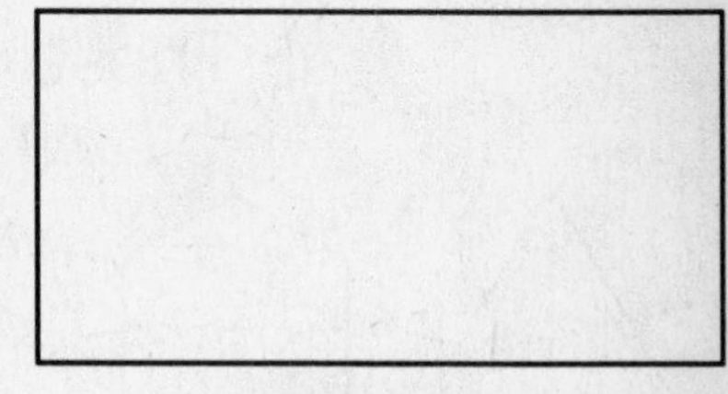

circle square triangle rectangle

Check

Ring the shapes that match.

1\. 

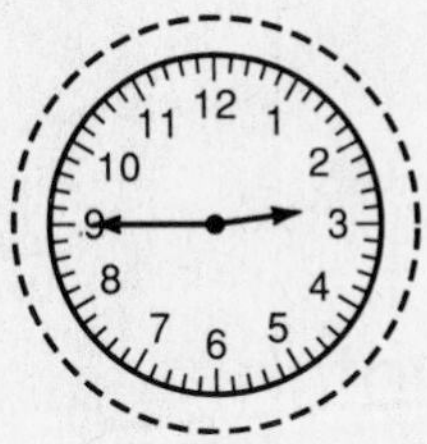

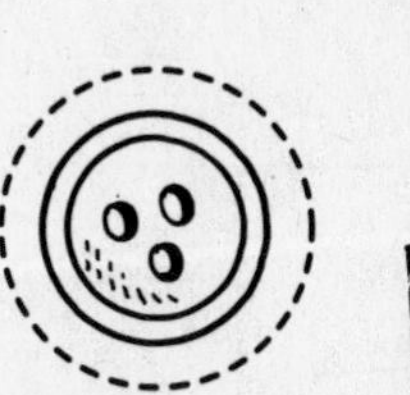

2\. 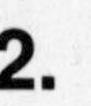

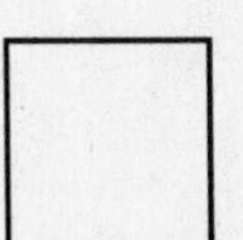

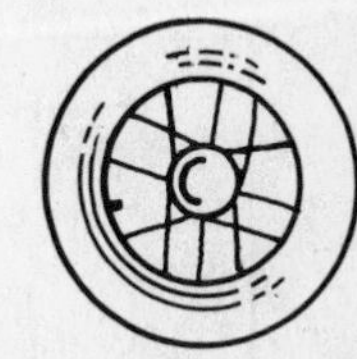

3\. 

4\. 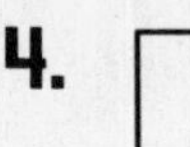

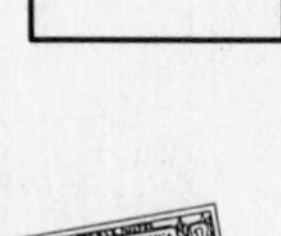

Name

SYMMETRY

Study

Check

Trace the line.
Ring the shape if both parts match.

1.

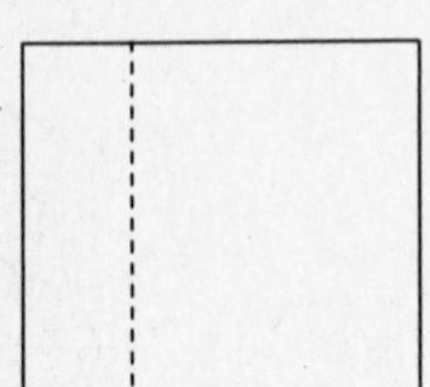

2.

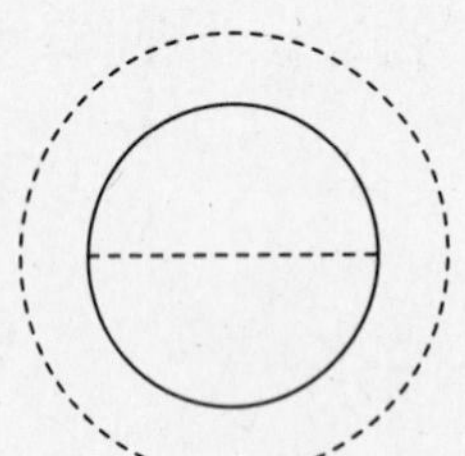

3.

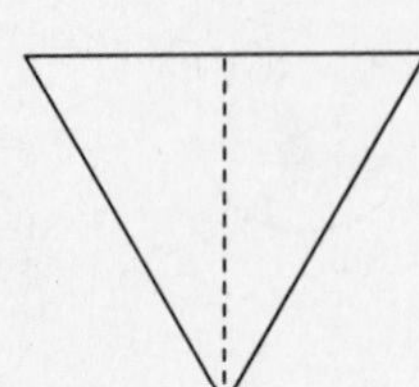

4.

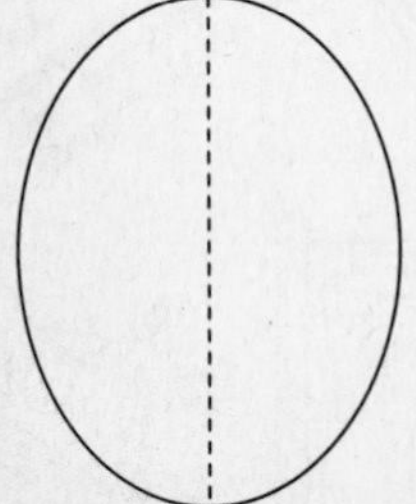

5.

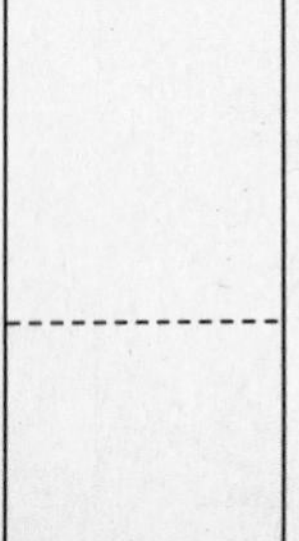

6.

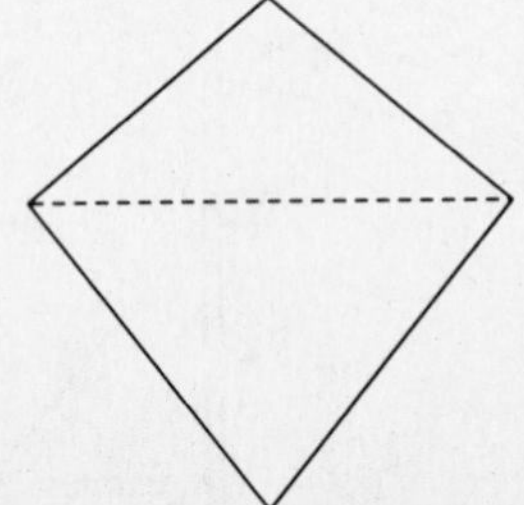

Name

PROBLEM SOLVING STRATEGY: FINDING A PATTERN

Study

Check

Color to show the pattern.

1. red blue red blue red blue red blue

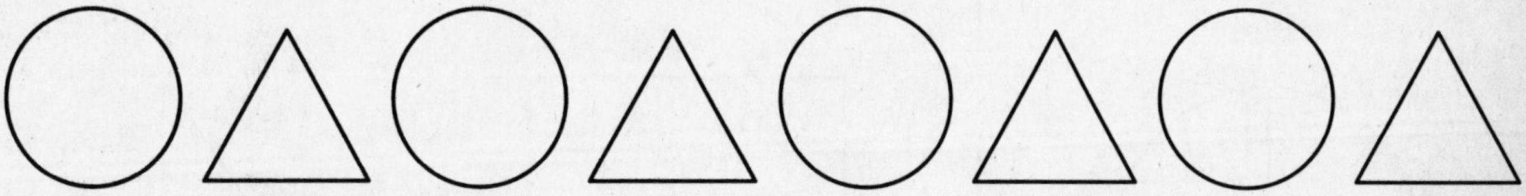

2. red yellow blue red yellow blue

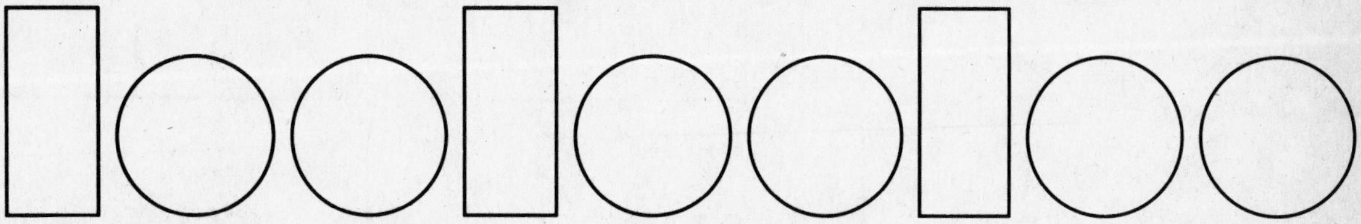

3. green orange blue green orange blue

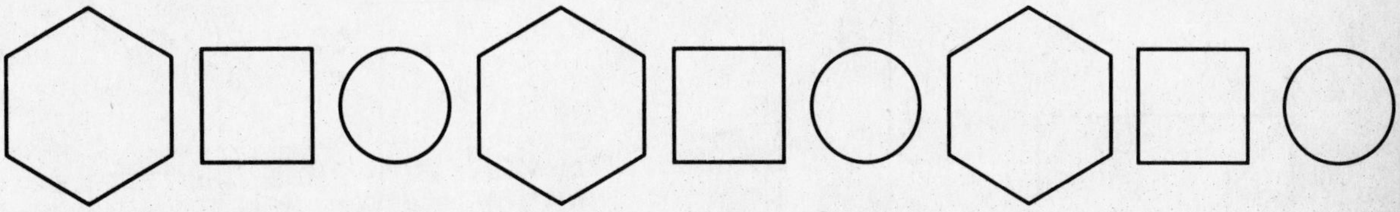

4. purple yellow red purple yellow red

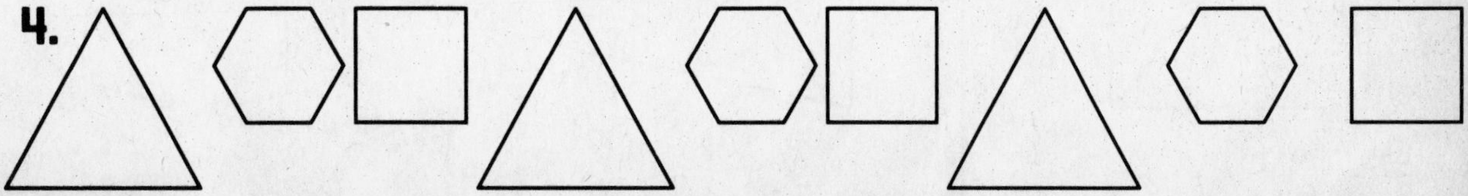

Macmillan/McGraw-Hill, MATHEMATICS IN ACTION
Grade 1, Chapter 11, Lesson 5, pages 329–330

Name

HALVES

Study

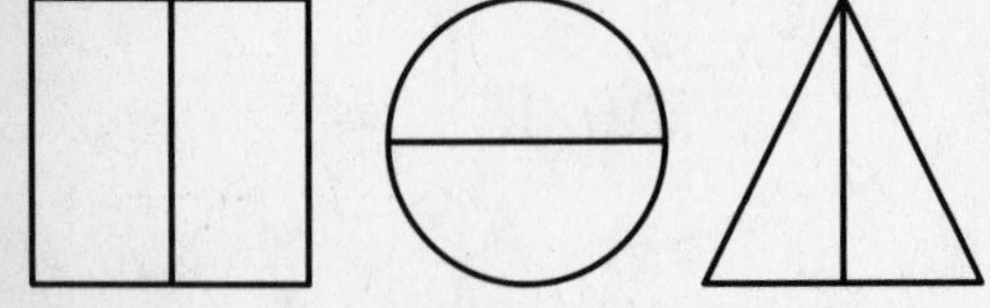

halves

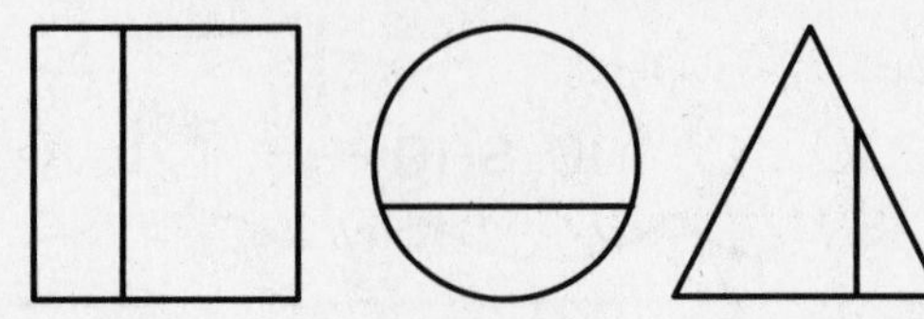

not halves

Check

Halves? Ring *yes* or *no*.

1.

yes no

2.

yes  no

3.

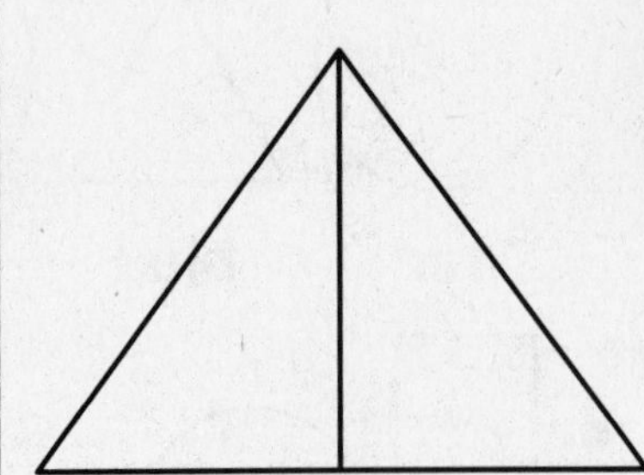

yes no

4.

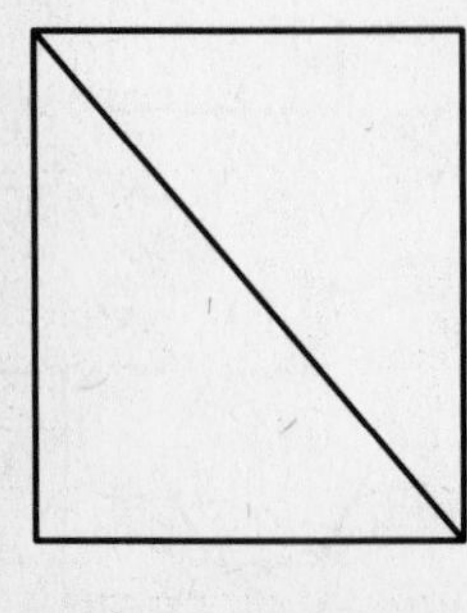

yes no

5.

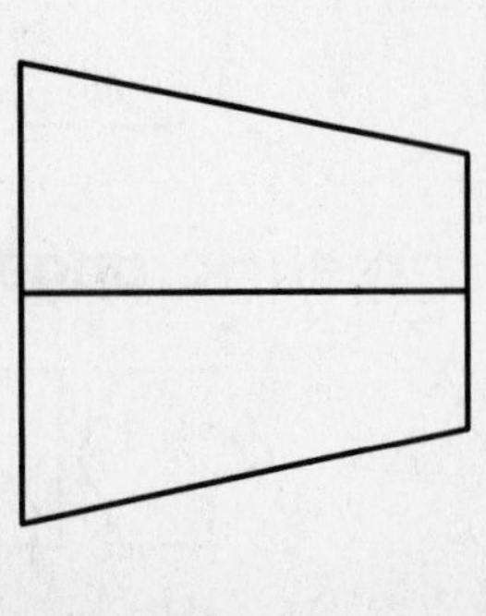
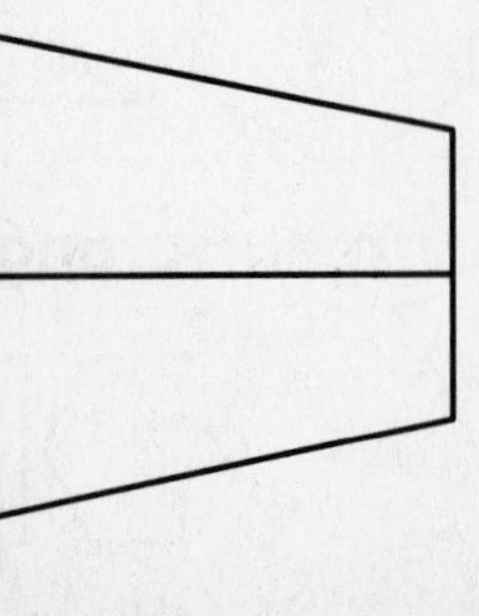
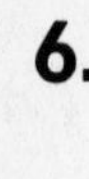

yes no

6.

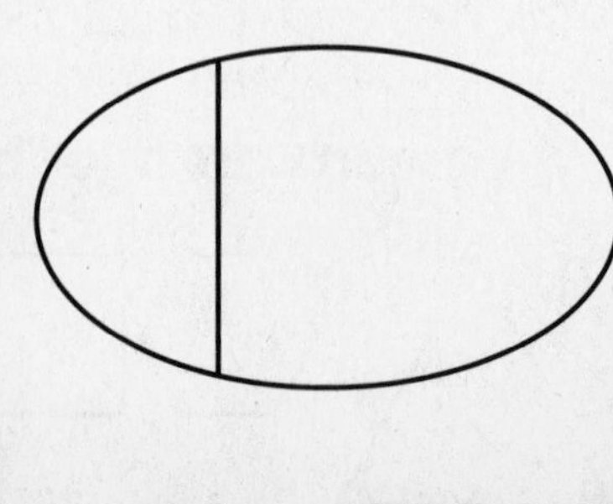

yes no

MACMILLAN/McGRAW-HILL

Name

FOURTHS

Study

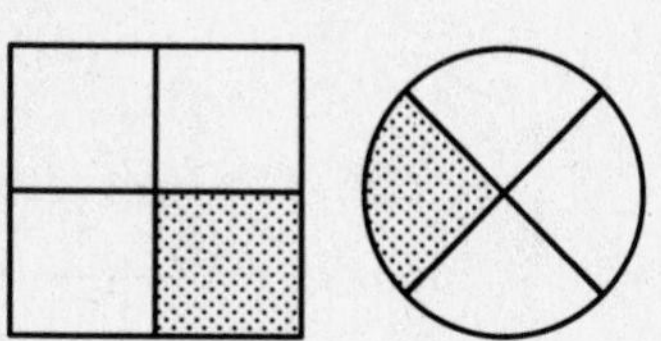

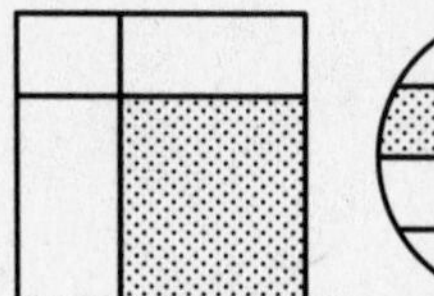

one fourth

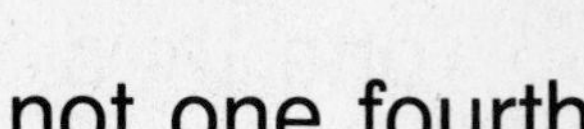

not one fourth

Check

Ring the shape that shows $\frac{1}{4}$.

1.

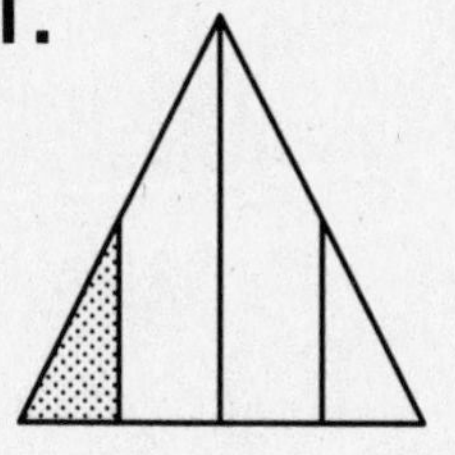

2.

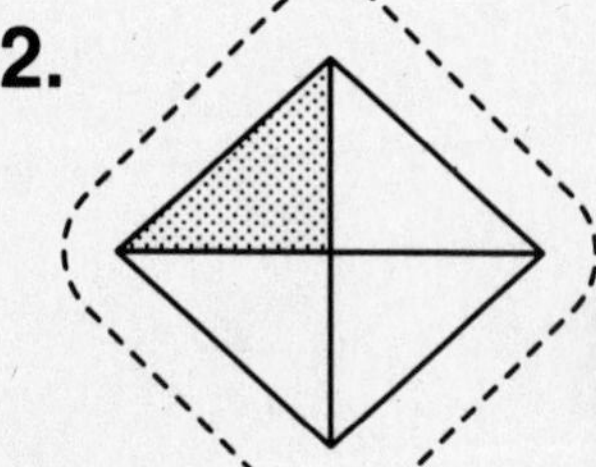

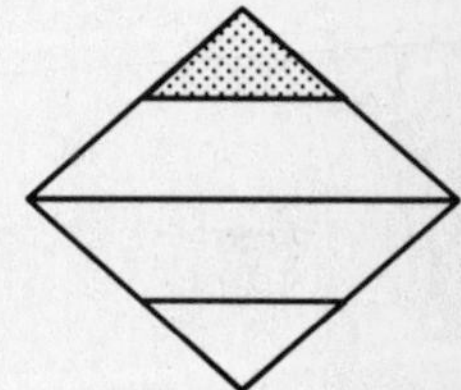

3.

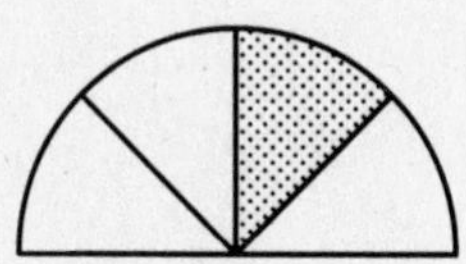

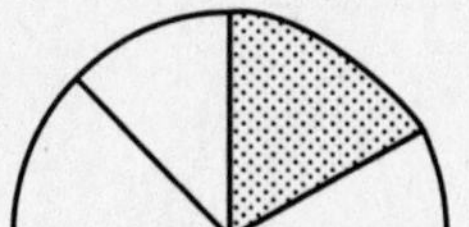

4.

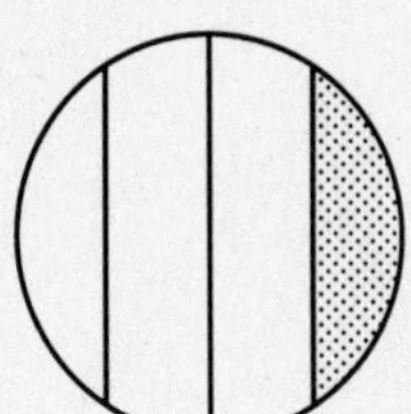

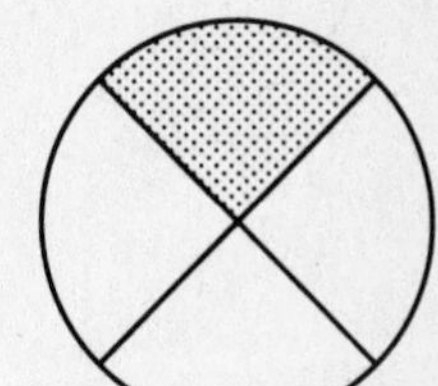

5.

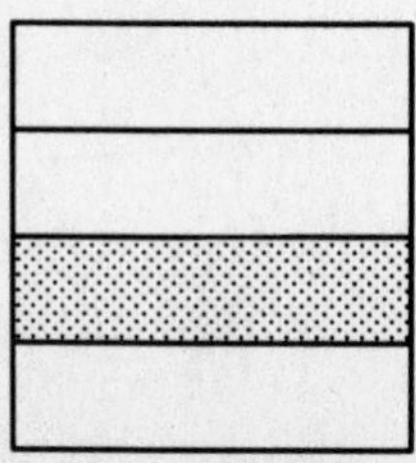

6.

Macmillan/McGraw-Hill, MATHEMATICS IN ACTION
Grade 1, Chapter 11, Lesson 8, pages 335–336

Name ______________________________

THIRDS

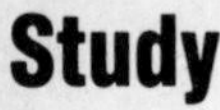

Study

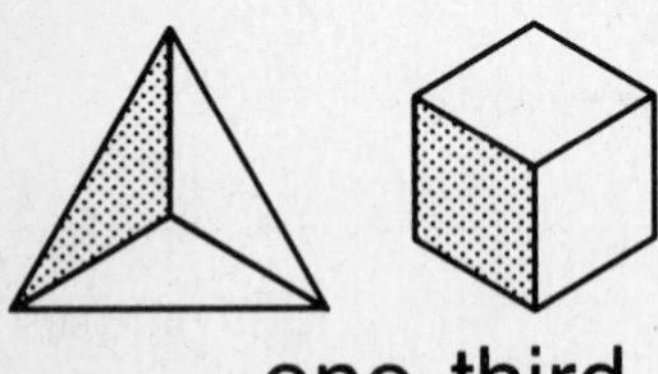

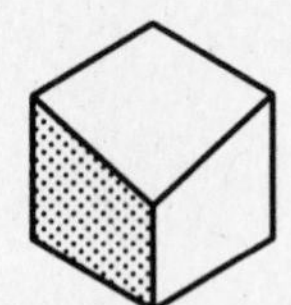

one third

not one third

Check

Ring the shapes that show thirds.

Color $\frac{1}{3}$ of those shapes.

1.

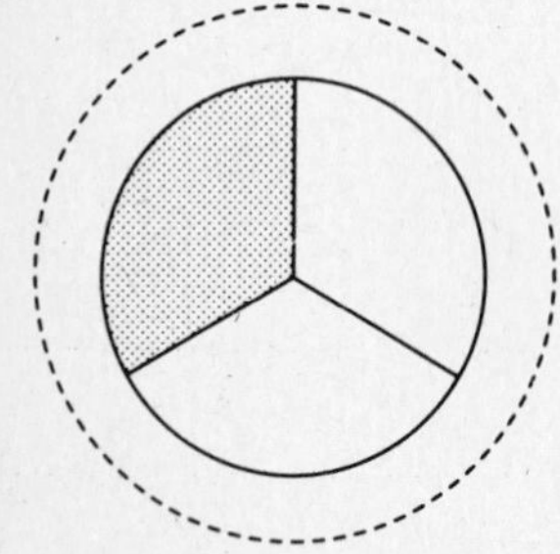

2.

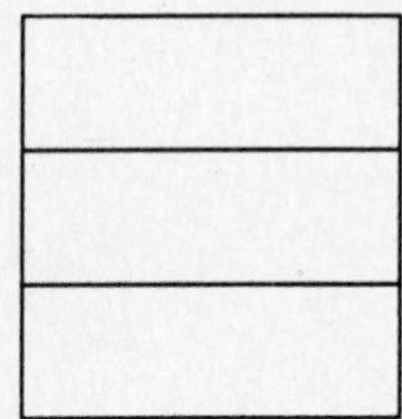

3.

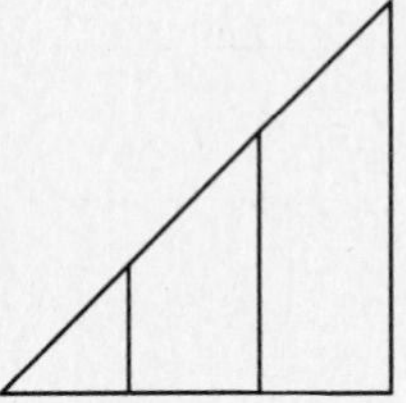

4.

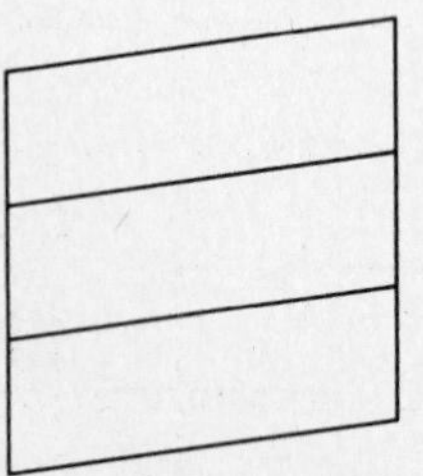

5.

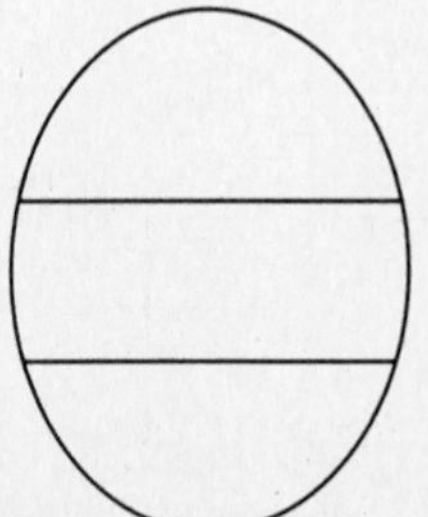

6.

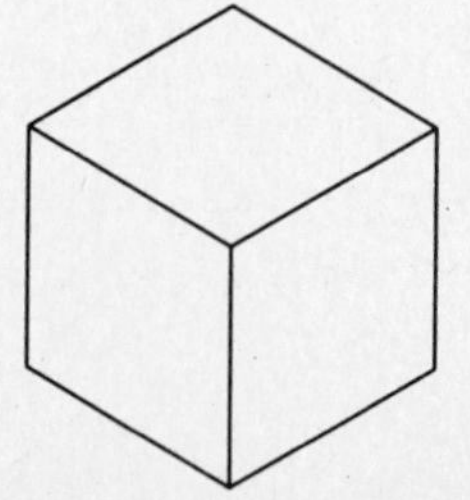

Name

PROBLEM SOLVING STRATEGY: DRAWING A PICTURE

Study

The 4 children will share the sheet of paper. How can they divide the paper into equal pieces?

Check

Draw a picture to show how the children share.

1.  3 children share the paper.

2.  2 children share the paper.

3.  3 children share the paper.

Macmillan/McGraw-Hill, MATHEMATICS IN ACTION
Grade 1, Chapter 11, Lesson 11, pages 341–342

Name

SUMS AND DIFFERENCES TO 13

Study

Addition Sentence

8 + 5 = 13

Subtraction Sentence

13 − 5 = 8

Check

Complete the number sentences.

1\. 6 + 7 = 13

2\. 13 − 7 = 6

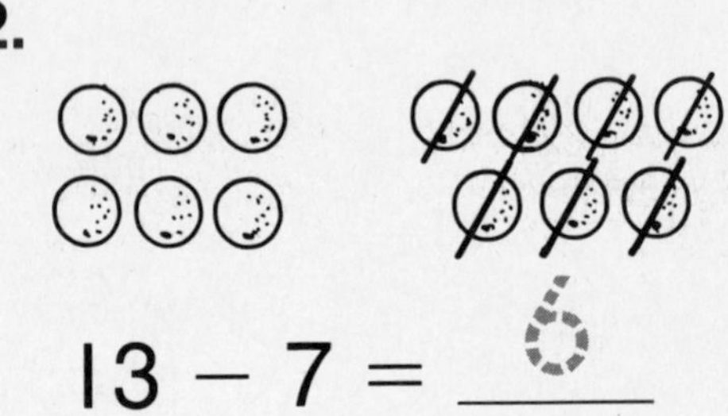

3\. 4 + 9 = ____

4\. 13 − 9 = ____

5\. 5 + 8 = ____

6\. 13 − 8 = ____

Name ____________________

MORE SUMS AND DIFFERENCES TO 13

Study

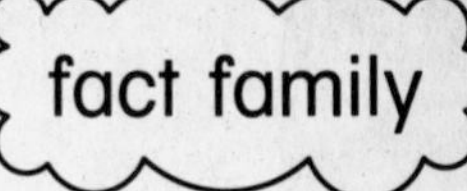

6 + 7 = 13
13 − 7 = 6

7 + 6 = 13
13 − 6 = 7

Check

Complete each fact family.

1. 

5 + 8 = 13 13 − 8 = 5

8 + 5 = 13 13 − 5 = 8

2.

9 + 4 = ____ 13 − 4 = ____

4 + 9 = ____ 13 − 9 = ____

3.

7 + 5 = ____ 12 − 5 = ____

5 + 7 = ____ 12 − 7 = ____

Name

SUMS AND DIFFERENCES TO 14

Study

9 + 5 = 14

Check

Write an addition fact and a subtraction fact.

1.

8 + 6 = 14

14 − 6 = 8

2.

___ + ___ = 14

14 − ___ = ___

3.

___ + ___ = 14

14 − ___ = ___

Name

MORE SUMS AND DIFFERENCES TO 14

Study

fact family

$5 + 9 = 14$

$14 - 9 = 5$

$9 + 5 = 14$

$14 - 5 = 9$

Check

Write the fact family.

1.
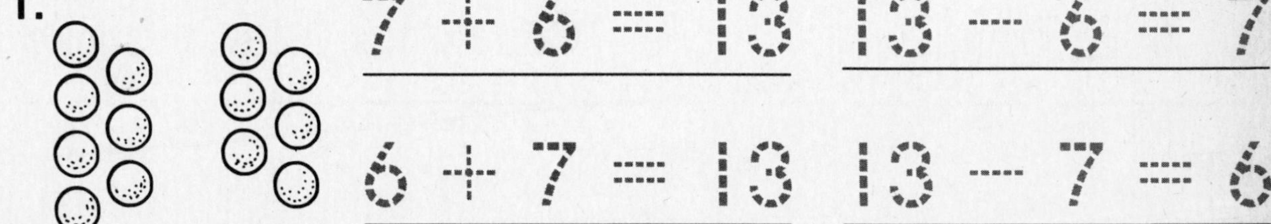

7 + 6 = 13 13 − 6 = 7

6 + 7 = 13 13 − 7 = 6

2.
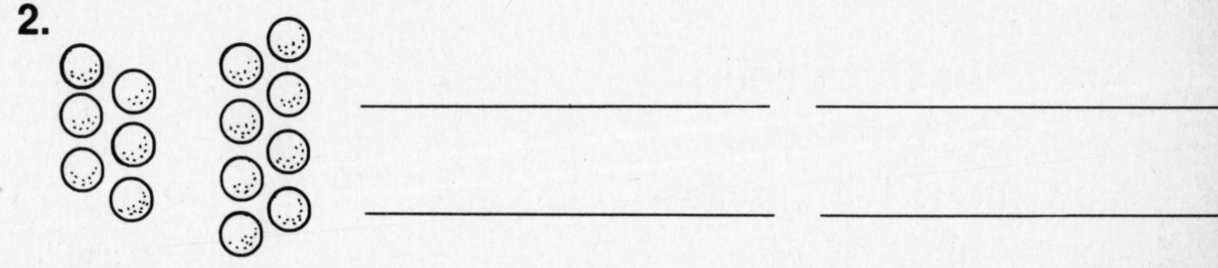

3.
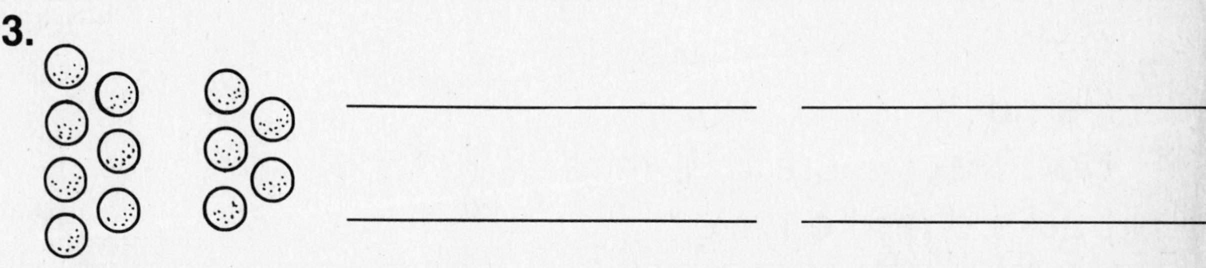

4.

Name

PROBLEM SOLVING STRATEGY: CHOOSING THE OPERATION

Study

Carlos has 7 stickers.
He has 9 stamps.
How many fewer stickers
than stamps does he have?

$9 - 7 = 2$ Carlos has 2 fewer stickers.

Check

Solve.

1. Anita has 8 toy bears.
   She has 6 toy cats.
   How many toy animals
   does Anita have?

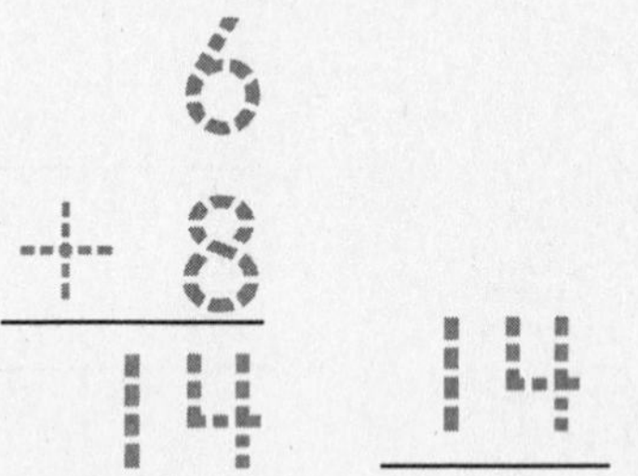

14 toy animals

2. George has 4 toy trucks.
   He has 9 toy cars.
   How many more cars than
   trucks does he have?

_____ more

3. Donny had 16 cookies.
   He gave 9 cookies to
   three friends.
   How many cookies does
   he have left?

_____ cookies

Name

Sums and Differences to 15

Study

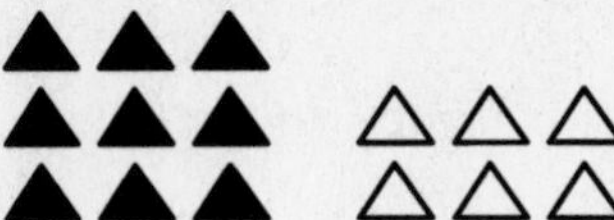

9 black	9	15
6 white	+ 6	− 6
	15	9

6 black	6	15
9 white	+ 9	− 9
	15	6

Check

Add or subtract.

1. 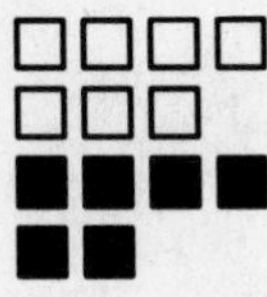
$7 + 6 = 13$ $\quad 13 - 6 = 7$

2. 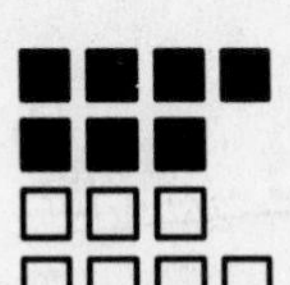
$7 + 7 = 14$ $\quad 14 - 7 = 7$

3. 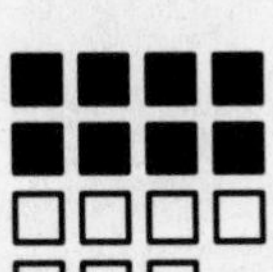
$8 + 7 =$ ___ $\quad 15 - 7 =$ ___

4. 
$4 + 9 =$ ___ $\quad 13 - 9 =$ ___

5. 
$6 + 8 =$ ___ $\quad 14 - 8 =$ ___

6. 
$7 + 8 =$ ___ $\quad 15 - 8 =$ ___

7. 
$6 + 9 =$ ___ $\quad 15 - 9 =$ ___

8. 
$9 + 5 =$ ___ $\quad 14 - 5 =$ ___

Macmillan/McGraw-Hill, MATHEMATICS IN ACTION
Grade 1, Chapter 12, Lesson 8, pages 367–368

Name

SUMS AND DIFFERENCES TO 16, 17, AND 18

Study

★★★ ★★★ ★★★ ☆☆☆ ☆☆☆ ☆

$$\begin{array}{r} 9 \\ +7 \\ \hline 16 \end{array} \quad \begin{array}{r} 16 \\ -7 \\ \hline 9 \end{array}$$

★★★ ★★★ ★★★ ☆☆☆ ☆☆☆ ☆☆

$$\begin{array}{r} 9 \\ +8 \\ \hline 17 \end{array} \quad \begin{array}{r} 17 \\ -8 \\ \hline 9 \end{array}$$

★★★ ★★★ ★★★ ☆☆☆ ☆☆☆ ☆☆☆

$$\begin{array}{r} 9 \\ +9 \\ \hline 18 \end{array} \quad \begin{array}{r} 18 \\ -9 \\ \hline 9 \end{array}$$

Check

Add or subtract.

1. ★★★ ★★★ ★★ ☆☆☆ ☆☆☆ ☆☆

$$\begin{array}{r} 8 \\ +8 \\ \hline 16 \end{array} \quad \begin{array}{r} 16 \\ -8 \\ \hline 8 \end{array}$$

2. ★★★ ★★★ ★★ ☆☆☆ ☆☆☆ ☆☆☆

$$\begin{array}{r} 8 \\ +9 \\ \hline \end{array} \quad \begin{array}{r} 17 \\ -9 \\ \hline \end{array}$$

3. $$\begin{array}{r} 16 \\ -9 \\ \hline \end{array} \quad \begin{array}{r} 17 \\ -8 \\ \hline \end{array} \quad \begin{array}{r} 16 \\ -8 \\ \hline \end{array} \quad \begin{array}{r} 18 \\ -9 \\ \hline \end{array} \quad \begin{array}{r} 16 \\ -7 \\ \hline \end{array}$$

4. $$\begin{array}{r} 9 \\ +8 \\ \hline \end{array} \quad \begin{array}{r} 8 \\ +8 \\ \hline \end{array} \quad \begin{array}{r} 9 \\ +9 \\ \hline \end{array} \quad \begin{array}{r} 8 \\ +9 \\ \hline \end{array} \quad \begin{array}{r} 9 \\ +7 \\ \hline \end{array}$$

5. $$\begin{array}{r} 17 \\ -9 \\ \hline \end{array} \quad \begin{array}{r} 7 \\ +9 \\ \hline \end{array} \quad \begin{array}{r} 16 \\ -9 \\ \hline \end{array} \quad \begin{array}{r} 9 \\ +8 \\ \hline \end{array} \quad \begin{array}{r} 18 \\ -9 \\ \hline \end{array}$$

Name

ADDITION AND SUBTRACTION PATTERNS

Study

3	4	5	6	7	8	9 ← one more
+ 2	+ 2	+ 2	+ 2	+ 2	+ 2	+ 2 ← same
5	6	7	8	9	10	11 ← one more

Check

Add or subtract.

1.

13	13	13	13	13	13
− 9	− 8	− 7	− 6	− 5	− 4
4	5	6			

2.

8	7	6	5	4	3
+ 1	+ 2	+ 3	+ 4	+ 5	+ 6

3.

12	12	12	12	12	12
− 4	− 5	− 6	− 7	− 8	− 9

4.

1	2	3	4	5	6
+ 1	+ 2	+ 3	+ 4	+ 5	+ 6

Macmillan/McGraw-Hill, MATHEMATICS IN ACTION
Grade 1, Chapter 12, Lesson 10, pages 371–372

Name

MONEY

Study

Check

Add or subtract.

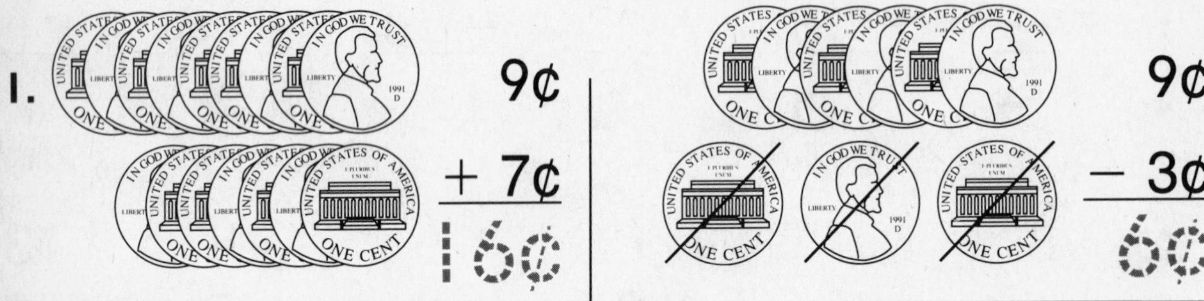

1. 9¢ + 7¢ = 16¢ | 9¢ − 3¢ = 6¢

2.	8¢ + 6¢	5¢ + 9¢	6¢ + 4¢	9¢ + 8¢	8¢ + 5¢
3.	14¢ − 7¢	16¢ − 7¢	18¢ − 9¢	17¢ − 8¢	15¢ − 9¢
4.	8¢ + 7¢	7¢ + 6¢	17¢ − 9¢	15¢ − 8¢	9¢ + 4¢

Name

ADDING THREE NUMBERS

Study

$$\begin{array}{r} 2 \\ 3 \\ +\ 2 \\ \hline 7 \end{array}$$ Add the double first. (3 and 2)

$$\begin{array}{r} 1 \\ 7 \\ +\ 8 \\ \hline 16 \end{array}$$ Add 1 first. (1 and 7)

$$\begin{array}{r} 3 \\ 3 \\ +\ 7 \\ \hline 13 \end{array}$$ Add a 10 first. (3 and 7)

Check.

Add the numbers in the arrow first.

1. $\begin{array}{r} 6 \\ 4 \\ +\ 2 \\ \hline 12 \end{array}$ (6 and 4) 10 $\qquad \begin{array}{r} 3 \\ 4 \\ +\ 3 \\ \hline 10 \end{array}$ (3 and 3) 6 $\qquad \begin{array}{r} 9 \\ 1 \\ +\ 5 \\ \hline \end{array}$ (9 and 1) ____

2. $\begin{array}{r} 6 \\ 7 \\ +\ 3 \\ \hline \end{array}$ (7 and 3) ____ $\qquad \begin{array}{r} 4 \\ 4 \\ +\ 5 \\ \hline \end{array}$ (4 and 4) ____ $\qquad \begin{array}{r} 7 \\ 2 \\ +\ 3 \\ \hline \end{array}$ (2 and 3) ____

3. $\begin{array}{r} 8 \\ 3 \\ +\ 1 \\ \hline \end{array}$ (3 and 1) ____ $\qquad \begin{array}{r} 5 \\ 6 \\ +\ 5 \\ \hline \end{array}$ (5 and 5) ____ $\qquad \begin{array}{r} 9 \\ 5 \\ +\ 4 \\ \hline \end{array}$ (5 and 4) ____

Name

PROBLEM SOLVING STRATEGIES REVIEW

Study

Choose a strategy.

15 horses are in the barn.
6 go out of the barn.
How many are left?

subtract: 15 − 6 = 9
9 horses left

Check

Solve.

1. Pam has 7 white hens.
   She has 8 red hens.
   How many hens does she have?

   add
   subtract

   15 hens

2. 9 cows in the field.
   8 horses in the field.
   How many more cows than horses are there?

   add
   subtract

   ______ more

3. There are 6 ducks in the pond.
   There are 7 ducks in the grass.
   How many ducks in all?

   add
   subtract

   ______ in all

Name

Adding ones and tens

Study

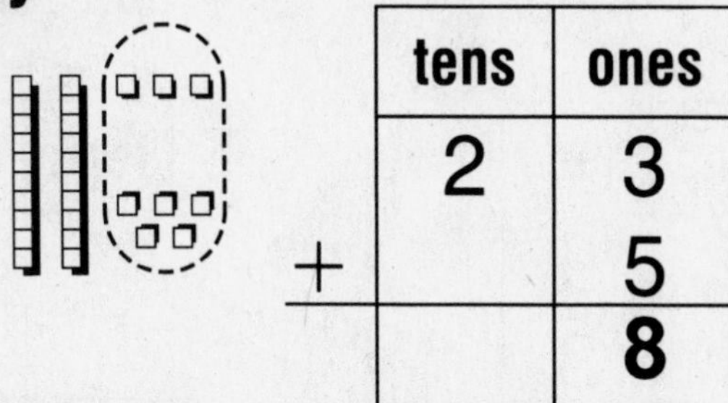

	tens	ones
	2	3
+		5
		8

	tens	ones
	2	3
+		5
	2	**8**

Check

Find the sum.

1.

	tens	ones
	4	1
+		6
	4	7

2.

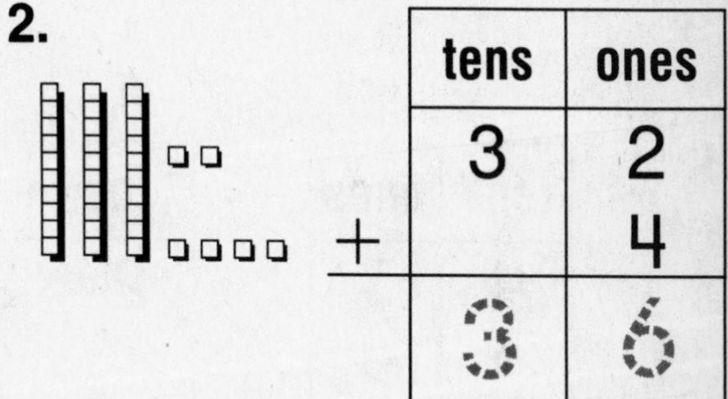

	tens	ones
	3	2
+		4
	3	6

3.

	tens	ones
	1	4
+		5

4.

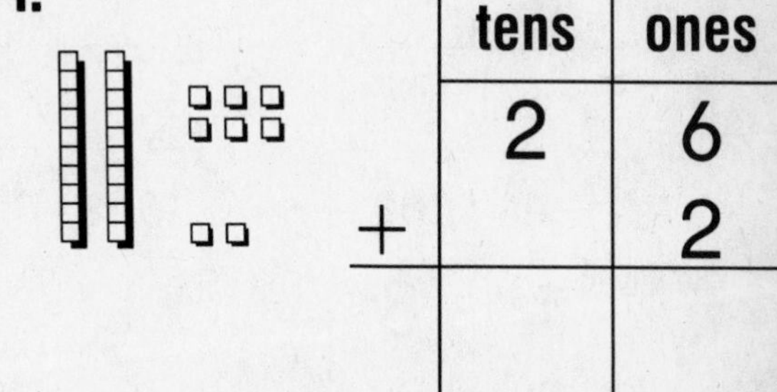

	tens	ones
	2	6
+		2

5.

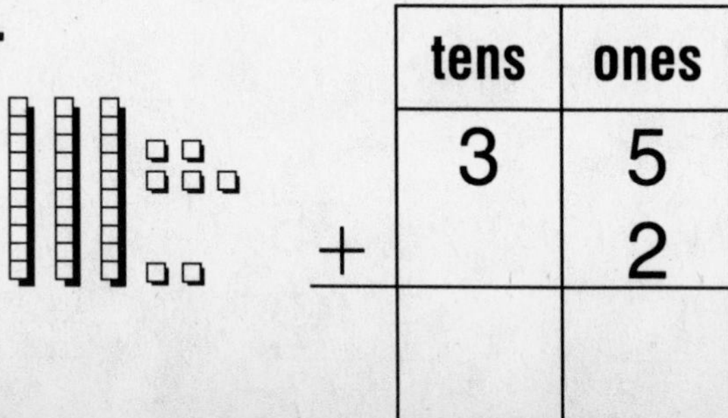

	tens	ones
	3	5
+		2

6.

	tens	ones
	1	3
+		4

Macmillan/McGraw-Hill, MATHEMATICS IN ACTION
Grade 1, Chapter 13, Lesson 2, pages 389–390

Name

MORE ADDING ONES AND TENS

Study

show the models

tens	ones
2	4
+ 1	3

add ones

tens	ones
2	4
+ 1	3
	7

add tens

tens	ones
2	4
+ 1	3
3	7

Check

Add.

1.

tens	ones
4	7
+ 3	2
7	9

tens	ones
2	2
+ 1	0
3	2

tens	ones
1	5
+ 7	1

tens	ones
3	5
+ 1	1

2.

tens	ones
1	8
+ 2	1

tens	ones
1	4
+ 6	2

tens	ones
3	6
+ 4	3

tens	ones
5	4
+ 2	3

3. $\begin{array}{r} 84 \\ +\ 15 \\ \hline \end{array}$ $\begin{array}{r} 52 \\ +\ 22 \\ \hline \end{array}$ $\begin{array}{r} 76 \\ +\ 13 \\ \hline \end{array}$ $\begin{array}{r} 35 \\ +\ 42 \\ \hline \end{array}$ $\begin{array}{r} 25 \\ +\ 30 \\ \hline \end{array}$

Name

PROBLEM SOLVING STRATEGY: USING INFORMATION FROM A TABLE

Study

PLAYING GAMES

	Grade 1	Grade 2
jumping	25	21
skipping	14	23
hopping	21	16

25 grade 1 children.
21 grade 2 children.
46 children jumping.

Check

Write the numbers. Solve.

1. 14 grade 1 children skipping.

   23 grade 2 children skipping.

   How many children skipping? 37

2. _____ grade 2 children hopping.

   _____ grade 2 children skipping.

   How many grade 2 children hopping and skipping? _____

3. _____ grade 1 children jumping.

   _____ grade 1 children hopping.

   How many grade 1 children jumping and hopping? _____

Name

Subtracting Ones and Tens

Study

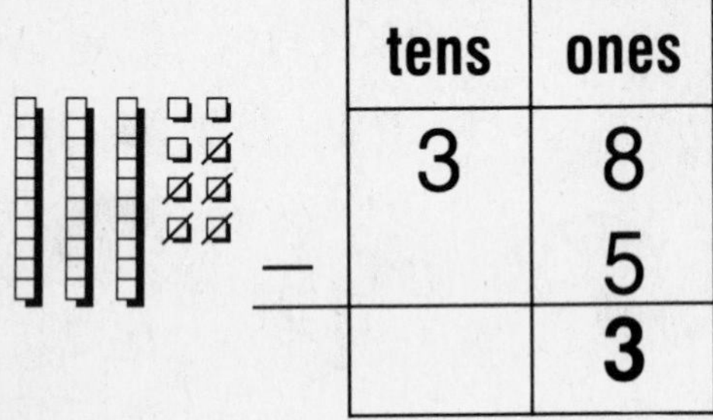

	tens	ones
	3	8
−		5
		3

	tens	ones
	3	8
−		5
	3	**3**

Check

Find the difference.

1.

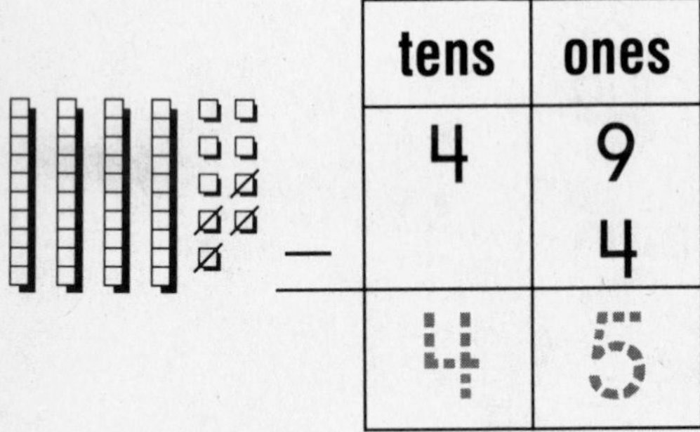

	tens	ones
	4	9
−		4
	4	5

2.

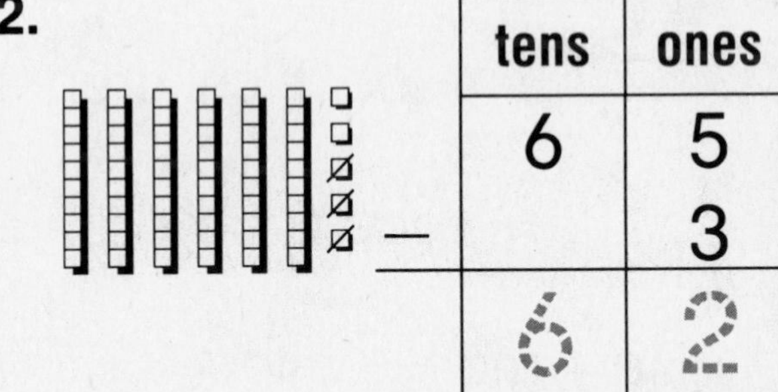

	tens	ones
	6	5
−		3
	6	2

3.

	tens	ones
	3	6
−		4

4.

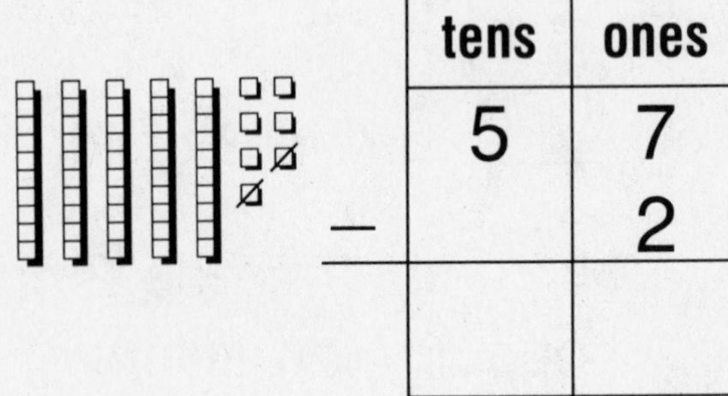

	tens	ones
	5	7
−		2

5.

	tens	ones
	2	8
−		4

6.

	tens	ones
	4	3
−		1

Name

MORE SUBTRACTING ONES AND TENS

Study

show the models

	tens	ones
	2	8
−	1	6

subtract ones

	tens	ones
	2	8
−	1	6
		2

subtract tens

	tens	ones
	2	8
−	1	6
	1	2

Check

Subtract.

1.

	tens	ones
	4	7
−	1	6
	3	1

	tens	ones
	7	5
−	3	2
	4	3

	tens	ones
	3	9
−	2	5

	tens	ones
	5	6
−	4	1

2.

	tens	ones
	6	9
−	3	3

	tens	ones
	3	7
−	1	4

	tens	ones
	8	4
−	2	2

	tens	ones
	4	8
−	3	3

3.

$$\begin{array}{r} 54 \\ -\ 30 \\ \hline \end{array} \qquad \begin{array}{r} 96 \\ -\ 15 \\ \hline \end{array} \qquad \begin{array}{r} 78 \\ -\ 24 \\ \hline \end{array} \qquad \begin{array}{r} 65 \\ -\ 41 \\ \hline \end{array} \qquad \begin{array}{r} 89 \\ -\ 58 \\ \hline \end{array}$$

Name

Adding and Subtracting Money

Study

22¢
+ 13¢
35¢

24¢
− 11¢
13¢

Check

Add or subtract.

1.

31¢
+ 24¢
55¢

2.

35¢
− 4¢
31¢

3.	60¢ + 10¢	47¢ + 21¢	86¢ + 3¢	15¢ + 43¢	64¢ + 25¢
4.	25¢ − 11¢	50¢ − 20¢	48¢ − 32¢	27¢ − 5¢	53¢ − 41¢
5.	67¢ − 5¢	32¢ + 16¢	57¢ + 20¢	56¢ − 33¢	98¢ − 54¢

Name

PROBLEM SOLVING STRATEGY: USING ESTIMATION

Study

There are 31 red bicycles.
There are 28 blue bicycles.
About how many bicycles are there in all?

31 is about 30
28 is about 30
30 + 30 = 60

About 60 bicycles in all.

Check

Ring the closer estimate.

1. There were 12 children in the park. There were 7 adults. About how many people were in the park?
   - (20 people)
   - 30 people

2. 29 children ride the bus to school. 12 children ride the van. About how many children ride the bus and the van to school?
   - 30 children
   - 40 children

3. 38 people saw the movie today. 19 people saw it yesterday. About how many people saw the movie during the two days?
   - 50 people
   - 60 people

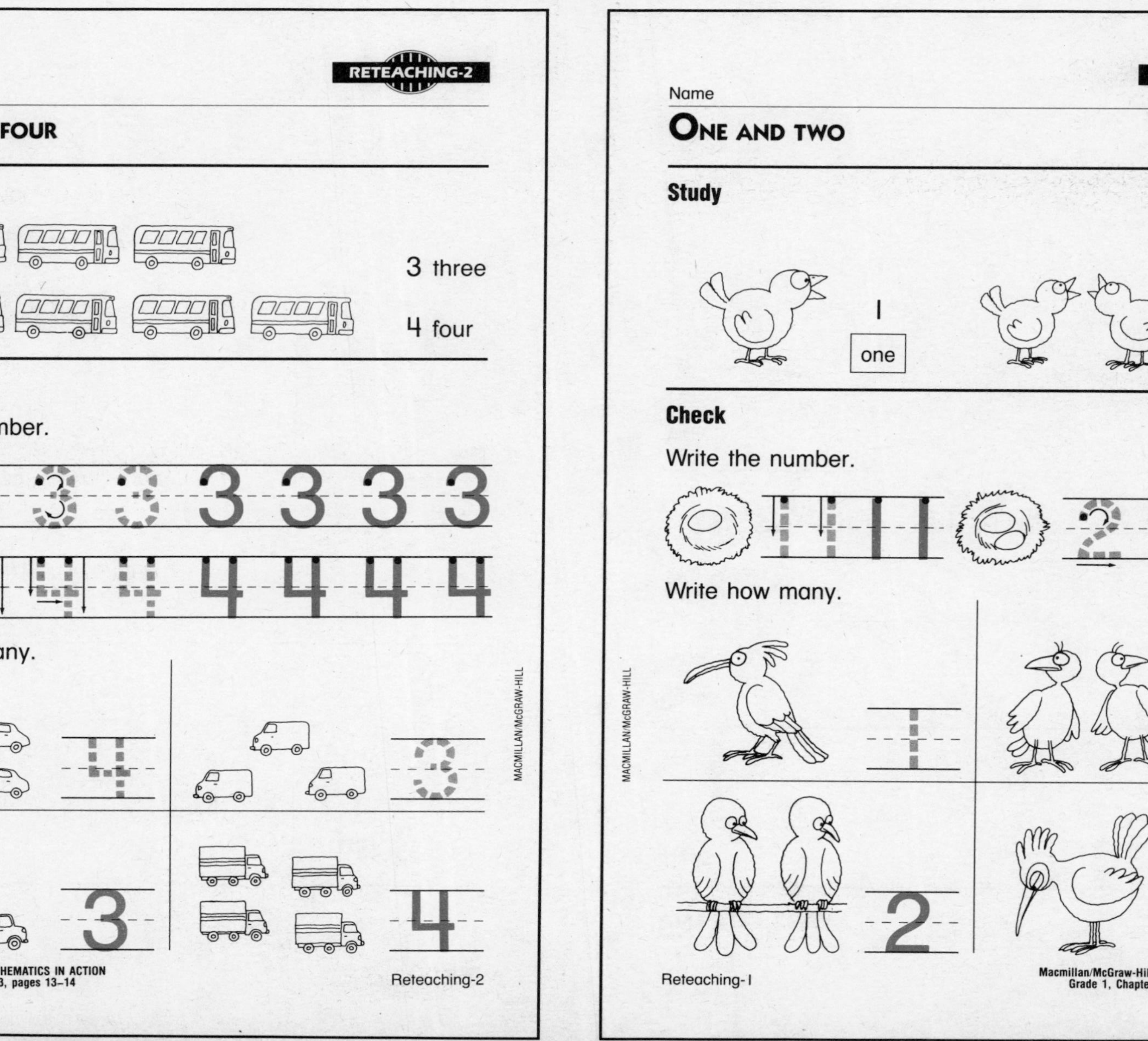

RETEACHING-2

Name

Three and Four

Study

3 three

4 four

Check

Write the number.

3 3 3 3

4 4 4 4

Write how many.

3

4

MACMILLAN/McGRAW-HILL

Macmillan/McGraw-Hill, MATHEMATICS IN ACTION
Grade 1, Chapter 1, Lesson 3, pages 13–14

Reteaching-2

RETEACHING-1

Name

One and Two

Study

1 one

2 two

Check

Write the number.

1 1

2

Write how many.

2

1

MACMILLAN/McGRAW-HILL

Reteaching-1

Macmillan/McGraw-Hill, MATHEMATICS IN ACTION
Grade 1, Chapter 1, Lesson 2, pages 11–12

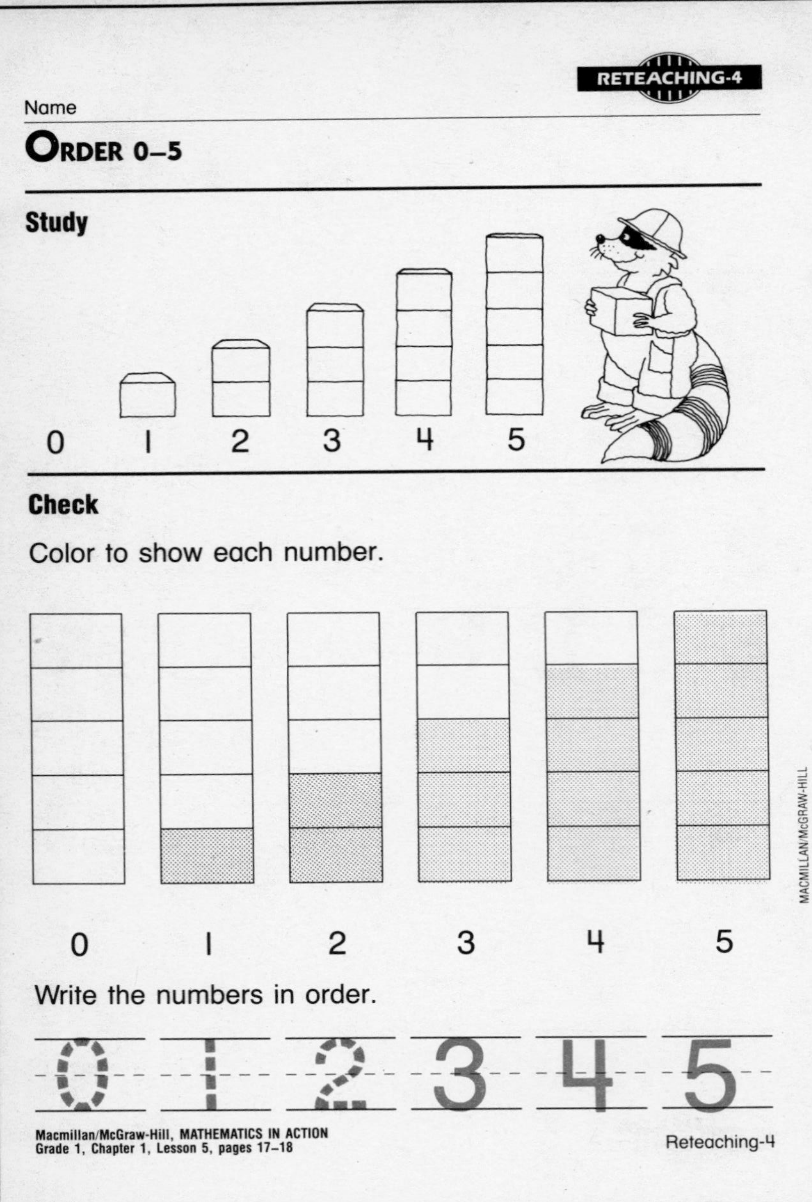

RETEACHING-4

Name

ORDER 0–5

Study

0 1 2 3 4 5

Check

Color to show each number.

0 1 2 3 4 5

Write the numbers in order.

0 1 2 3 4 5

Macmillan/McGraw-Hill, MATHEMATICS IN ACTION
Grade 1, Chapter 1, Lesson 5, pages 17–18

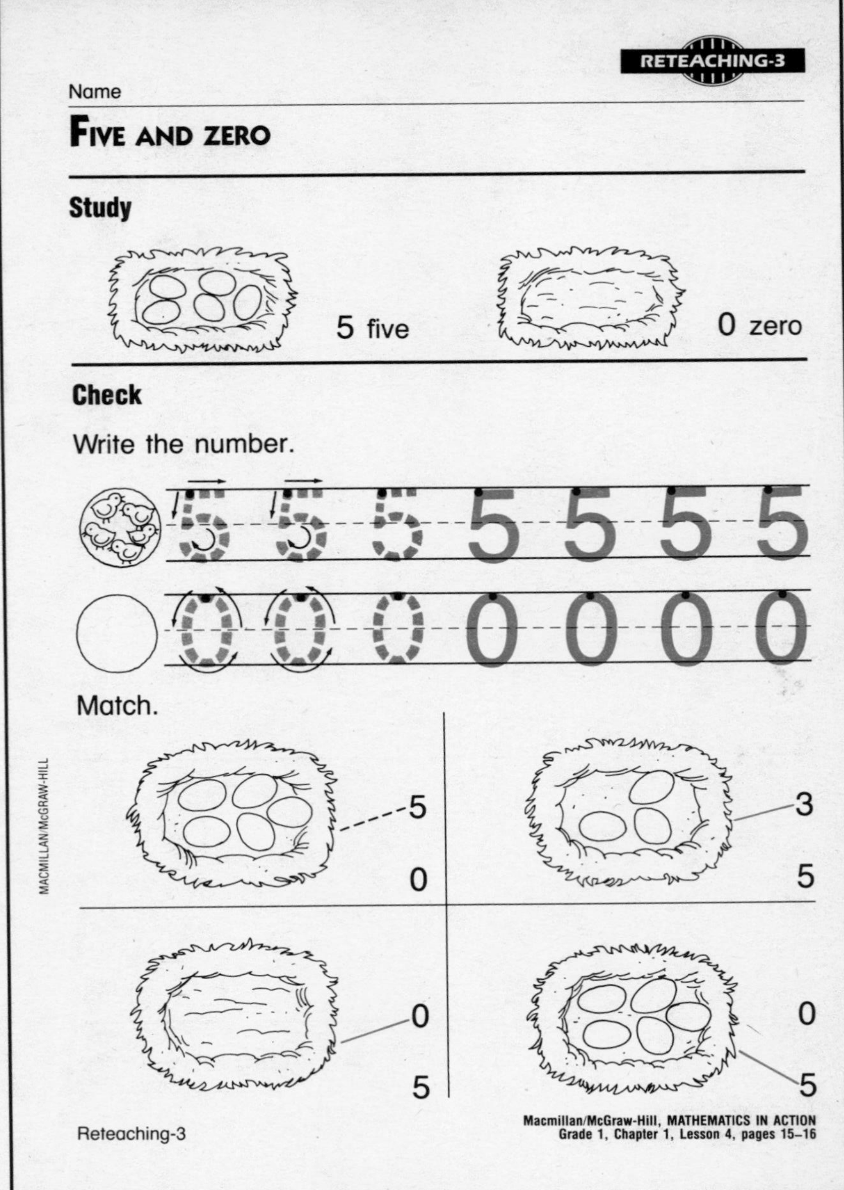

RETEACHING-3

Name

FIVE AND ZERO

Study

5 five

0 zero

Check

Write the number.

5 5 5 5 5 5 5

0 0 0 0 0 0 0

Match.

5 0

3 5

0 5

0 5

Macmillan/McGraw-Hill, MATHEMATICS IN ACTION
Grade 1, Chapter 1, Lesson 4, pages 15–16

RETEACHING-6

Name

SIX AND SEVEN

Study

6 six

7 seven

Write the number.

6 6 6 6 6 6 6

7 7 7 7 7 7 7

Write how many.

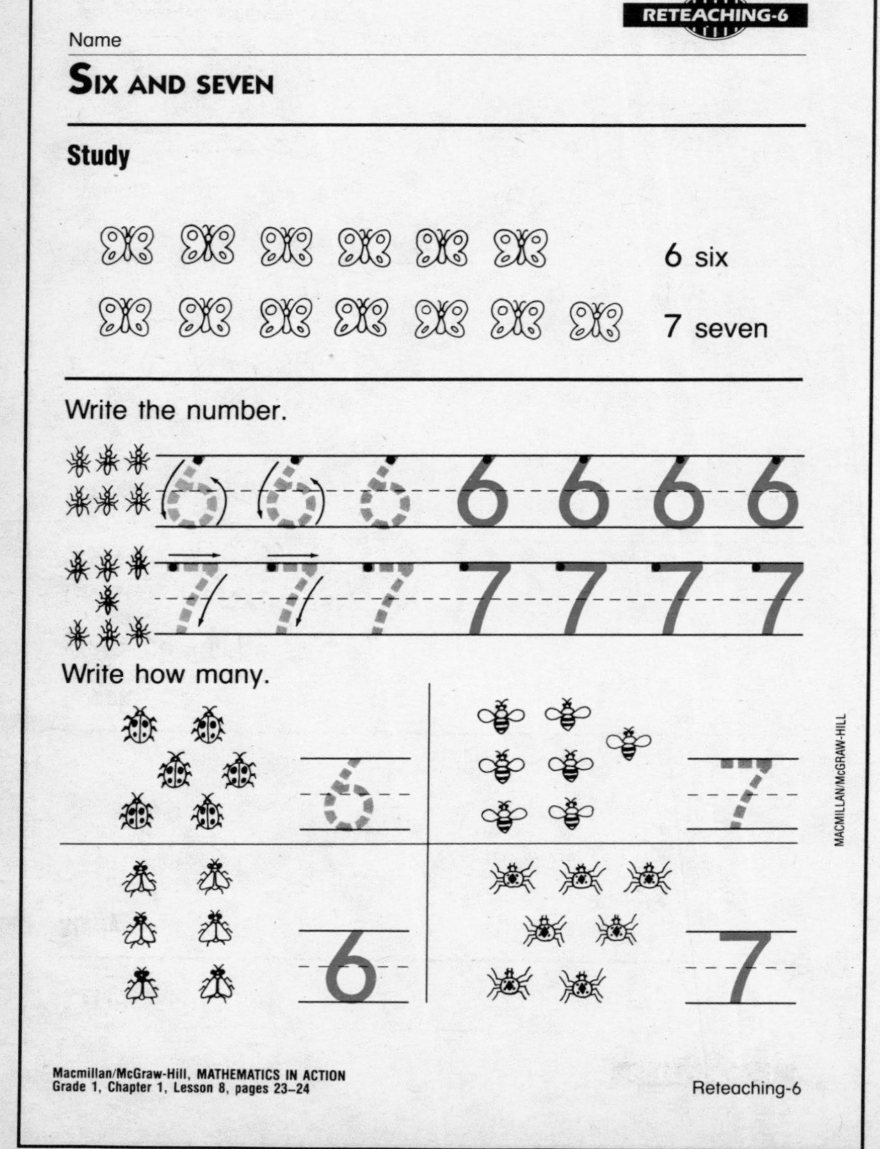

6 7

6 7

RETEACHING-5

Name

PROBLEM SOLVING: USING INFORMATION FROM A PICTURE

Study

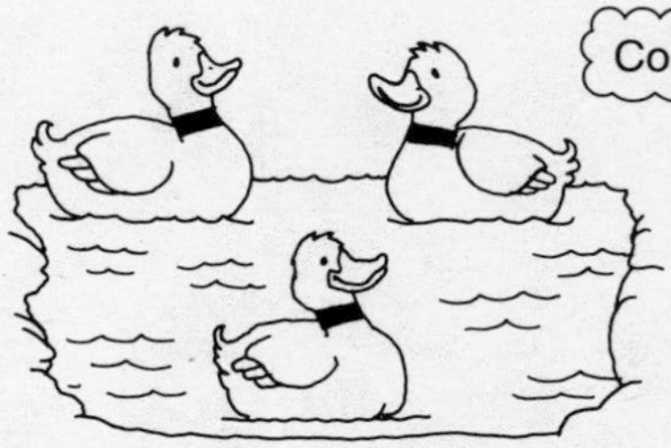

Count.

3

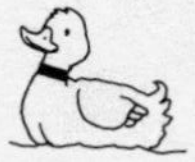

Check

Write how many.

1. 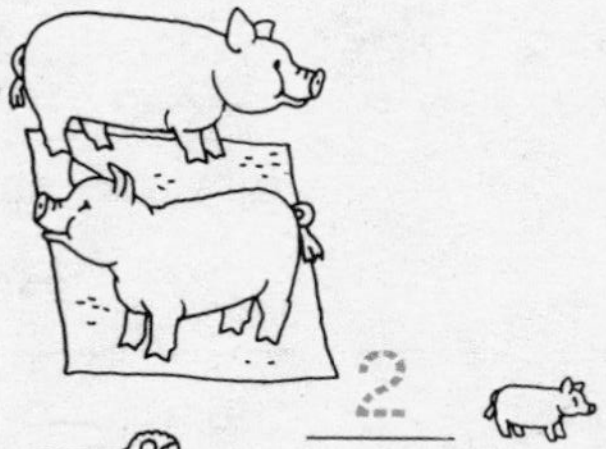 2

2. 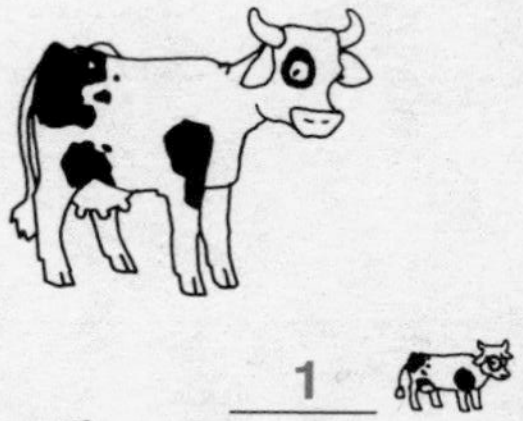 1

3. 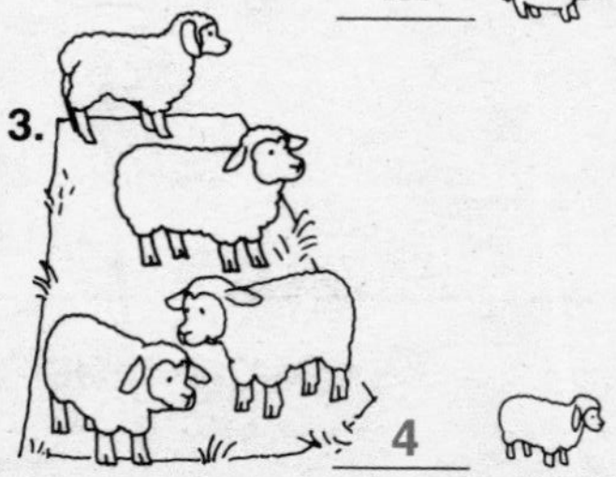 4

4. 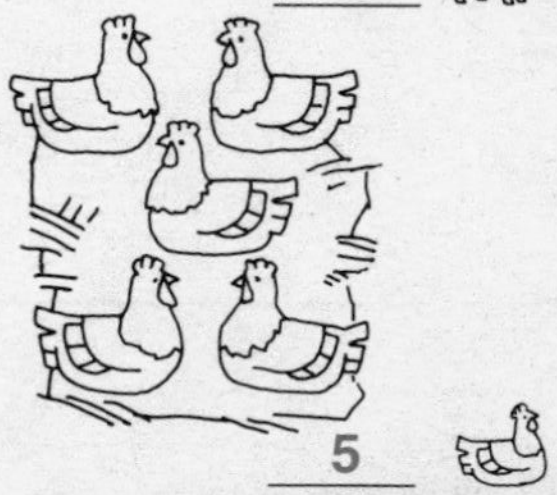 5

RETEACHING-8

Name

TEN

Study

10 ten

Check

Write the number.

10 10 10 10 10

Ring how many.

(9) 10

9 (10)

9 (10)

(9) 10

Macmillan/McGraw-Hill, MATHEMATICS IN ACTION
Grade 1, Chapter 1, Lesson 10, pages 27–28

RETEACHING-7

Name

EIGHT AND NINE

Study

8 eight

9 nine

Check

Write the number.

8 8 8 8 8 8 8

9 9 9 9 9 9 9

How many? Ring the number.

(8) 9

8 (9)

(8) 9

Macmillan/McGraw-Hill, MATHEMATICS IN ACTION
Grade 1, Chapter 1, Lesson 9, pages 25–26

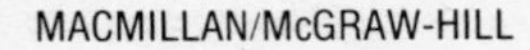

RETEACHING-10

Name

NUMBER WORDS TO TEN

Study

0 zero

1 one	💧	6 six	💧💧💧💧💧💧
2 two	💧💧	7 seven	💧💧💧💧💧💧💧
3 three	💧💧💧	8 eight	💧💧💧💧💧💧💧💧
4 four	💧💧💧💧	9 nine	💧💧💧💧💧💧💧💧💧
5 five	💧💧💧💧💧	10 ten	💧💧💧💧💧💧💧💧💧💧

Check

Match.

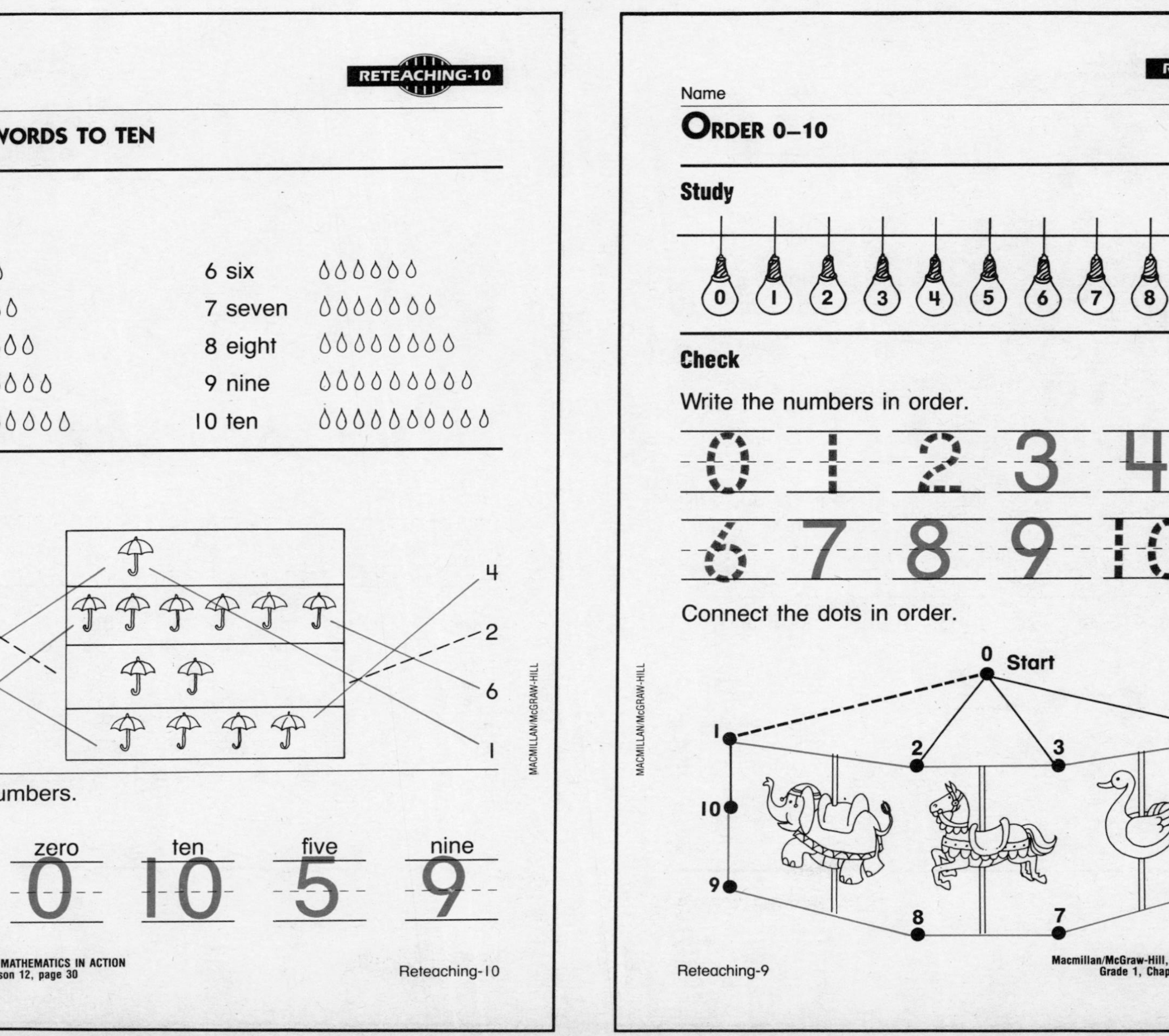

Write the numbers.

seven 7 zero 0 ten 10 five 5 nine 9

Macmillan/McGraw-Hill, MATHEMATICS IN ACTION
Grade 1, Chapter 1, Lesson 12, page 30

RETEACHING-9

Name

ORDER 0–10

Study

0 1 2 3 4 5 6 7 8 9 10

Check

Write the numbers in order.

0 1 2 3 4 5

6 7 8 9 10

Connect the dots in order.

Macmillan/McGraw-Hill, MATHEMATICS IN ACTION
Grade 1, Chapter 1, Lesson 11, page 29

RETEACHING-12

Name

Ordinal Numbers

Study

first, second, third, fourth, fifth, sixth, seventh, eighth, ninth, tenth

1st, 2nd, 3rd, 4th, 5th, 6th, 7th, 8th, 9th, 10th

Check

Start at the left.
Ring the fifth.

Ring the seventh.

Ring the fourth.

Ring the tenth.

Macmillan/McGraw-Hill, MATHEMATICS IN ACTION
Grade 1, Chapter 1, Lesson 14, pages 33–34

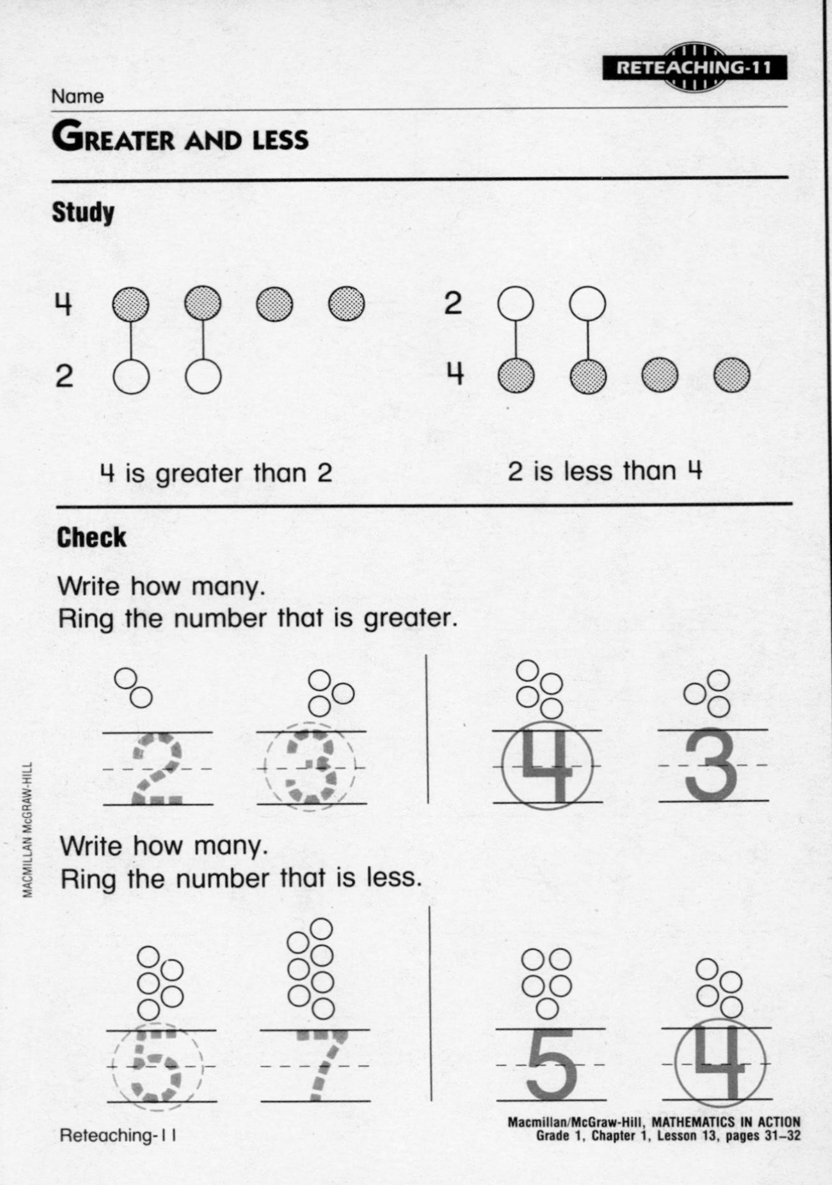

RETEACHING-11

Name

Greater and Less

Study

4 is greater than 2

2 is less than 4

Check

Write how many.
Ring the number that is greater.

Write how many.
Ring the number that is less.

Macmillan/McGraw-Hill, MATHEMATICS IN ACTION
Grade 1, Chapter 1, Lesson 13, pages 31–32

RETEACHING-14

Name

ADDITION READINESS

Study

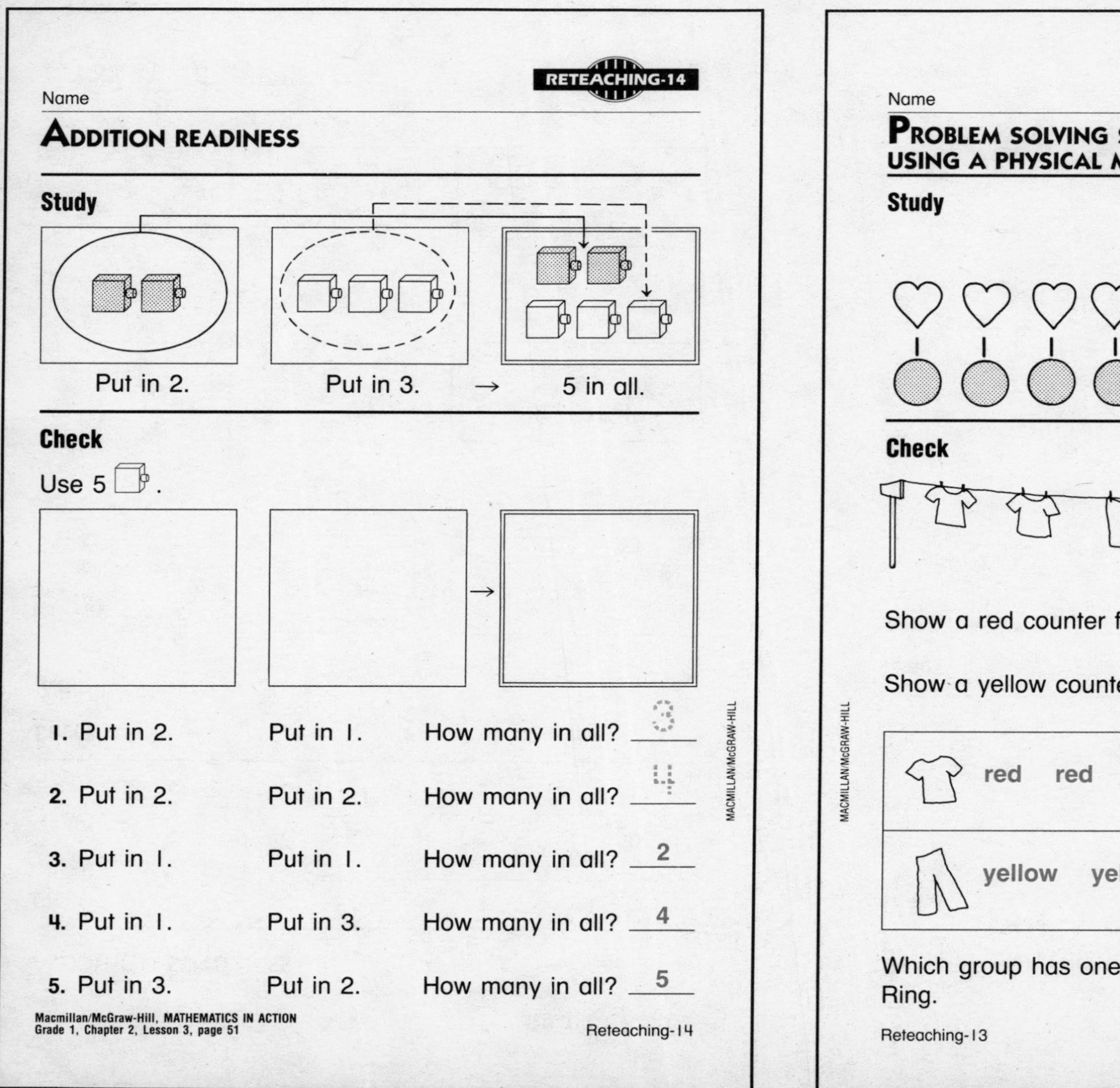

Put in 2. Put in 3. → 5 in all.

Check

Use 5 .

1. Put in 2. Put in 1. How many in all? 3
2. Put in 2. Put in 2. How many in all? 4
3. Put in 1. Put in 1. How many in all? 2
4. Put in 1. Put in 3. How many in all? 4
5. Put in 3. Put in 2. How many in all? 5

RETEACHING-13

Name

PROBLEM SOLVING STRATEGY: USING A PHYSICAL MODEL

Study

You can show a counter for each item.

Check

Show a red counter for each .

Show a yellow counter for each .

	red	red	red	red
	yellow	yellow	yellow	

Which group has one more? Ring.

RETEACHING-16

Name

Addition Sentences

Study

2 + 1 = 3

Check

Write how many in all.

1. 3 + 2 = 5

2. 1 + 3 = 4

3. 1 + 1 = 2

Macmillan/McGraw-Hill, MATHEMATICS IN ACTION
Grade 1, Chapter 2, Lesson 5, pages 53–54

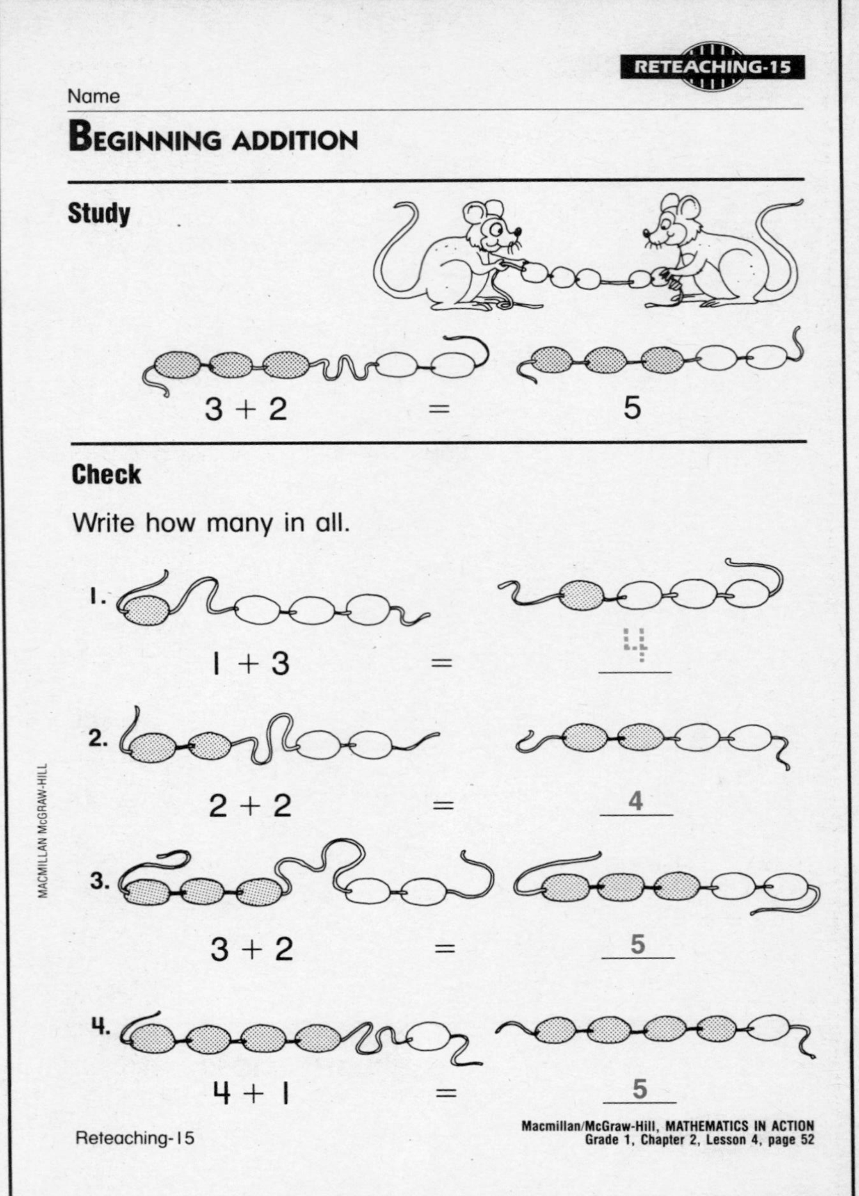

RETEACHING-15

Name

Beginning Addition

Study

3 + 2 = 5

Check

Write how many in all.

1. 1 + 3 = 4

2. 2 + 2 = 4

3. 3 + 2 = 5

4. 4 + 1 = 5

Macmillan/McGraw-Hill, MATHEMATICS IN ACTION
Grade 1, Chapter 2, Lesson 4, page 52

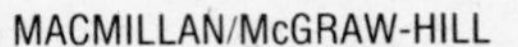

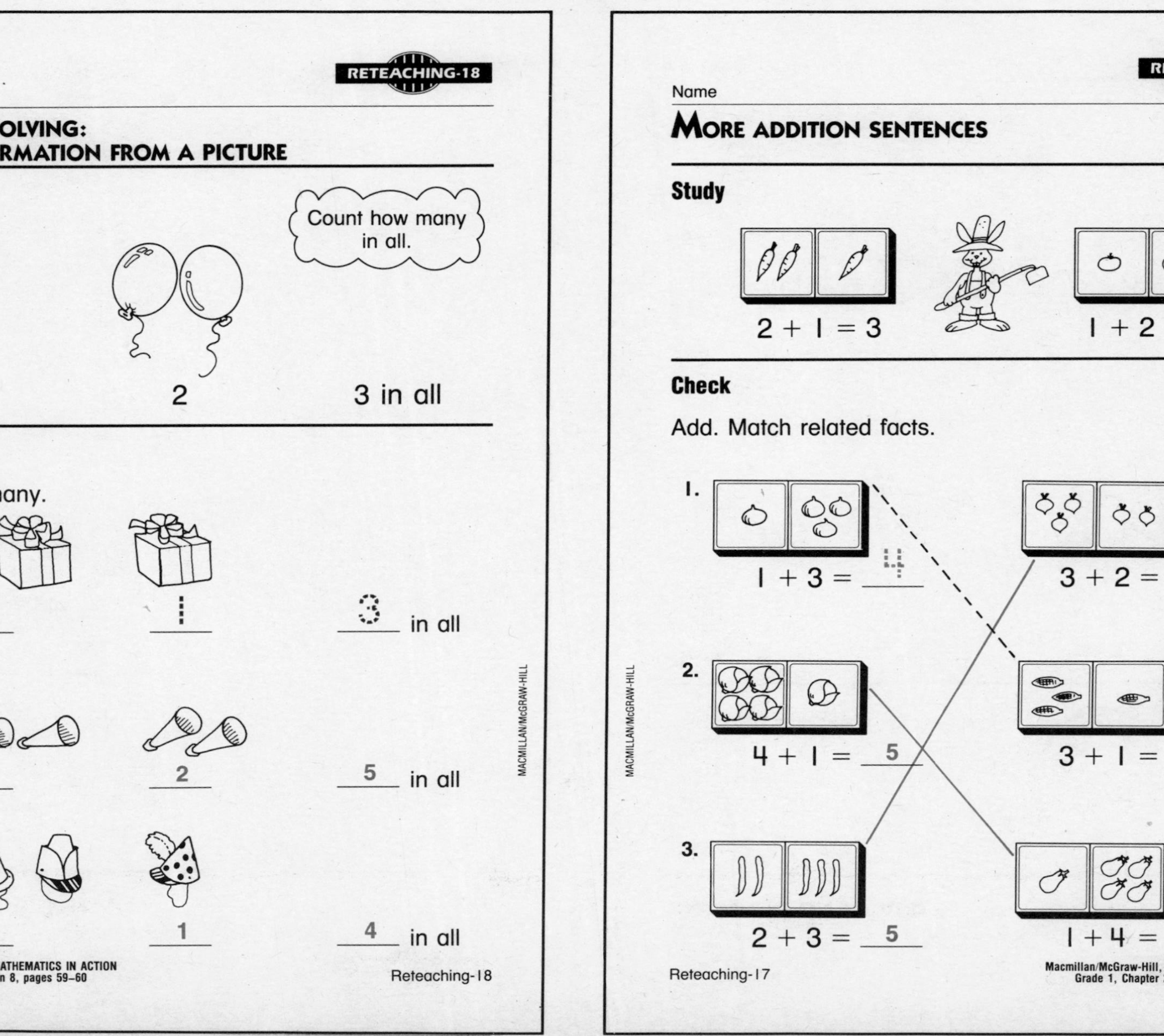

RETEACHING-18

Name

PROBLEM SOLVING: USING INFORMATION FROM A PICTURE

Study

Count how many in all.

1	2	3 in all

Check

Write how many.

1. 2   1   3 in all

2. 3   2   5 in all

3. 3   1   4 in all

Macmillan/McGraw-Hill, MATHEMATICS IN ACTION
Grade 1, Chapter 2, Lesson 8, pages 59–60

RETEACHING-17

Name

MORE ADDITION SENTENCES

Study

$2 + 1 = 3$ $1 + 2 = 3$

Check

Add. Match related facts.

1. $1 + 3 =$ 4 $3 + 2 =$ 5

2. $4 + 1 =$ 5 $3 + 1 =$ 4

3. $2 + 3 =$ 5 $1 + 4 =$ 5

Macmillan/McGraw-Hill, MATHEMATICS IN ACTION
Grade 1, Chapter 2, Lesson 6, pages 55–56

RETEACHING-20

Name

Vertical Addition

Study

2 + 1 = 3

$$\begin{array}{r} 2 \\ +\ 1 \\ \hline 3 \end{array}$$

Check

Draw dots. Find the sum.

1. 1 + 4 = 5

$$\begin{array}{r} 1 \\ +\ 4 \\ \hline 5 \end{array}$$

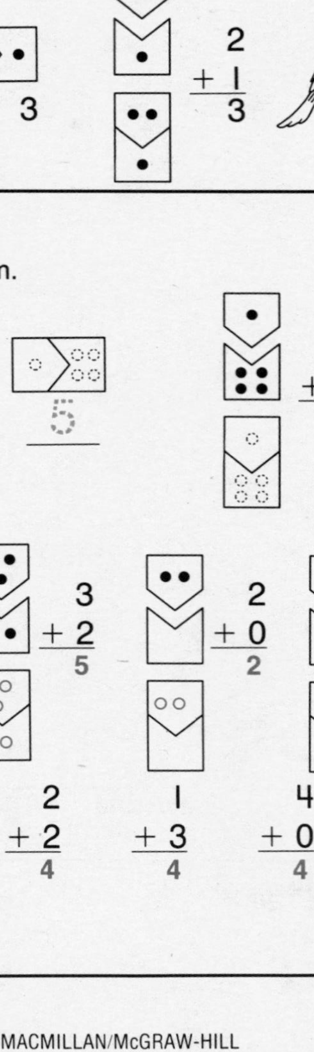

2. $\begin{array}{r} 2 \\ +\ 2 \\ \hline 4 \end{array}$ $\begin{array}{r} 3 \\ +\ 2 \\ \hline 5 \end{array}$ $\begin{array}{r} 2 \\ +\ 0 \\ \hline 2 \end{array}$ $\begin{array}{r} 1 \\ +\ 1 \\ \hline 2 \end{array}$

3. $\begin{array}{r} 4 \\ +\ 1 \\ \hline 5 \end{array}$ $\begin{array}{r} 0 \\ +\ 3 \\ \hline 3 \end{array}$ $\begin{array}{r} 2 \\ +\ 2 \\ \hline 4 \end{array}$ $\begin{array}{r} 1 \\ +\ 3 \\ \hline 4 \end{array}$ $\begin{array}{r} 4 \\ +\ 0 \\ \hline 4 \end{array}$ $\begin{array}{r} 1 \\ +\ 2 \\ \hline 3 \end{array}$

Macmillan/McGraw-Hill, MATHEMATICS IN ACTION
Grade 1, Chapter 2, Lesson 10, pages 63–64

RETEACHING-19

Name

Counting on to Add

Study

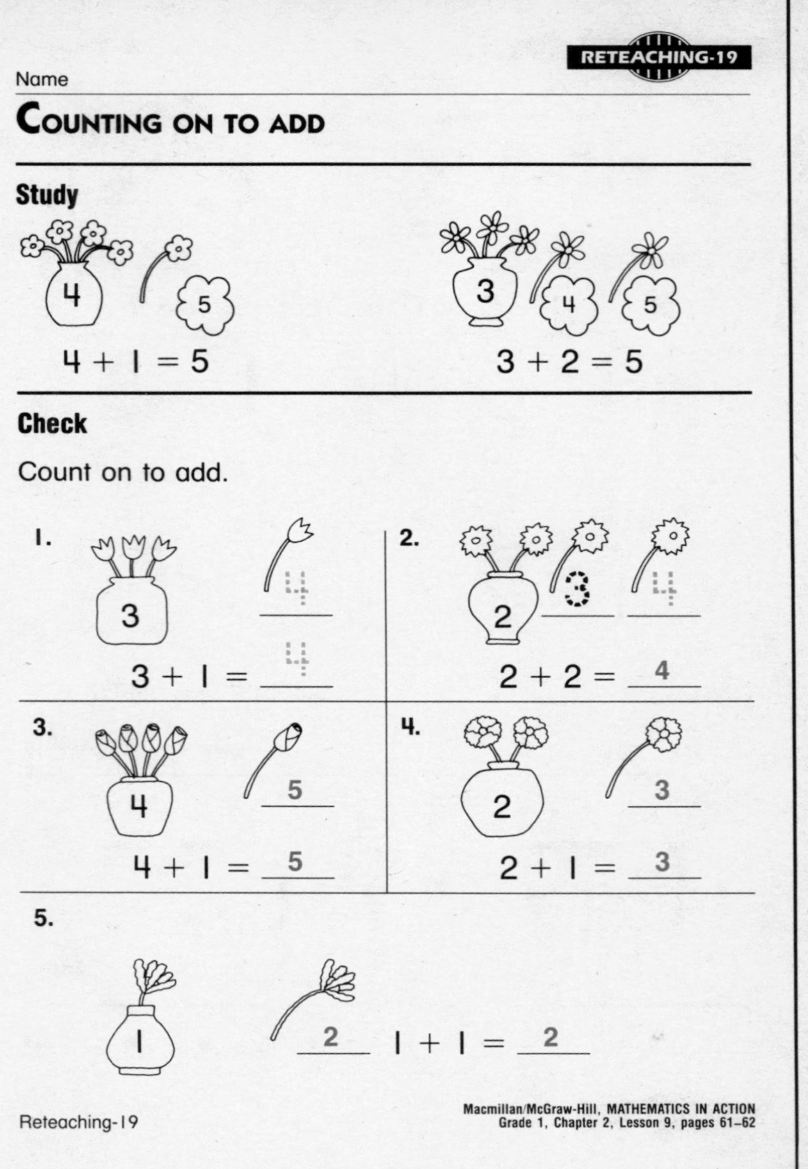

4 + 1 = 5

3 + 2 = 5

Check

Count on to add.

1. 3 + 1 = 4

2. 2 + 2 = 4

3. 4 + 1 = 5

4. 2 + 1 = 3

5. 1 + 1 = 2

Macmillan/McGraw-Hill, MATHEMATICS IN ACTION
Grade 1, Chapter 2, Lesson 9, pages 61–62

RETEACHING-22

Name

SUBTRACTION READINESS

Study

Put in 4. Take away 2. 2 are left.

Check

Use 5 ☐.

1. Put in 4. Take away 4. How many are left? 0
2. Put in 3. Take away 1. How many are left? 2
3. Put in 2. Take away 1. How many are left? 1
4. Put in 4. Take away 1. How many are left? 3
5. Put in 5. Take away 2. How many are left? 3

Macmillan/McGraw-Hill, MATHEMATICS IN ACTION
Grade 1, Chapter 3, Lesson 3, page 81

RETEACHING-21

Name

PROBLEM SOLVING STRATEGY: COMPLETING AN ADDITION SENTENCE

Study

2 + 1 = 3

Check

How many in all?

1. 2 + 2 = 4
2. 3 + 1 = 4
3. 3 + 2 = 5
4. 1 + 2 = 3

Macmillan/McGraw-Hill, MATHEMATICS IN ACTION
Grade 1, Chapter 2, Lesson 11, pages 65–66

RETEACHING-24

Name

SUBTRACTION SENTENCES

Study

5 − 2 = 3

Check

Write how many are left.

1. 3 − 1 = 2

2. 4 − 3 = 1

3. 5 − 1 = 4

Macmillan/McGraw-Hill, MATHEMATICS IN ACTION
Grade 1, Chapter 3, Lesson 5, pages 83–84

RETEACHING-23

Name

BEGINNING SUBTRACTION

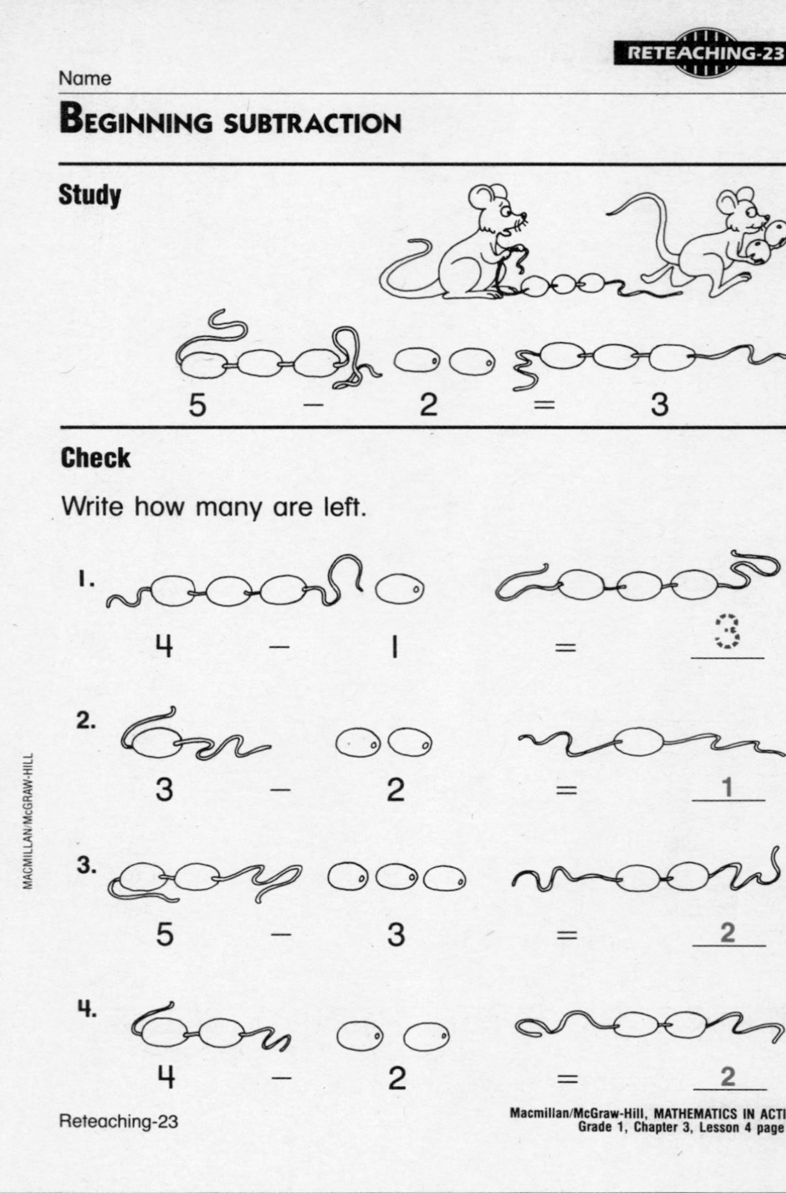

Study

5 − 2 = 3

Check

Write how many are left.

1. 4 − 1 = 3

2. 3 − 2 = 1

3. 5 − 3 = 2

4. 4 − 2 = 2

Macmillan/McGraw-Hill, MATHEMATICS IN ACTION
Grade 1, Chapter 3, Lesson 4 page 82

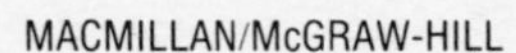

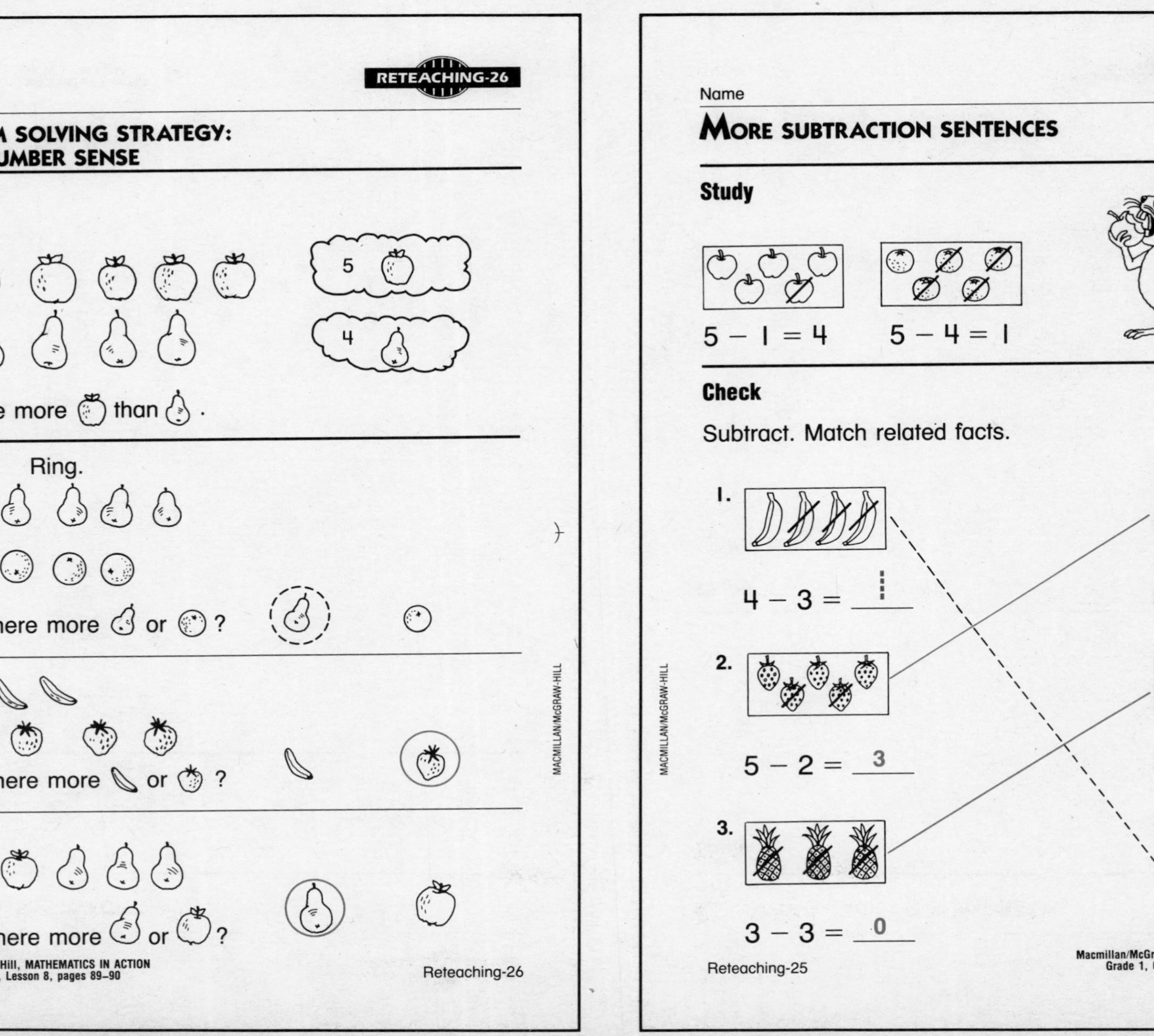

RETEACHING-26

Name

PROBLEM SOLVING STRATEGY: USING NUMBER SENSE

Study

5

4

There are more [apple] than [pear].

Check Ring.

1. Are there more [pear] or [orange] ?

2. Are there more [banana] or [strawberry] ?

3. Are there more [pear] or [apple] ?

Macmillan/McGraw-Hill, MATHEMATICS IN ACTION
Grade 1, Chapter 3, Lesson 8, pages 89–90

RETEACHING-25

Name

MORE SUBTRACTION SENTENCES

Study

5 − 1 = 4 5 − 4 = 1

Check

Subtract. Match related facts.

1. 4 − 3 = 1

5 − 3 = 2

2. 5 − 2 = 3

3 − 0 = 3

3. 3 − 3 = 0

4 − 1 = 3

Macmillan/McGraw-Hill, MATHEMATICS IN ACTION
Grade 1, Chapter 3, Lesson 6, pages 85–86

RETEACHING-28

Name

Vertical Subtraction

Study

5 − 4 = 1

$$\begin{array}{r} 5 \\ -\ 4 \\ \hline 1 \end{array}$$

Check

Cross out. Then subtract.

1. 4 − 1 = 3

$$\begin{array}{r} 4 \\ -\ 1 \\ \hline 3 \end{array}$$

2. 3 − 2 = 1

$$\begin{array}{r} 3 \\ -\ 2 \\ \hline 1 \end{array}$$

3.

$$\begin{array}{r} 2 \\ -\ 2 \\ \hline \end{array} \quad \begin{array}{r} 4 \\ -\ 3 \\ \hline \end{array} \quad \begin{array}{r} 3 \\ -\ 1 \\ \hline \end{array} \quad \begin{array}{r} 5 \\ -\ 3 \\ \hline 2 \end{array}$$

4.

$$\begin{array}{r} 4 \\ -\ 4 \\ \hline 0 \end{array} \quad \begin{array}{r} 2 \\ -\ 0 \\ \hline 2 \end{array} \quad \begin{array}{r} 5 \\ -\ 2 \\ \hline 3 \end{array} \quad \begin{array}{r} 3 \\ -\ 0 \\ \hline 3 \end{array} \quad \begin{array}{r} 1 \\ -\ 1 \\ \hline 0 \end{array} \quad \begin{array}{r} 4 \\ -\ 0 \\ \hline 4 \end{array}$$

RETEACHING-27

Name

Counting Back to Subtract

Study

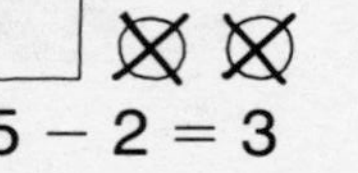

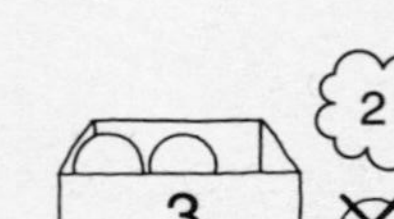

5 − 2 = 3

3 − 1 = 2

Check

Count back to subtract.

1.

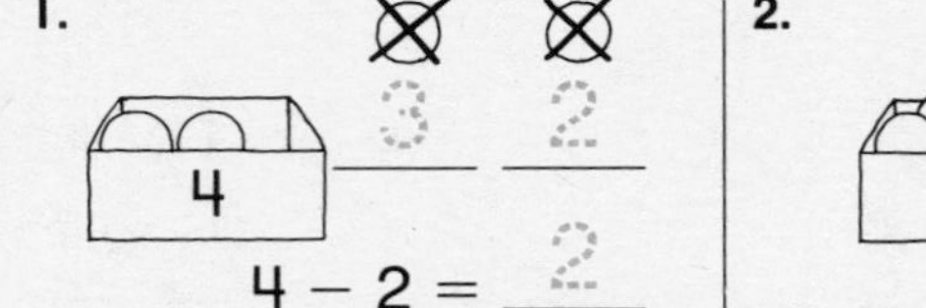

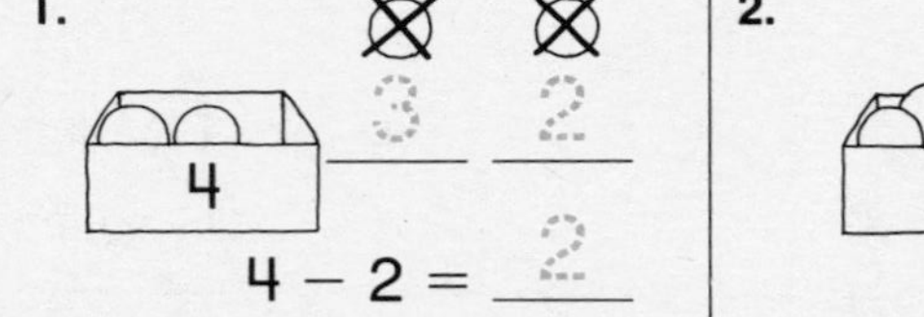

3 2

4 − 2 = 2

2.

5

4

5 − 1 = 4

3.

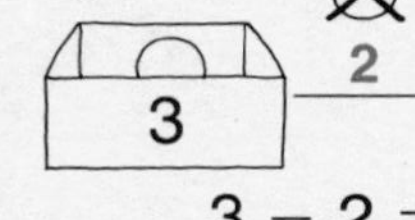

2 1

3 − 2 = 1

4.

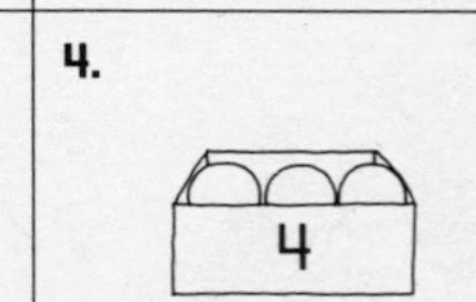

3

4 − 1 = 3

5.

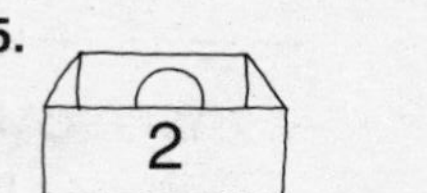

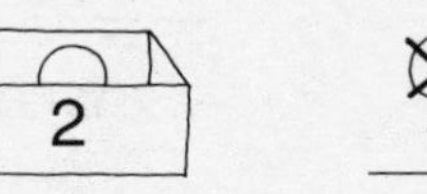

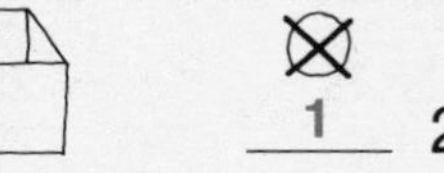

1

2 − 1 = 1

RETEACHING-30

Name

PROBLEM SOLVING STRATEGY: COMPLETING A SUBTRACTION SENTENCE

Study

5 − 2 = 3

Check

How many are left?

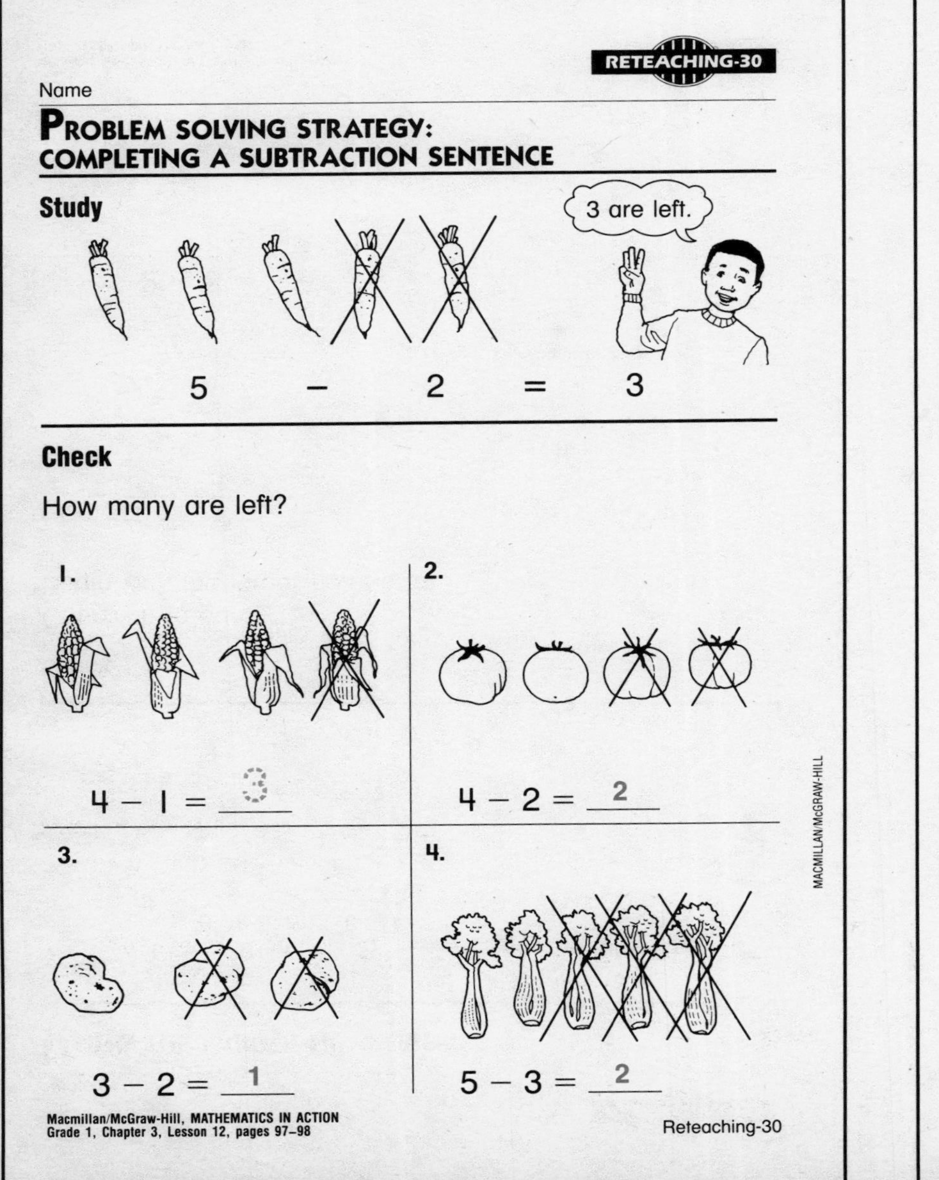

1. 4 − 1 = 3

2. 4 − 2 = 2

3. 3 − 2 = 1

4. 5 − 3 = 2

Macmillan/McGraw-Hill, MATHEMATICS IN ACTION
Grade 1, Chapter 3, Lesson 12, pages 97–98

RETEACHING-29

Name

FACT FAMILIES

Study

1 + 3 = 4 3 + 1 = 4 4 − 3 = 1 4 − 1 = 3

Check

Complete each fact family.

1. 2 + 3 = 5
3 + 2 = 5
5 − 3 = 2
5 − 2 = 3

2. 2 + 1 = 3
1 + 2 = 3
3 − 1 = 2
3 − 2 = 1

3. 4 + 1 = 5
1 + 4 = 5
5 − 1 = 4
5 − 4 = 1

4. 5 + 0 = 5
0 + 5 = 5
5 − 0 = 5
5 − 5 = 0

Macmillan/McGraw-Hill, MATHEMATICS IN ACTION
Grade 1, Chapter 3, Lesson 11, pages 95–96

RETEACHING-32

Name

USING THE LARGER NUMBER FIRST

Study

I counted on from 2.
2, **3**, **4**, **5**, **6**, **7**, **8**

I counted on from 6.
6, **7**, **8**

2 + 6 = 8

Check

Count on to add.
Begin with the larger number.

1. 1 + 7 = 8
2. 2 + 5 = 7
3. 2 + 8 = 10
4. 1 + 6 = 7
5. 1 + 9 = 10
6. 2 + 7 = 9

Macmillan/McGraw-Hill, MATHEMATICS IN ACTION
Grade 1, Chapter 4, Lesson 4, page 115

RETEACHING-31

Name

COUNTING ON

Study

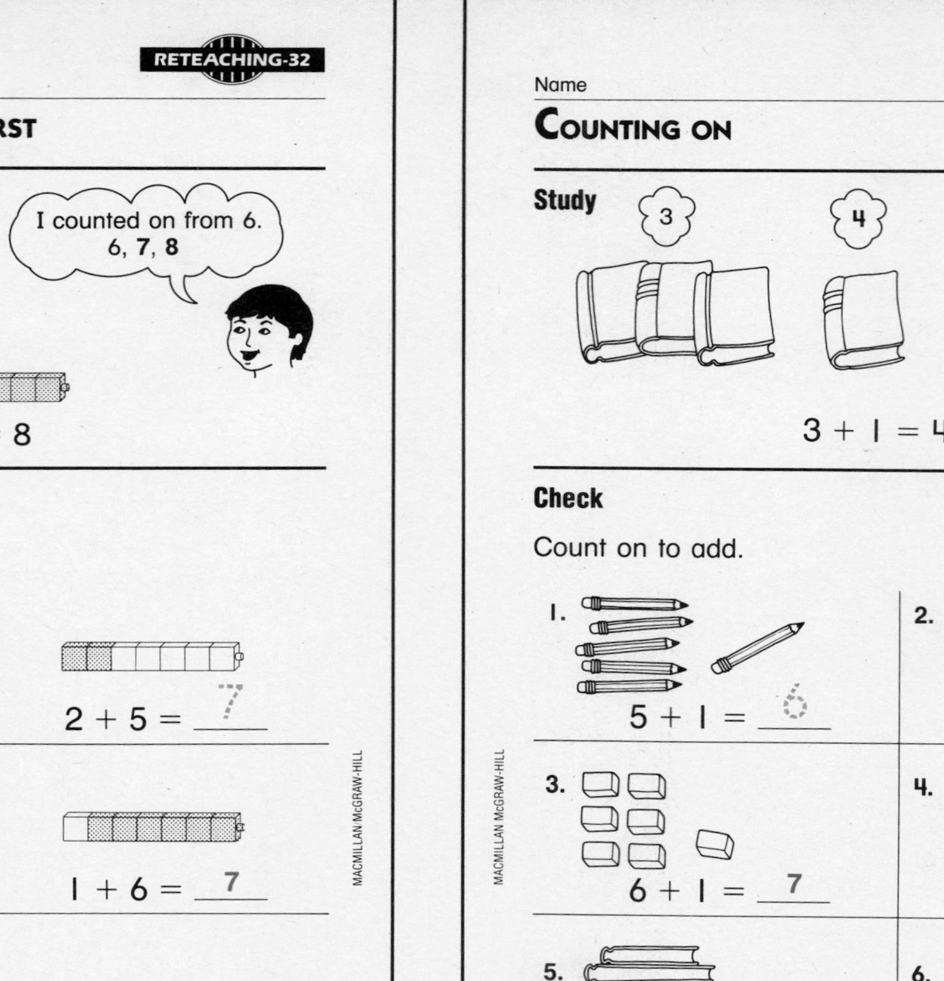

3 4

3 + 1 = 4

Check

Count on to add.

1. 5 + 1 = 6
2. 7 + 2 = 9
3. 6 + 1 = 7
4. 8 + 2 = 10
5. 5 + 2 = 7
6. 9 + 1 = 10

Macmillan/McGraw-Hill, MATHEMATICS IN ACTION
Grade 1, Chapter 4, Lesson 3, pages 113–114

RETEACHING-34

Name

USING DOUBLES

Study

$1 + 1 = 2$ $1 + 2 = 3$ (1 more) (1 more) $2 + 2 = 4$ $2 + 3 = 5$ (1 more) (1 more)

Check

Add.

1.	$3 + 3 = 6$	$3 + 4 = 7$	$4 + 4 = 8$	$4 + 5 = 9$		
2.	$2 + 2 = 4$	$3 + 2 = 5$	$1 + 1 = 2$	$2 + 1 = 3$	$3 + 3 = 6$	$4 + 3 = 7$
3.	$5 + 5 = 10$	$5 + 3 = 8$	$2 + 4 = 6$	$5 + 4 = 9$	$3 + 6 = 9$	$8 + 1 = 9$
4.	$7 + 0 = 7$	$6 + 1 = 7$	$9 + 1 = 10$	$8 + 2 = 10$	$7 + 3 = 10$	$2 + 6 = 8$

RETEACHING-33

Name

PATTERNS

Study

$2 + 1 = 3$ $3 + 1 = 4$ $4 + 1 = 5$ $5 + 1 = 6$ $6 + 1 = 7$

Check

Add. Look for patterns.

1.	$1 + 2 = 3$	$2 + 2 = 4$	$3 + 2 = 5$	$4 + 2 = 6$	$5 + 2 = 7$	$6 + 2 = 8$
2.	$3 + 0 = 3$	$3 + 1 = 4$	$3 + 2 = 5$	$3 + 3 = 6$	$3 + 4 = 7$	$3 + 5 = 8$
3.	$4 + 6 = 10$	$4 + 5 = 9$	$4 + 4 = 8$	$4 + 3 = 7$	$4 + 2 = 6$	$4 + 1 = 5$
4.	$8 + 2 = 10$	$7 + 2 = 9$	$6 + 2 = 8$	$5 + 2 = 7$	$4 + 2 = 6$	$3 + 2 = 5$

RETEACHING-36

Name

ADDING THREE NUMBERS

Study

(4) (4 + 1)

2 + 2 + 1 = 5

$$\begin{array}{r} 2 \\ 2 \\ +\ 1 \\ \hline 5 \end{array}$$

(4) (4 + 1)

Check

Add.

1.

$$\begin{array}{r} 2 \\ 3 \\ +\ 4 \\ \hline 9 \end{array}$$ (5)

$$\begin{array}{r} 3 \\ 4 \\ +\ 1 \\ \hline 8 \end{array}$$ (7)

$$\begin{array}{r} 1 \\ 2 \\ +\ 4 \\ \hline 7 \end{array}$$ (3)

2.

$$\begin{array}{r} 5 \\ 2 \\ +\ 3 \\ \hline 10 \end{array}$$ (7)

$$\begin{array}{r} 2 \\ 2 \\ +\ 3 \\ \hline 7 \end{array}$$ (4)

$$\begin{array}{r} 2 \\ 1 \\ +\ 3 \\ \hline 6 \end{array}$$ (3)

Use ○ if you need help.

3.

$$\begin{array}{r} 1 \\ 4 \\ +\ 5 \\ \hline 10 \end{array}$$

$$\begin{array}{r} 2 \\ 1 \\ +\ 2 \\ \hline 5 \end{array}$$

$$\begin{array}{r} 1 \\ 2 \\ +\ 5 \\ \hline 8 \end{array}$$

$$\begin{array}{r} 3 \\ 1 \\ +\ 4 \\ \hline 8 \end{array}$$

$$\begin{array}{r} 2 \\ 2 \\ +\ 2 \\ \hline 6 \end{array}$$

RETEACHING-35

Name

PROBLEM SOLVING STRATEGY: WRITING AN ADDITION SENTENCE

Study

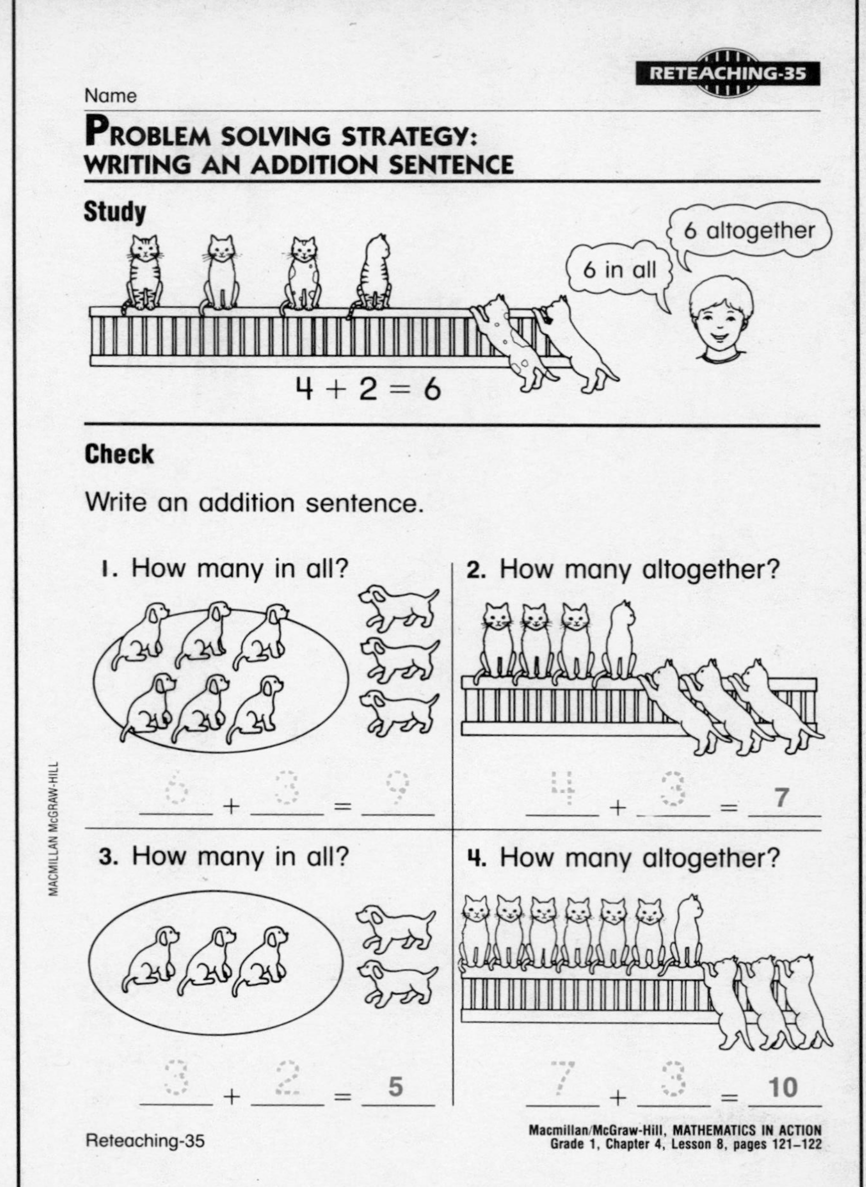

4 + 2 = 6

Check

Write an addition sentence.

1. How many in all?

6 + 3 = 9

2. How many altogether?

4 + 3 = 7

3. How many in all?

3 + 2 = 5

4. How many altogether?

7 + 3 = 10

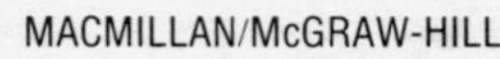

RETEACHING-38

Name

COUNTING BACK TO SUBTRACT

Study

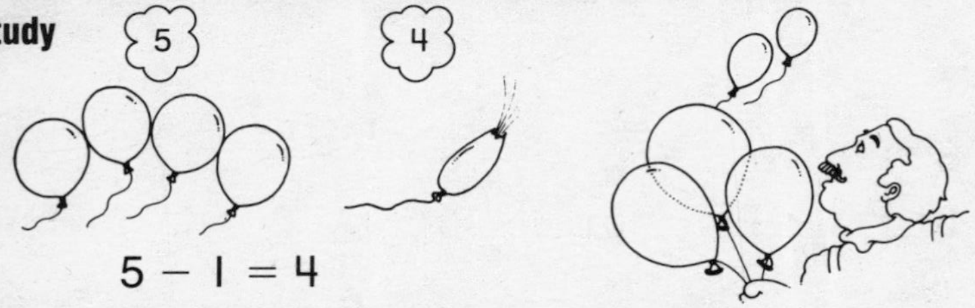

5 4

5 − 1 = 4

Check

Count back to subtract.

1. 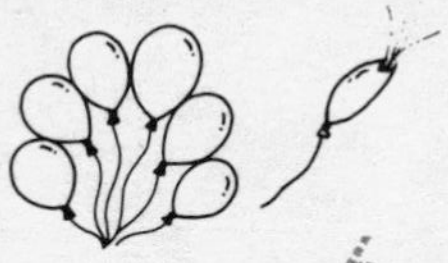 7 − 1 = 6

2. 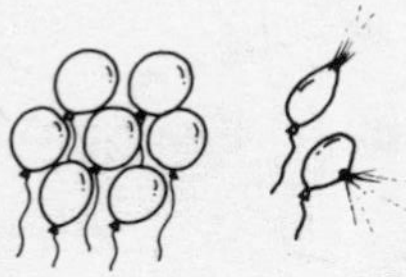 9 − 2 = 7

3.  4 − 1 = 3

4.  6 − 2 = 4

5. 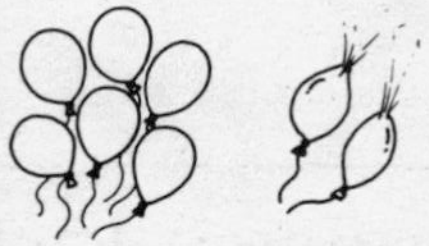 8 − 2 = 6

6. 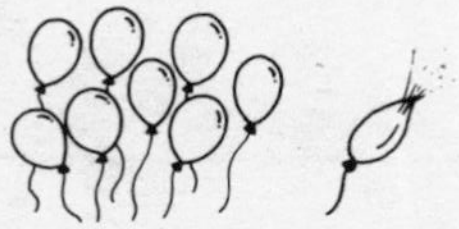 9 − 1 = 8

Macmillan/McGraw-Hill, MATHEMATICS IN ACTION
Grade 1, Chapter 5, Lesson 3, pages 141–142

RETEACHING-37

Name

PROBLEM SOLVING STRATEGY: LOOKING FOR A PATTERN

Study

The next one should be

Check

Color. Next.

Guide children in coloring the patterns.

1. red red red red | red

2. blue blue blue blue blue blue | blue

3. green blue green blue green blue green blue | green

4. red blue blue red blue blue red blue blue | red

Macmillan/McGraw-Hill, MATHEMATICS IN ACTION
Grade 1, Chapter 4, Lesson 10, pages 125–126

RETEACHING-40

Name

SUBTRACTION PATTERNS

Study

5	5	5	5	5	5
− 0	− 1	− 2	− 3	− 4	− 5
5	4	3	2	1	0

Check

Subtract. Look for patterns.

1.	9 − 3 = 6	8 − 3 = 5	7 − 3 = 4	6 − 3 = 3	5 − 3 = 2	4 − 3 = 1
2.	7 − 7 = 0	7 − 6 = 1	7 − 5 = 2	7 − 4 = 3	7 − 3 = 4	7 − 2 = 5
3.	10 − 1 = 9	10 − 2 = 8	10 − 3 = 7	10 − 4 = 6	10 − 5 = 5	10 − 6 = 4
4.	8 − 2 = 6	7 − 2 = 5	6 − 2 = 4	5 − 2 = 3	4 − 2 = 2	3 − 2 = 1

RETEACHING-39

Name

USING RELATED SUBTRACTION FACTS

Study

This shows 7 − 3 = 4.

This shows 7 − 4 = 3.

These are related facts.

Check

Complete each pair of facts.

1. 9 − 5 = 4
   9 − 4 = 5

2. 10 − 6 = 4
   10 − 4 = 6

3. 8 − 3 = 5   7 − 5 = 2   9 − 6 = 3
   8 − 5 = 3   7 − 2 = 5   9 − 3 = 6

4. 6 − 1 = 5   10 − 8 = 2   8 − 2 = 6
   6 − 5 = 1   10 − 2 = 8   8 − 6 = 2

RETEACHING-42

Name

Subtraction and Addition

Study

7 ○
How many ○
in the box?

Outside the box.

7 − 3 = 4

Inside the box.

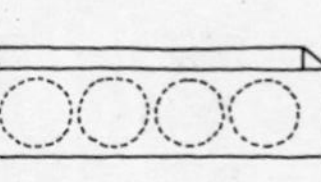

3 + 4 = 7

Check

Write the missing numbers.
Use ○ if you need help.

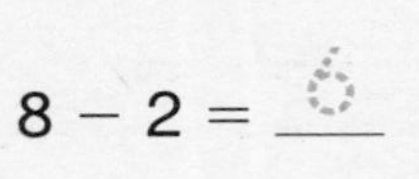

1. 9 − 4 = 5   4 + 5 = 9   8 − 2 = 6   2 + 6 = 8

2. 10 − 6 = 4   9 − 6 = 3   8 − 5 = 3

   6 + 4 = 10   6 + 3 = 9   5 + 3 = 8

3. 8 − 4 = 4   7 − 2 = 5   6 − 2 = 4

   4 + 4 = 8   2 + 5 = 7   2 + 4 = 6

Macmillan/McGraw-Hill, MATHEMATICS IN ACTION
Grade 1, Chapter 5, Lesson 8, pages 149–150

RETEACHING-41

Name

Problem Solving Strategy: Writing a Subtraction Sentence

Study

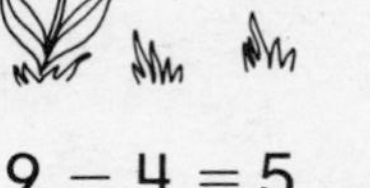

9 − 4 = 5

Check

How many are left?

1.

9 − 3 = 6

2.

7 − 3 = 4

3.

10 − 5 = 5

4.

6 − 3 = 3

Macmillan/McGraw-Hill, MATHEMATICS IN ACTION
Grade 1, Chapter 5, Lesson 6, pages 145–146

Name

PROBLEM SOLVING STRATEGY: USING A PHYSICAL MODEL

Study

Ted had 7 shells.

He lost 2 shells.

How many were left?

You can use a counter to show each shell.

7 − 2 = 5

5 were left

Check

Solve. Use counters.

1. Lisa had 6 shells.

   She gave 3 shells away.

   How many were left?

   6 − 3 = 3

   3 were left

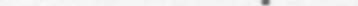

2. Pat had 8 shells.

   She broke 4 shells.

   How many were left?

   8 − 4 = 4

   4 were left

Name

FACT FAMILIES

Study

5 + 3 = 8 8 − 3 = 5 3 + 5 = 8 8 − 5 = 3

fact family

Check

Complete each fact family.

1.

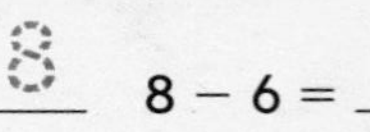
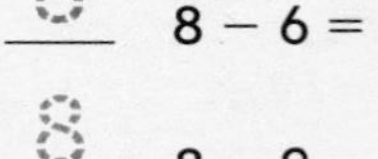

2 + 6 = 8 8 − 6 = 2

6 + 2 = 8 8 − 2 = 6

2.

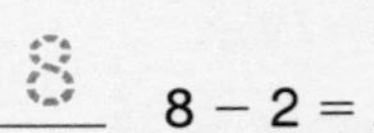
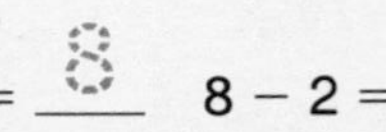

7 + 3 = 10 10 − 3 = 7

3 + 7 = 10 10 − 7 = 3

3.

4 + 5 = 9 9 − 5 = 4

5 + 4 = 9 9 − 4 = 5

4.

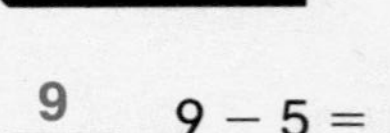

8 + 1 = 9 9 − 1 = 8

1 + 8 = 9 9 − 8 = 1

RETEACHING-46

Name

COUNTING BY TENS

Study

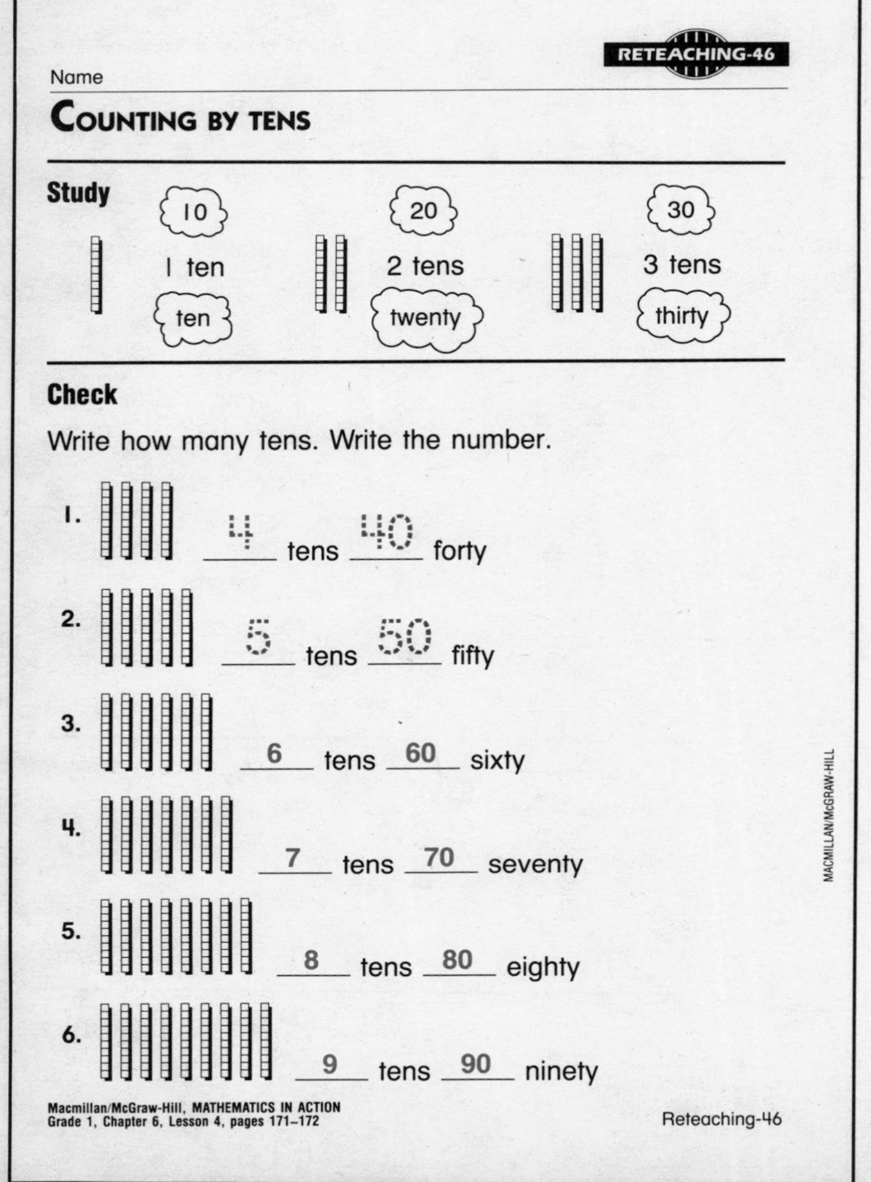

Check

Write how many tens. Write the number.

1. 4 tens 40 forty
2. 5 tens 50 fifty
3. 6 tens 60 sixty
4. 7 tens 70 seventy
5. 8 tens 80 eighty
6. 9 tens 90 ninety

Macmillan/McGraw-Hill, MATHEMATICS IN ACTION
Grade 1, Chapter 6, Lesson 4, pages 171–172

RETEACHING-45

Name

NUMBERS TO 19

Study

1 ten 0 ones
10

1 ten 5 ones
15

Check

Color each ten.
Write how many tens and ones. Write the number.

1 ten 1 ones
11

1 ten 2 ones
12

1 ten 3 ones
13

1 ten 4 ones
14

1 ten 6 ones
16

1 ten 7 ones
17

1 ten 8 ones
18

1 ten 9 ones
19

Macmillan/McGraw-Hill, MATHEMATICS IN ACTION
Grade 1, Chapter 6, Lesson 3, pages 169–170

RETEACHING-48

Name

NUMBERS TO 59

Study

5 [10] 2 ○

5 tens 2 ones 52

Check.

Match. Then write the number.

1. 4 [10] 7 ○
   4 tens 7 ones — 47
2. 5 [10] 4 ○
   5 tens 4 ones — 54
3. 3 [10] 5 ○
   3 tens 5 ones — 35
4. 5 [10] 8 ○
   5 tens 8 ones — 58

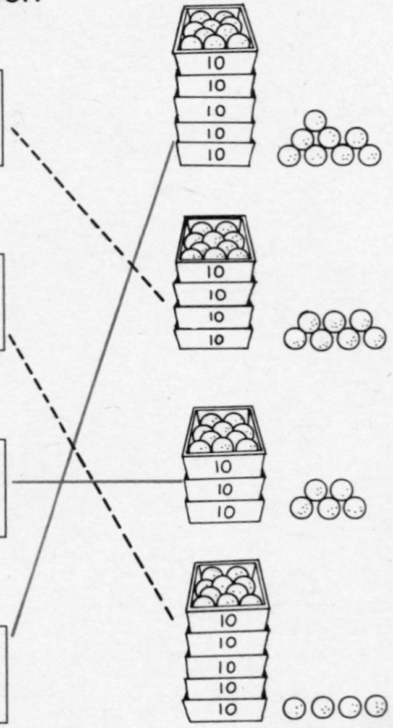

Macmillan/McGraw-Hill, MATHEMATICS IN ACTION
Grade 1, Chapter 6, Lesson 6, pages 175–176

RETEACHING-47

Name

NUMBERS TO 39

Study

tens	ones
2	3

23

First I count the tens.
Then I count the ones.

Check

Write how many tens and ones.
Then write the number.

	tens	ones	number
1.	2	5	25
2.	2	8	28
3.	3	0	30
4.	3	6	36
5.	3	2	32

Macmillan/McGraw-Hill, MATHEMATICS IN ACTION
Grade 1, Chapter 6, Lesson 5, pages 173–174

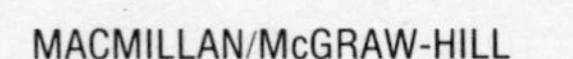

RETEACHING-50

Name

Numbers to 79

Study

3 tens is not the same as 3 ones.

3 tens 7 ones 37

7 tens 3 ones 73

Check

Write the numbers.

1. 5 tens 6 ones 56	2. 6 tens 5 ones 65
3. 7 tens 5 ones 75	4. 5 tens 7 ones 57
5. 4 tens 7 ones 47	6. 7 tens 4 ones 74

RETEACHING-49

Name

Problem Solving Strategy: Choosing the Operation

Study

Bob had 5 .
He got 3 more .
How many in all?

Add to join groups.

5 + 3 = 8

8 in all

Sue had 7.
She gave away 4.
How many were left?

Subtract to take away some from a group.

7 − 4 = 3

3 were left

Check

Ring the number sentence that solves the problem.

Andy had 4 .
He got 3 more .
How many in all?

4 + 3 = 7

4 − 3 = 1

7 in all

Lien had 8 .
She gave away 2 .
How many were left?

8 + 2 = 10

8 − 2 = 6

6 were left

RETEACHING-52

Name

ORDER

Study

1 2 3 4 5 6 7 8 9 10

21 22 23 24 25 26 27 28 29 30

Check

Count by ones. Write the numbers.

1. 31 32 33 34 35 36 37 38 39 40
2. 61 62 63 64 65 66 67 68 69 70
3. 81 82 83 84 85 86 87 88 89 90

4. What number comes just after?

6 7 8

24 25 26

76 77 78

88 89 90

5. What number comes just before?

13 14 15

30 31 32

64 65 66

97 98 99

Macmillan/McGraw-Hill, MATHEMATICS IN ACTION
Grade 1, Chapter 6, Lesson 11, pages 185–186

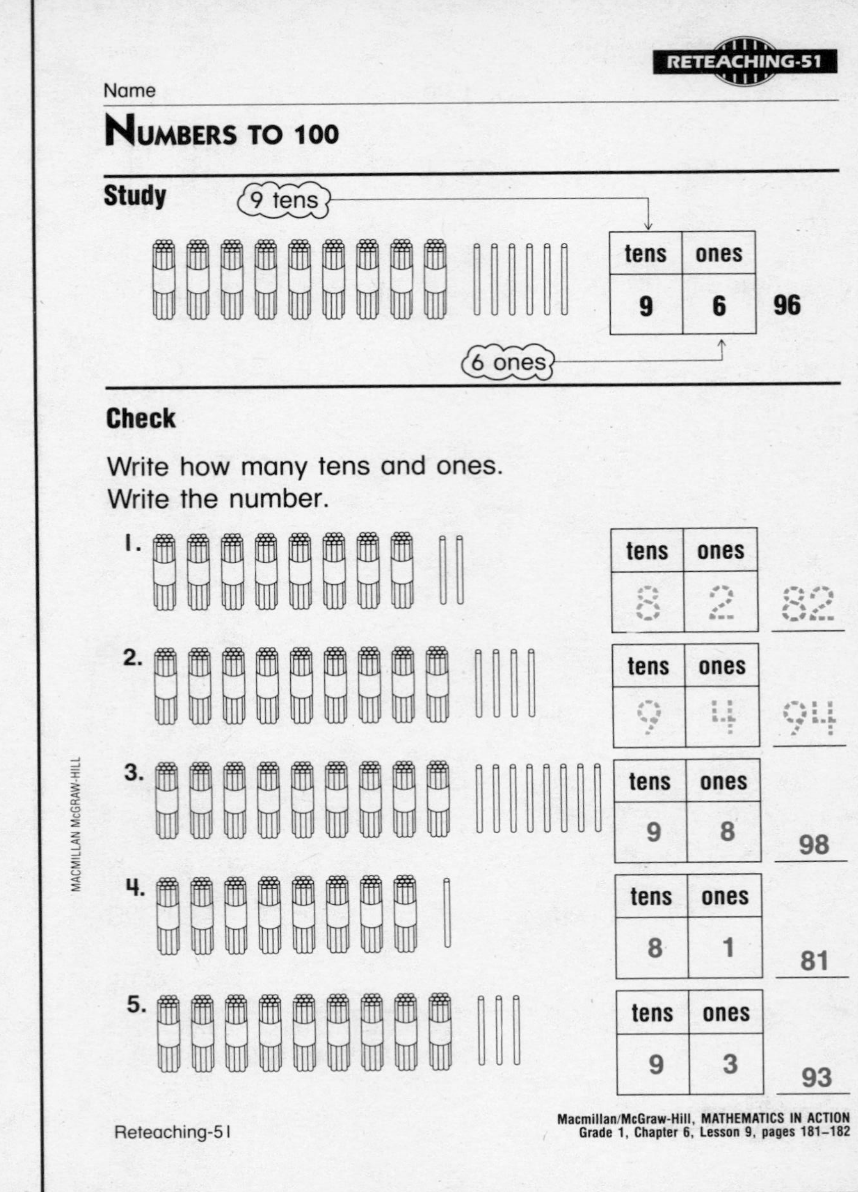

RETEACHING-51

Name

NUMBERS TO 100

Study

9 tens

6 ones

tens	ones
9	6

96

Check

Write how many tens and ones.
Write the number.

1.

tens	ones
8	2

82

2.

tens	ones
9	4

94

3.

tens	ones
9	8

98

4.

tens	ones
8	1

81

5.

tens	ones
9	3

93

Macmillan/McGraw-Hill, MATHEMATICS IN ACTION
Grade 1, Chapter 6, Lesson 9, pages 181–182

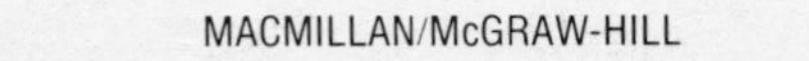

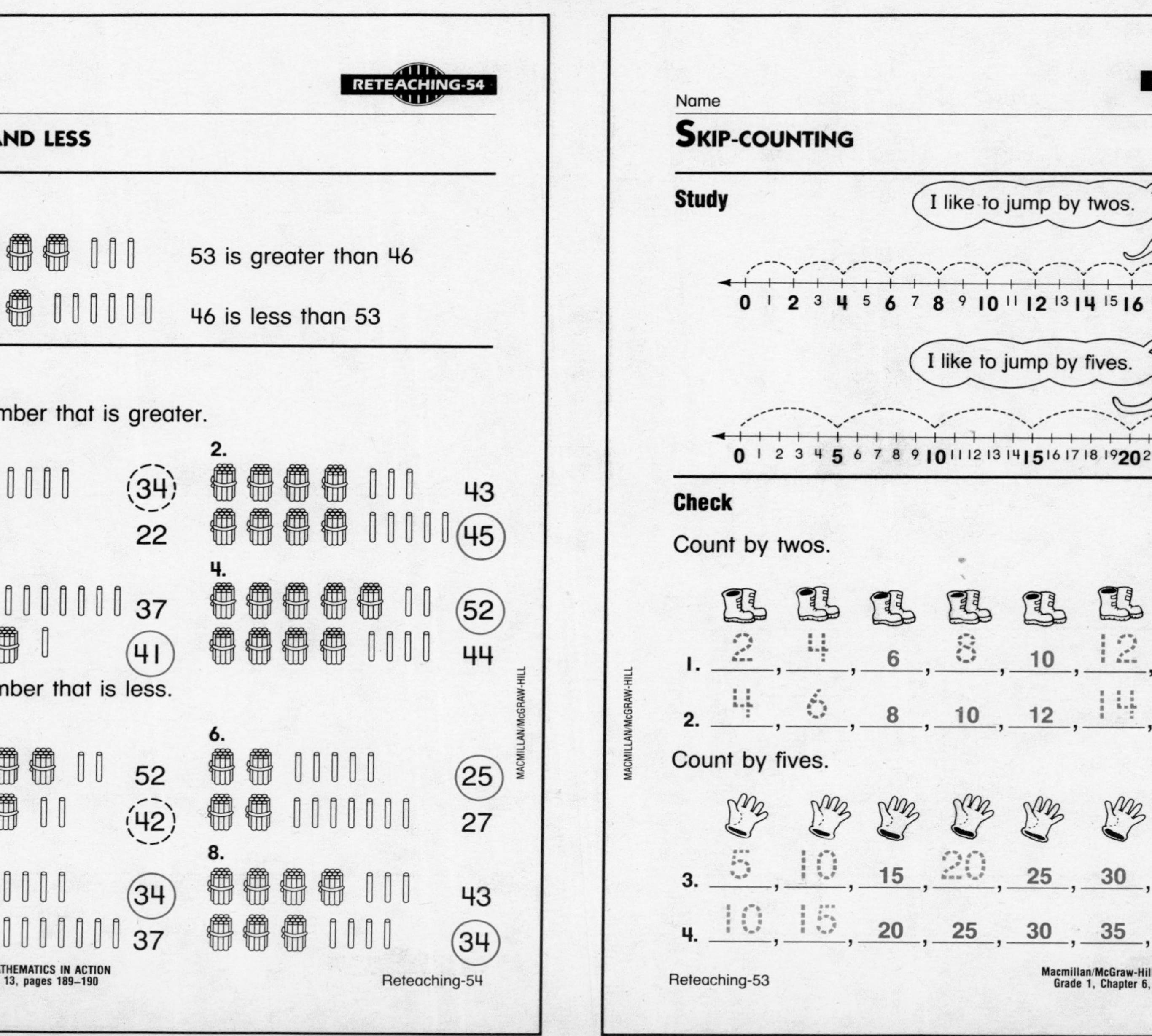

RETEACHING-54

Name

GREATER AND LESS

Study

53 is greater than 46

46 is less than 53

Check

Ring the number that is greater.

1. 34 22
2. 43 45
3. 37 41
4. 52 44

Ring the number that is less.

5. 52 42
6. 25 27
7. 34 37
8. 43 34

Macmillan/McGraw-Hill, MATHEMATICS IN ACTION
Grade 1, Chapter 6, Lesson 13, pages 189–190

RETEACHING-53

Name

SKIP-COUNTING

Study

Check

Count by twos.

1. 2, 4, 6, 8, 10, 12, 14, 16
2. 4, 6, 8, 10, 12, 14, 16, 18

Count by fives.

3. 5, 10, 15, 20, 25, 30, 35, 40
4. 10, 15, 20, 25, 30, 35, 40, 45

Macmillan/McGraw-Hill, MATHEMATICS IN ACTION
Grade 1, Chapter 6, Lesson 12, pages 187–188

RETEACHING-56

Name

PROBLEM SOLVING: USING INFORMATION FROM A GRAPH

Study

Mark 1 box for each item.
Go left to right.

Aircraft

0 1 2 3 4 5 6

There are 3 [airplane].
There are 5 [helicopter].

Color 1 box for each [airplane].

Color 1 box for each [helicopter].

6 [airplane]

8 [helicopter]

Aircraft

0 1 2 3 4 5 6 7 8

Macmillan/McGraw-Hill, MATHEMATICS IN ACTION
Grade 1, Chapter 6, Lesson 15, pages 193–194

RETEACHING-55

Name

GRAPHING

Study

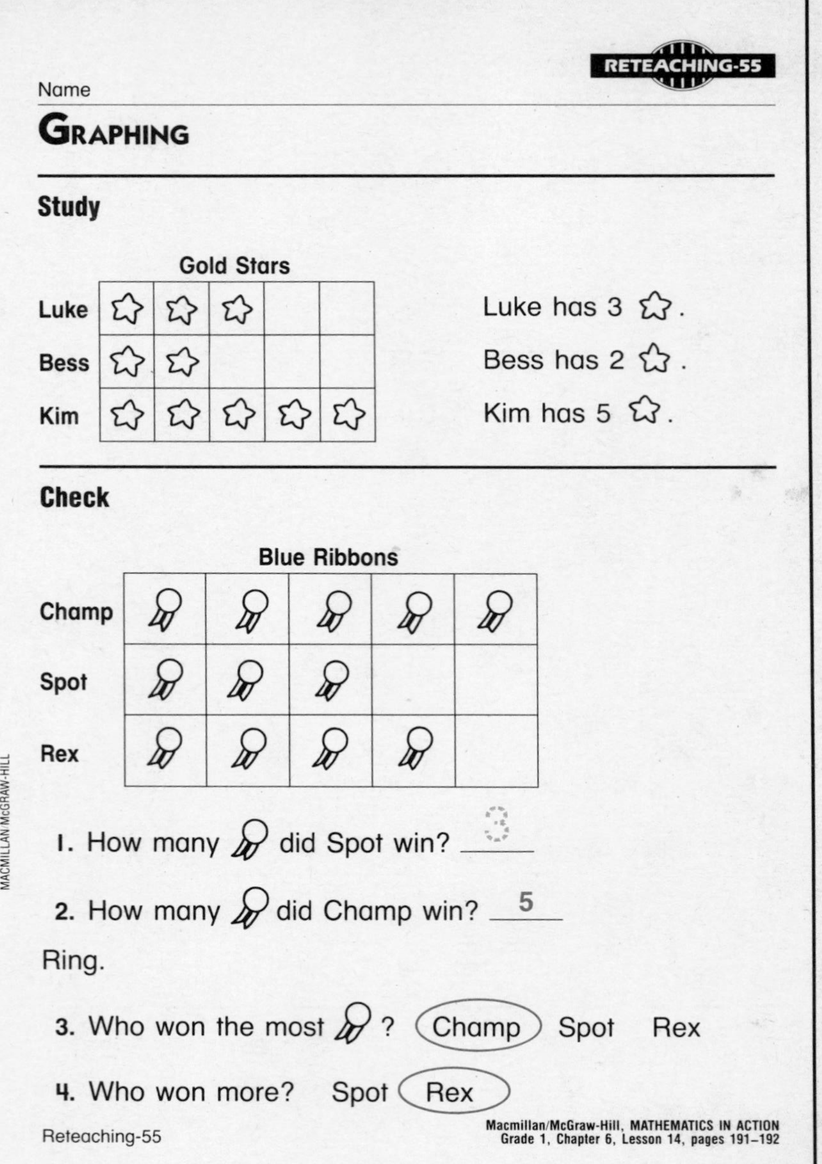

Gold Stars

Luke has 3 [star].
Bess has 2 [star].
Kim has 5 [star].

Check

Blue Ribbons

1. How many [ribbon] did Spot win? 3
2. How many [ribbon] did Champ win? 5

Ring.

3. Who won the most [ribbon]? (Champ) Spot Rex
4. Who won more? Spot (Rex)

Macmillan/McGraw-Hill, MATHEMATICS IN ACTION
Grade 1, Chapter 6, Lesson 14, pages 191–192

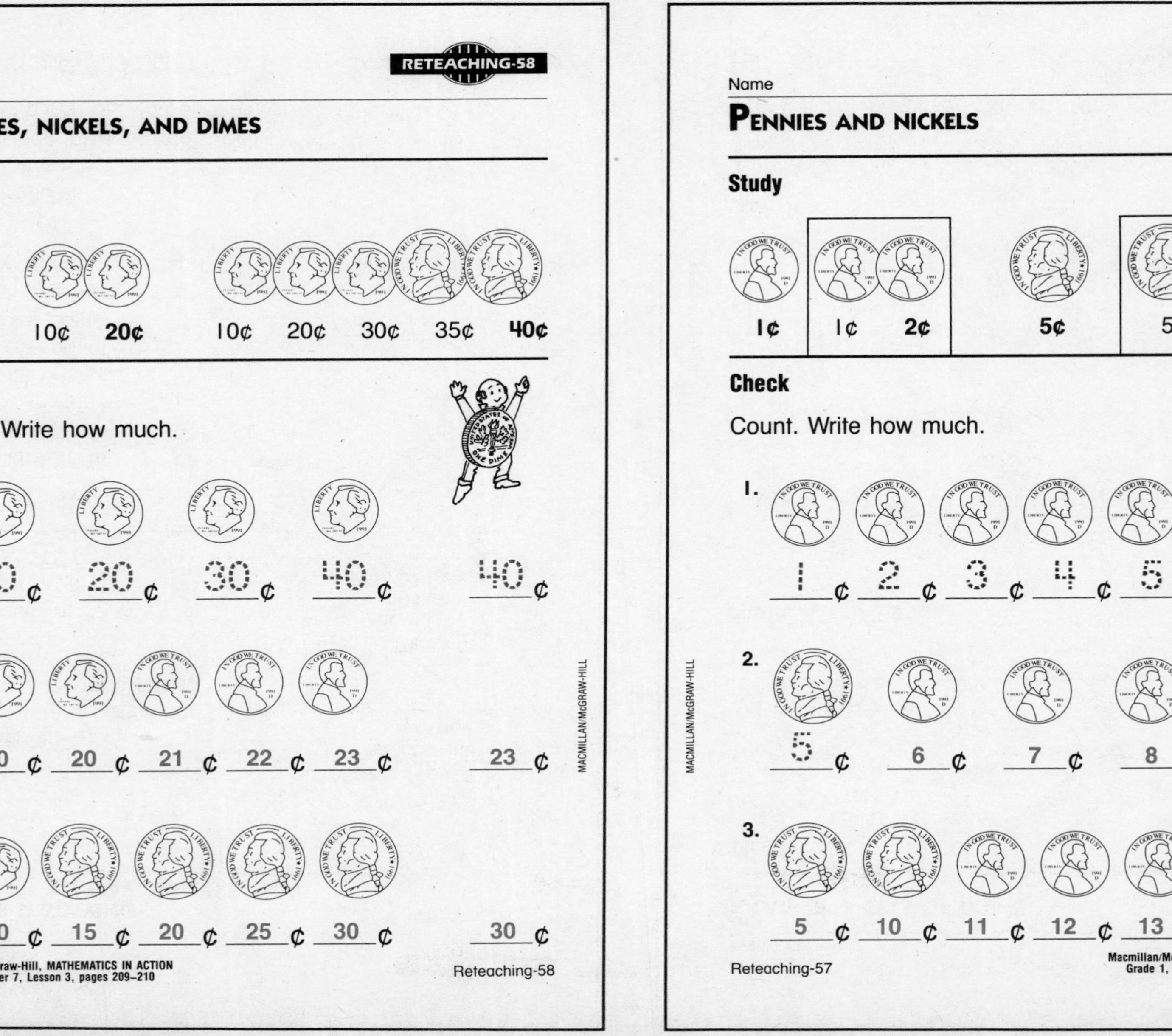

RETEACHING-58

Name

PENNIES, NICKELS, AND DIMES

Study

10¢ | 10¢ 20¢ | 10¢ 20¢ 30¢ 35¢ 40¢

Check

Count. Write how much.

1. 10 ¢ 20 ¢ 30 ¢ 40 ¢ — 40 ¢

2. 10 ¢ 20 ¢ 21 ¢ 22 ¢ 23 ¢ — 23 ¢

3. 10 ¢ 15 ¢ 20 ¢ 25 ¢ 30 ¢ — 30 ¢

Macmillan/McGraw-Hill, MATHEMATICS IN ACTION
Grade 1, Chapter 7, Lesson 3, pages 209–210

RETEACHING-57

Name

PENNIES AND NICKELS

Study

1¢ | 1¢ 2¢ | 5¢ | 5¢ 10¢ 15¢

Check

Count. Write how much.

1. 1 ¢ 2 ¢ 3 ¢ 4 ¢ 5 ¢ — 5 ¢

2. 5 ¢ 6 ¢ 7 ¢ 8 ¢ — 8 ¢

3. 5 ¢ 10 ¢ 11 ¢ 12 ¢ 13 ¢ — 13 ¢

Macmillan/McGraw-Hill, MATHEMATICS IN ACTION
Grade 1, Chapter 7, Lesson 2, pages 207–208

RETEACHING-60

Name

PROBLEM SOLVING: IDENTIFYING EXTRA INFORMATION

Study

A pencil costs 3¢.
A ball costs 5¢.
~~A top costs 7¢.~~
Rosa bought a pencil and a ball.
How much did she spend?

Cross out what is not needed.

Think:
pencil 3¢
ball 5¢
Add to join groups.

$$\begin{array}{r} 3¢ \\ +\ 5¢ \\ \hline 8¢ \end{array}$$

Rosa spent 8¢.

Check

Cross out the fact you do not need.
Solve.

1. A pen costs 5¢.
   ~~A yoyo costs 7¢.~~
   A ruler costs 4¢.
   Neal bought a pen and a ruler.
   How much did he spend?

$$\begin{array}{r} 5¢ \\ +\ 4¢ \\ \hline 9¢ \end{array}$$

Neal spent 9 ¢

2. ~~A hat costs 5¢.~~
   A tie costs 5¢.
   A belt costs 2¢.
   Jeff bought a tie and a belt.
   How much did Jeff spend?

$$\begin{array}{r} 5¢ \\ +\ 2¢ \\ \hline 7¢ \end{array}$$

Jeff spent 7 ¢

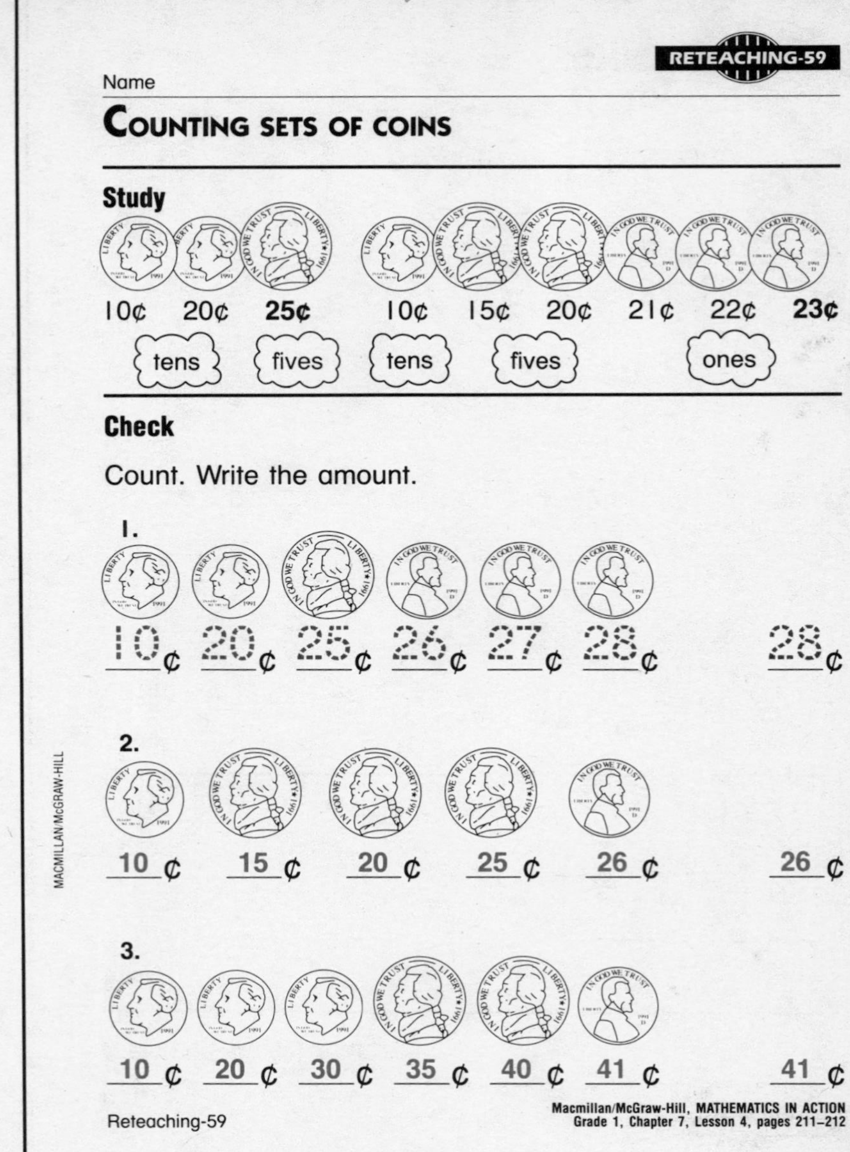

RETEACHING-59

Name

COUNTING SETS OF COINS

Study

10¢ 20¢ **25¢** 10¢ 15¢ 20¢ 21¢ 22¢ **23¢**

tens fives tens fives ones

Check

Count. Write the amount.

1. 10 ¢ 20 ¢ 25 ¢ 26 ¢ 27 ¢ 28 ¢ 28 ¢

2. 10 ¢ 15 ¢ 20 ¢ 25 ¢ 26 ¢ 26 ¢

3. 10 ¢ 20 ¢ 30 ¢ 35 ¢ 40 ¢ 41 ¢ 41 ¢

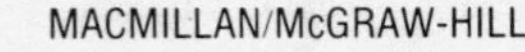

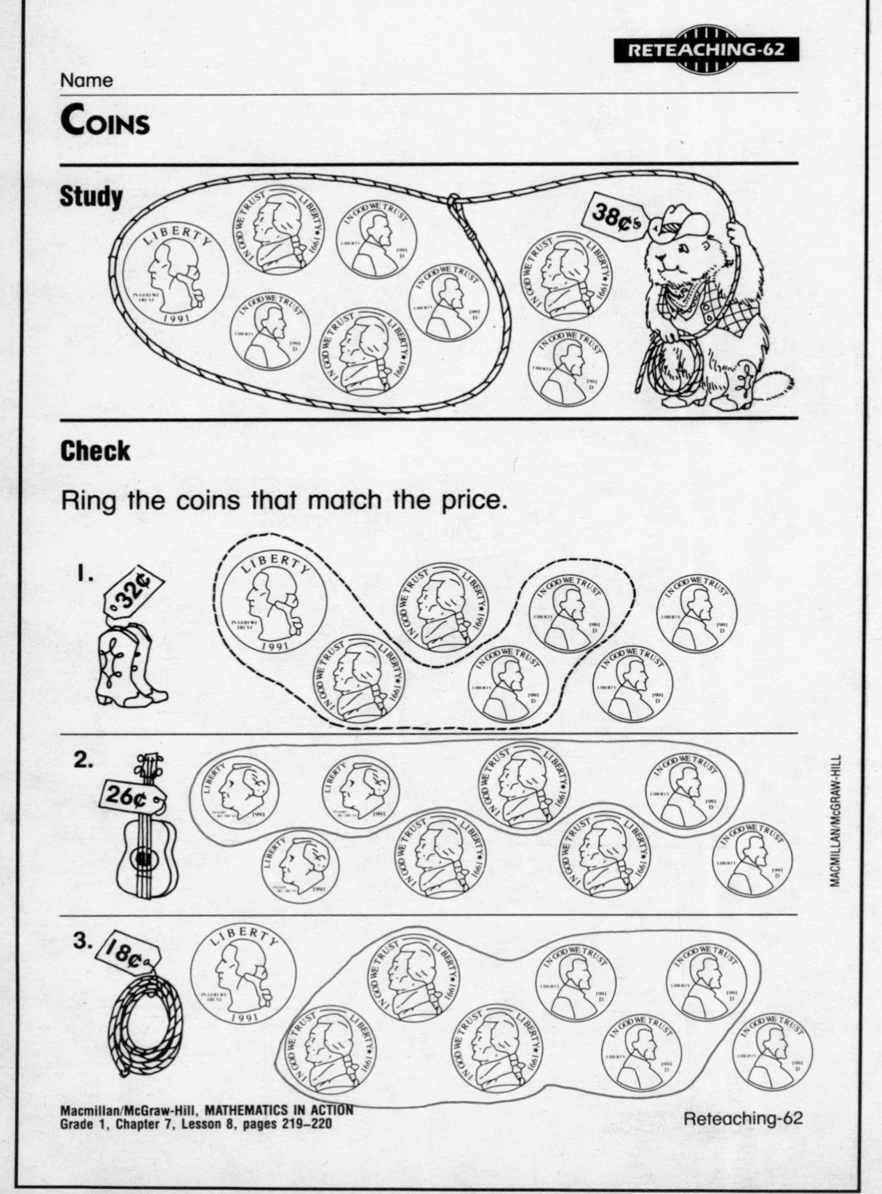

RETEACHING-62

Name

Coins

Study

Check

Ring the coins that match the price.

1. 32¢

2. 26¢

3. 18¢

Macmillan/McGraw-Hill, MATHEMATICS IN ACTION
Grade 1, Chapter 7, Lesson 8, pages 219–220

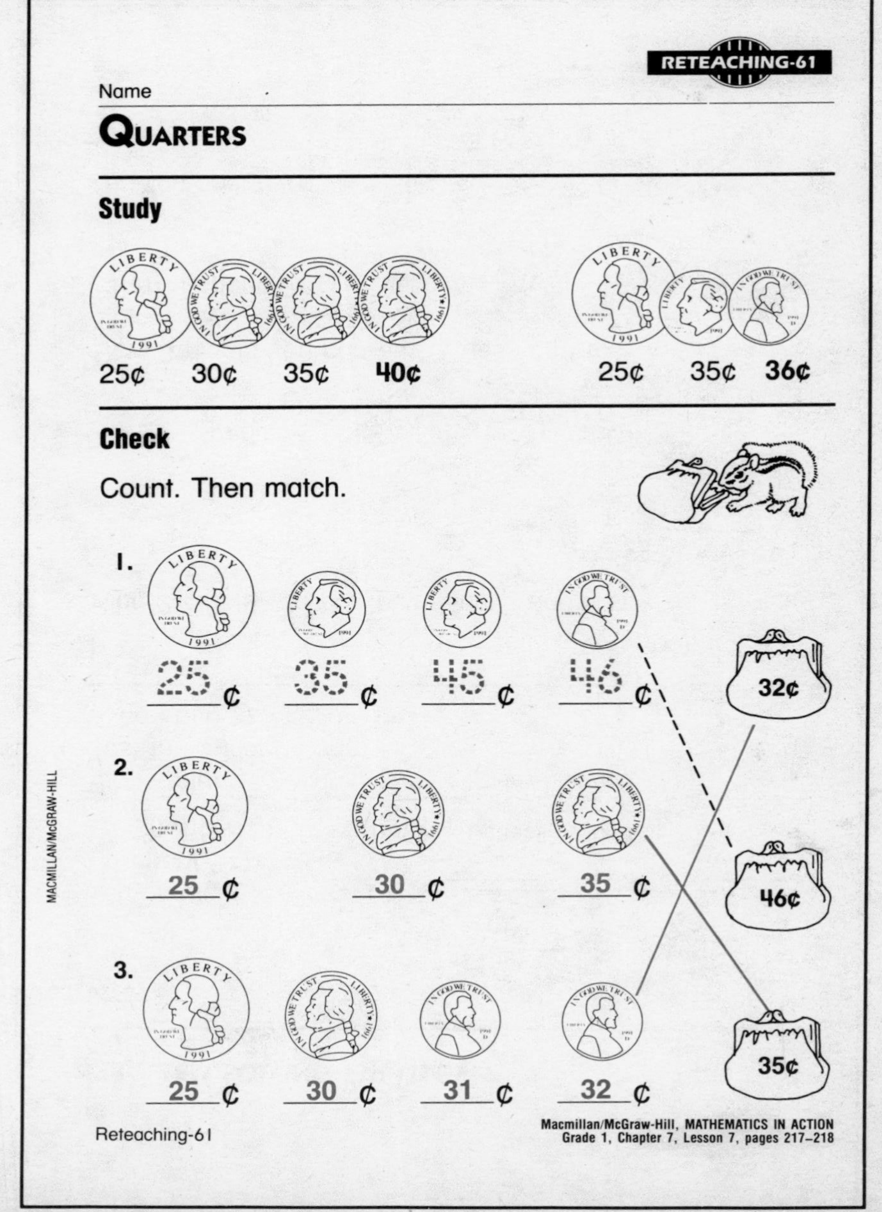

RETEACHING-61

Name

Quarters

Study

25¢ 30¢ 35¢ **40¢**

25¢ 35¢ **36¢**

Check

Count. Then match.

1. 25 ¢ 35 ¢ 45 ¢ 46 ¢

2. 25 ¢ 30 ¢ 35 ¢

3. 25 ¢ 30 ¢ 31 ¢ 32 ¢

Macmillan/McGraw-Hill, MATHEMATICS IN ACTION
Grade 1, Chapter 7, Lesson 7, pages 217–218

RETEACHING-64

Name

Centimeters and Decimeters

Study

I centimeter
I cm

3 centimeters

3 cm

Check

Use your [ruler] to measure.

1. 7 cm

2. 10 cm

3. 11 cm

4. 4 cm

5. 13 cm

RETEACHING-63

Name

Problem Solving Strategy: Guess and Test

Study

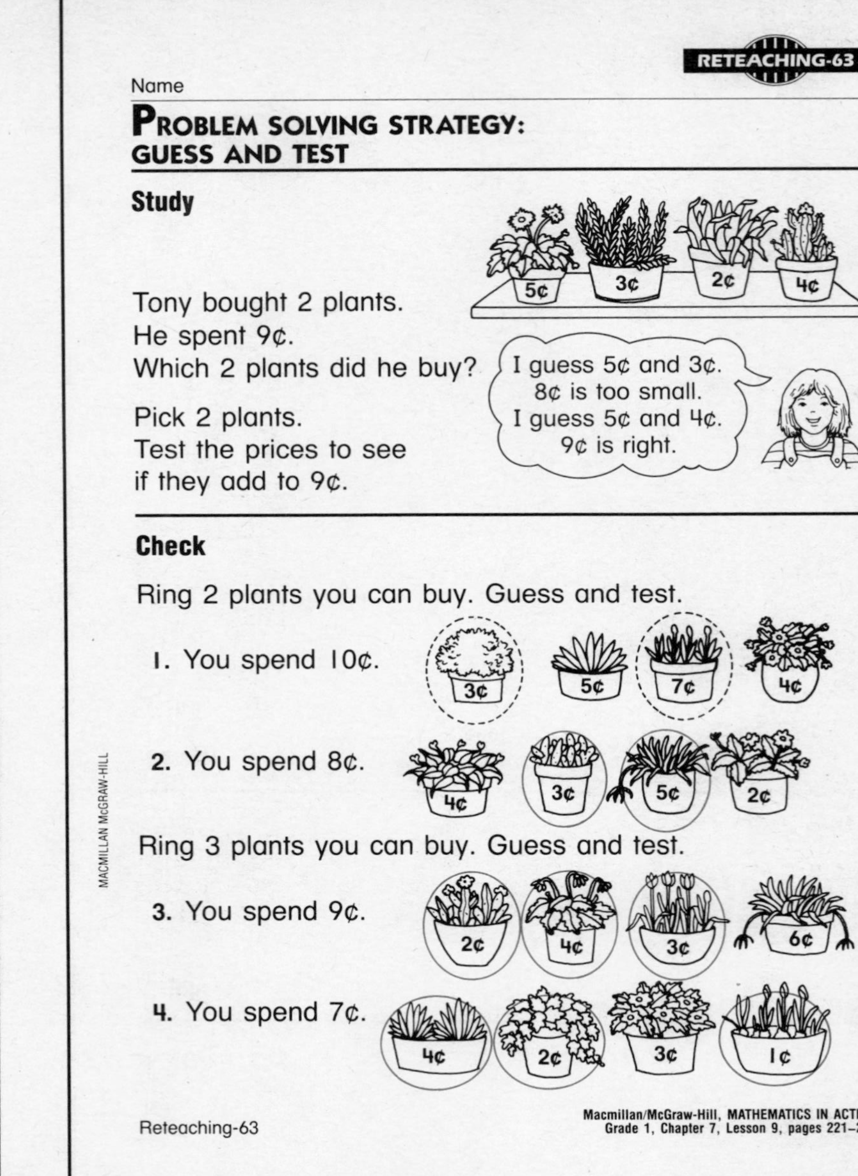

Tony bought 2 plants.
He spent 9¢.
Which 2 plants did he buy?

Pick 2 plants.
Test the prices to see if they add to 9¢.

Check

Ring 2 plants you can buy. Guess and test.

1. You spend 10¢. (3¢, 5¢, 7¢, 4¢)

2. You spend 8¢. (4¢, 3¢, 5¢, 2¢)

Ring 3 plants you can buy. Guess and test.

3. You spend 9¢. (2¢, 4¢, 3¢, 6¢)

4. You spend 7¢. (4¢, 2¢, 3¢, 1¢)

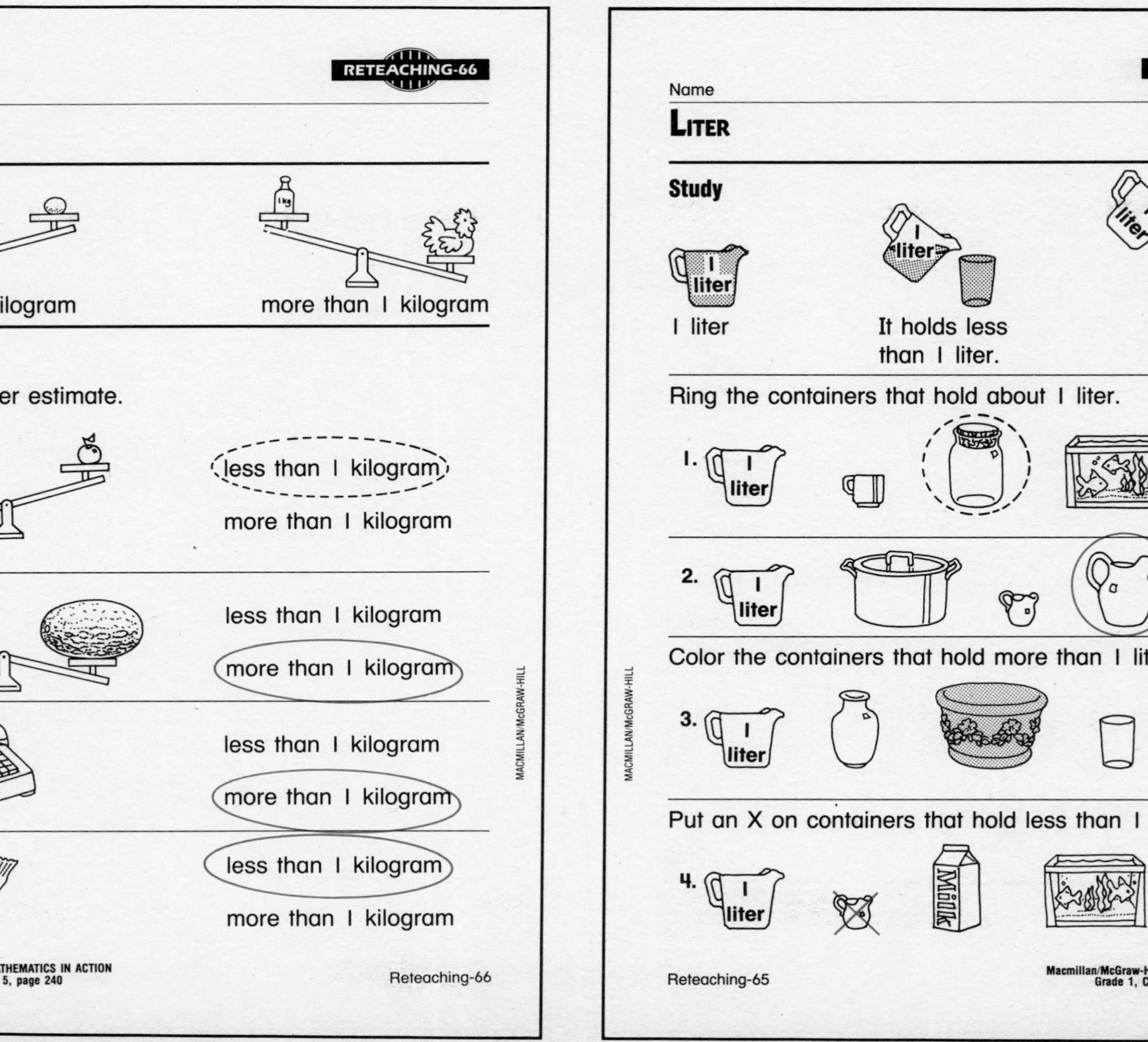

RETEACHING-66

Name

KILOGRAM

Study

less than I kilogram

more than I kilogram

Check

Ring the better estimate.

1. less than I kilogram / more than I kilogram
2. less than I kilogram / more than I kilogram
3. less than I kilogram / more than I kilogram
4. less than I kilogram / more than I kilogram

RETEACHING-65

Name

LITER

Study

I liter

It holds less than I liter.

It holds more than I liter.

Ring the containers that hold about I liter.

1.

2.

Color the containers that hold more than I liter.

3.

Put an X on containers that hold less than I liter.

4.

RETEACHING-68

Name

INCH AND FOOT

Study

I inch

3 inches

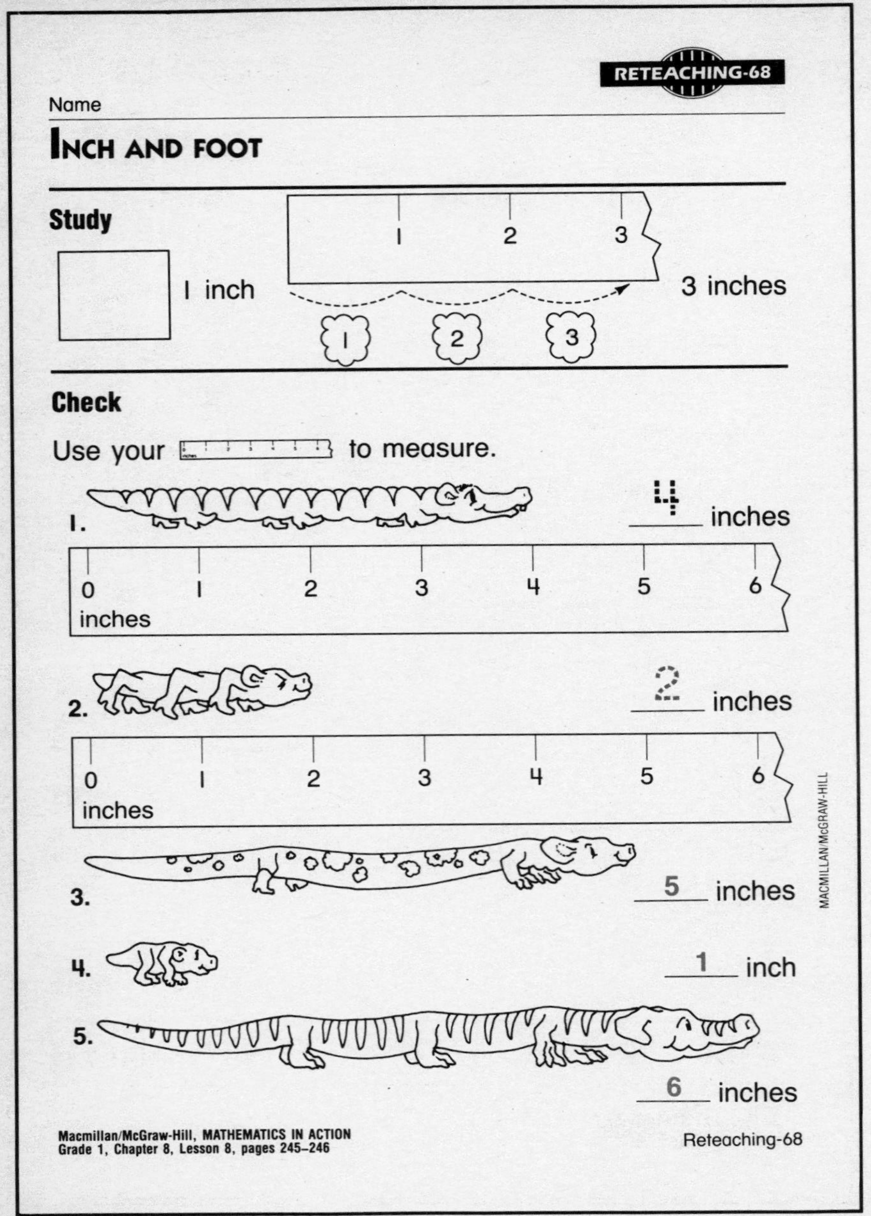

Check

Use your ruler to measure.

1. 4 inches

2. 2 inches

3. 5 inches

4. 1 inch

5. 6 inches

Macmillan/McGraw-Hill, MATHEMATICS IN ACTION
Grade 1, Chapter 8, Lesson 8, pages 245–246

RETEACHING-67

Name

PROBLEM SOLVING STRATEGY: USING ESTIMATION

Study

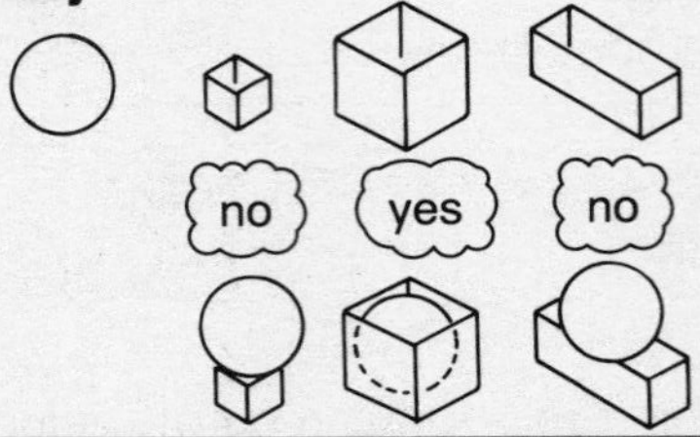

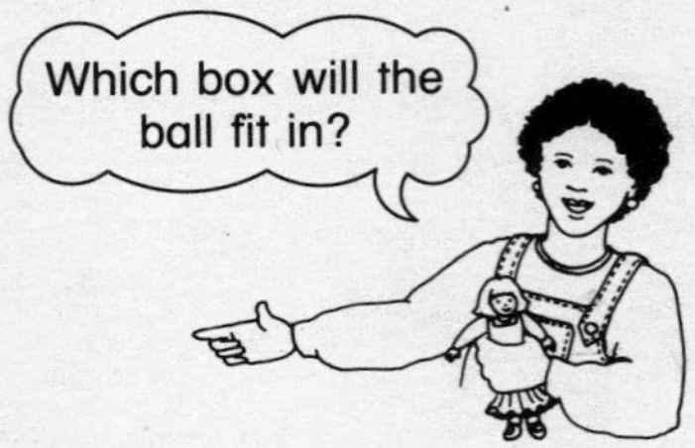

Which box will the ball fit in?

no yes no

Check

Color the box that best fits the toy.

1.

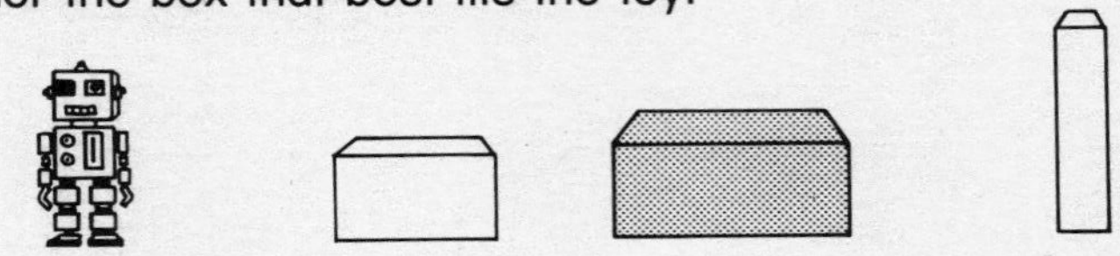

2.

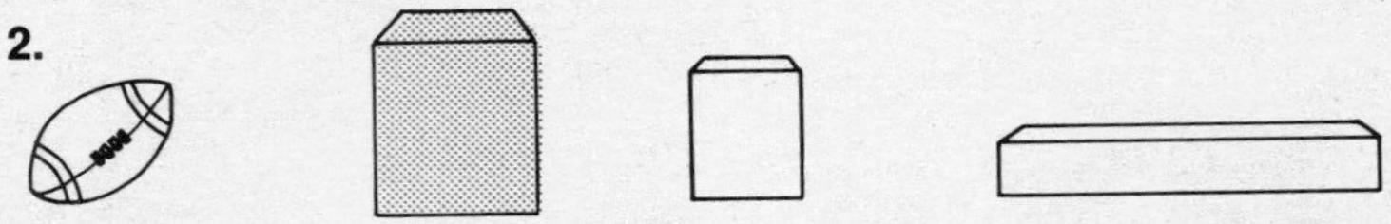

3.

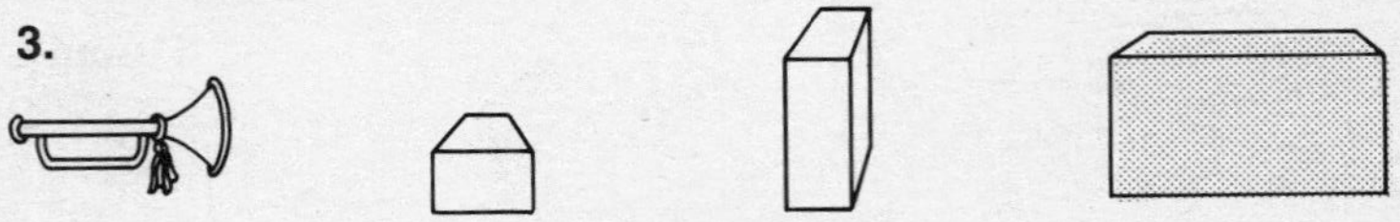

4.

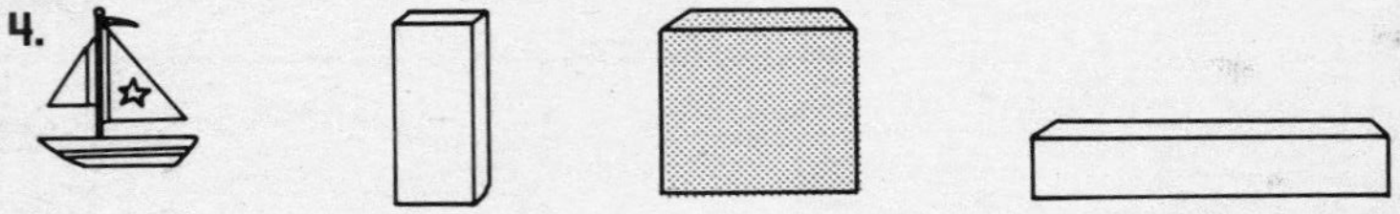

Macmillan/McGraw-Hill, MATHEMATICS IN ACTION
Grade 1, Chapter 8, Lesson 6, pages 241–242

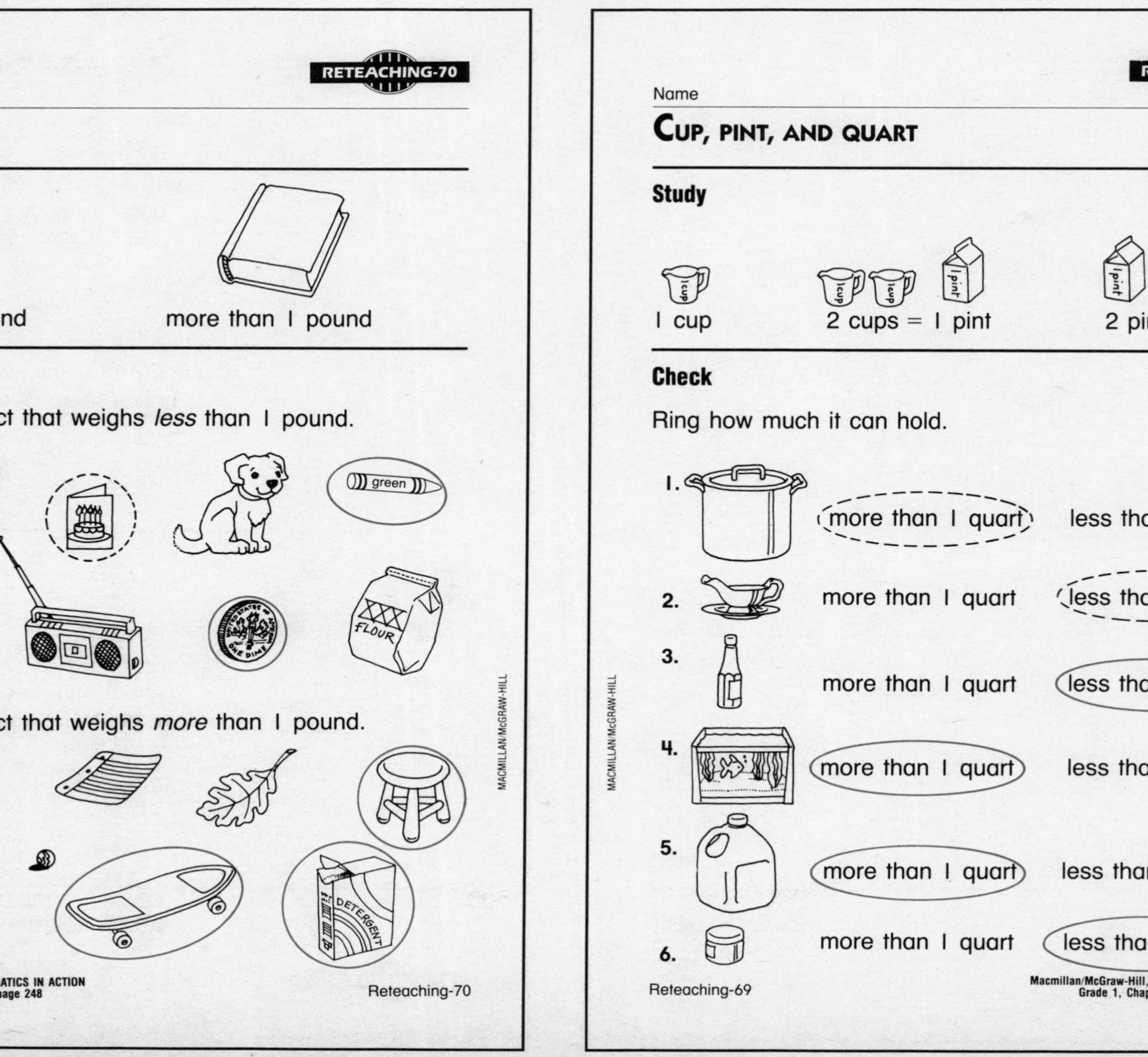

RETEACHING-70

Name

Pound

Study

less than 1 pound — more than 1 pound

Check

Ring each object that weighs *less* than 1 pound.

1.

Ring each object that weighs *more* than 1 pound.

2.

Macmillan/McGraw-Hill, MATHEMATICS IN ACTION
Grade 1, Chapter 8, Lesson 10, page 248

RETEACHING-69

Name

Cup, Pint, and Quart

Study

1 cup — 2 cups = 1 pint — 2 pints = 1 quart

Check

Ring how much it can hold.

1. more than 1 quart — less than 1 quart
2. more than 1 quart — less than 1 quart
3. more than 1 quart — less than 1 quart
4. more than 1 quart — less than 1 quart
5. more than 1 quart — less than 1 quart
6. more than 1 quart — less than 1 quart

Macmillan/McGraw-Hill, MATHEMATICS IN ACTION
Grade 1, Chapter 8, Lesson 9, page 247

RETEACHING-72

Name

Problem Solving Strategy: Drawing a Picture

Study

Ted has 4 inches of tape.
He needs 2 inches for each card.
How many cards can he make?

Ted can make 2 cards.

Check

Draw a picture to solve.

1. Alice has 6 inches of ribbon.
   She needs 3 inches for each bow.
   How many bows can she make? 2 bows

2. Ellen has 5 inches of paper.
   She needs 1 inch for each card.
   How many cards can she make? 5 cards

Macmillan/McGraw-Hill, MATHEMATICS IN ACTION
Grade 1, Chapter 8, Lesson 12, pages 251–252

RETEACHING-71

Name

Temperature

Study

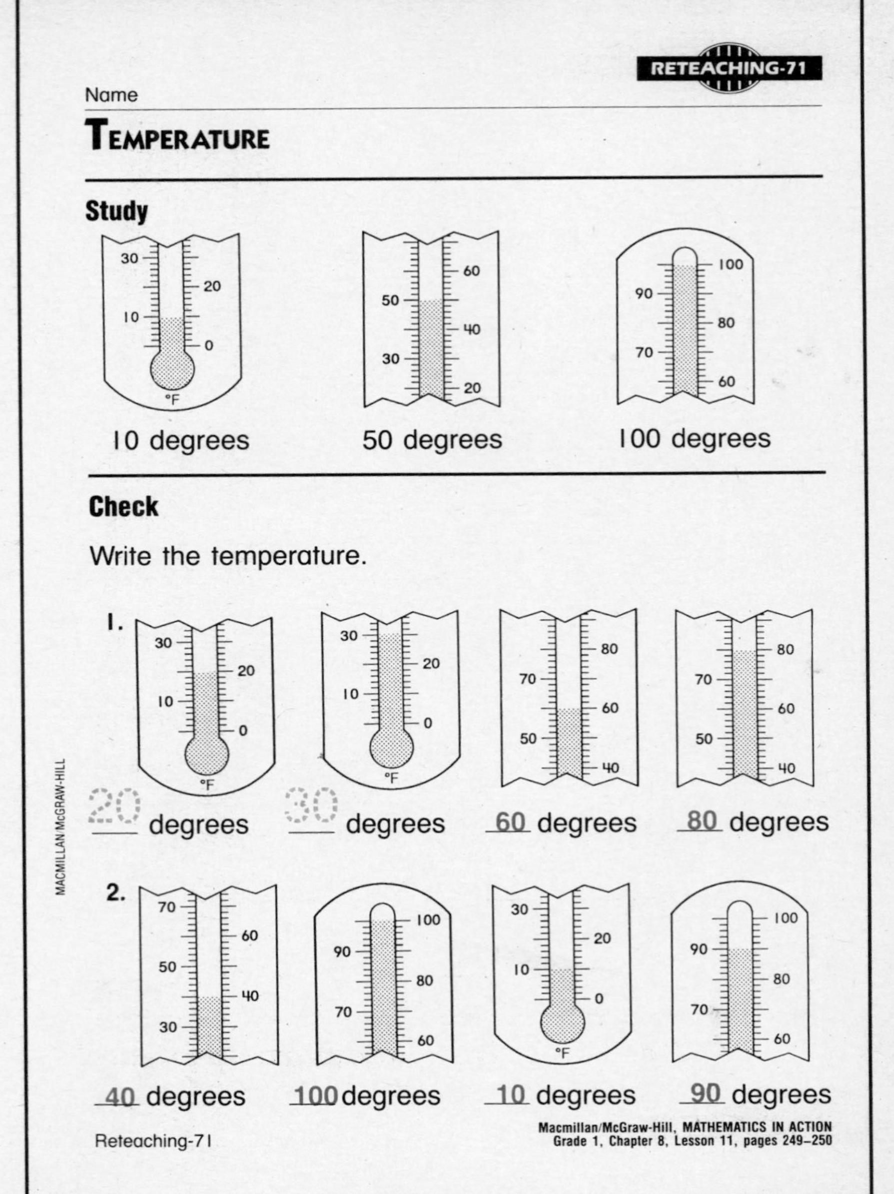

10 degrees | 50 degrees | 100 degrees

Check

Write the temperature.

1. 20 degrees | 30 degrees | 60 degrees | 80 degrees

2. 40 degrees | 100 degrees | 10 degrees | 90 degrees

Macmillan/McGraw-Hill, MATHEMATICS IN ACTION
Grade 1, Chapter 8, Lesson 11, pages 249–250

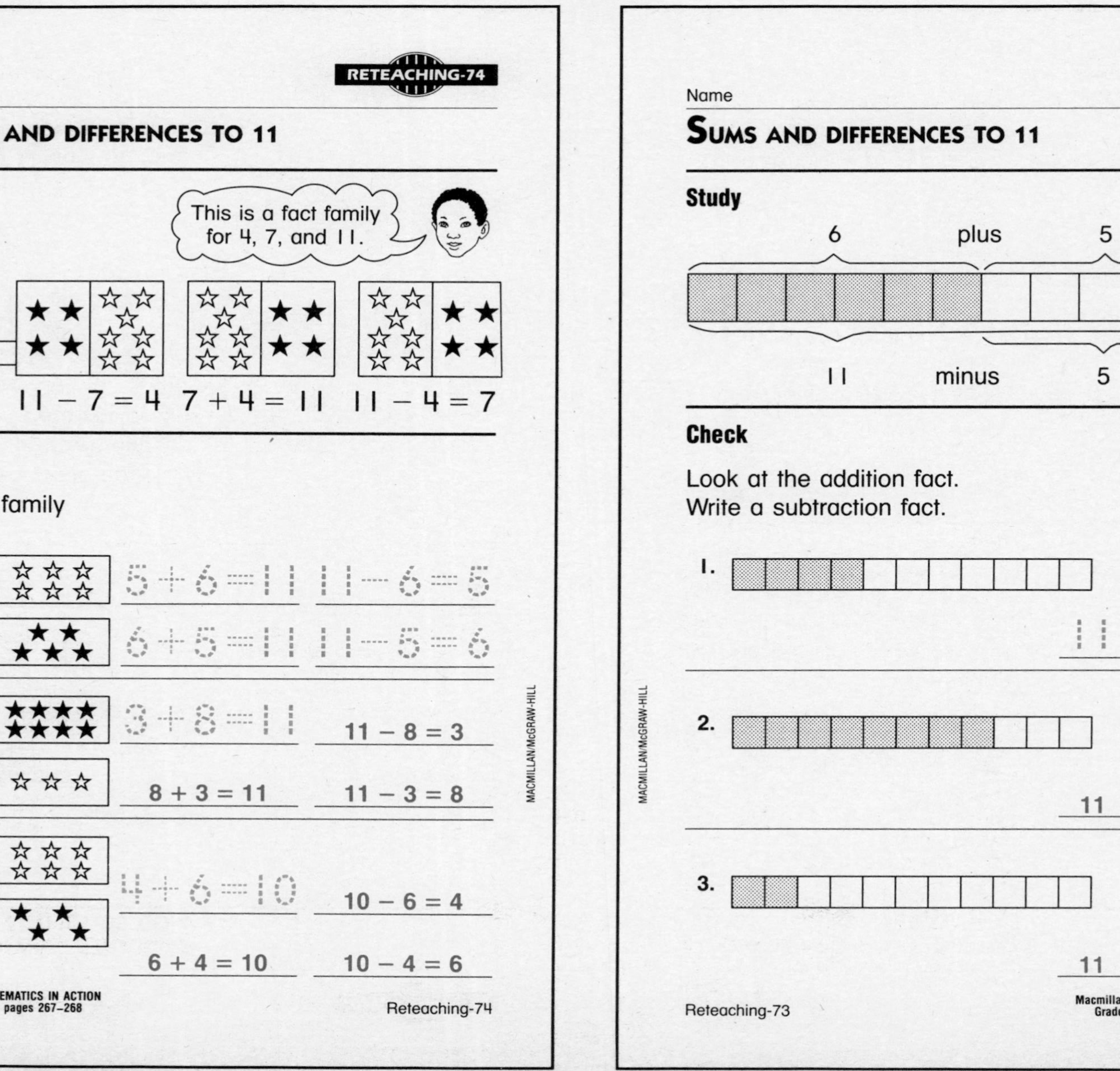

RETEACHING-74

Name

MORE SUMS AND DIFFERENCES TO 11

Study

This is a fact family for 4, 7, and 11.

4 + 7 = 11 11 − 7 = 4 7 + 4 = 11 11 − 4 = 7

Check

Write the fact family

1. 5 + 6 = 11 11 − 6 = 5
6 + 5 = 11 11 − 5 = 6

2. 3 + 8 = 11 11 − 8 = 3
8 + 3 = 11 11 − 3 = 8

3. 4 + 6 = 10 10 − 6 = 4
6 + 4 = 10 10 − 4 = 6

Macmillan/McGraw-Hill, MATHEMATICS IN ACTION
Grade 1, Chapter 9, Lesson 3, pages 267–268

RETEACHING-73

Name

SUMS AND DIFFERENCES TO 11

Study

6 plus 5 equals 11

11 minus 5 equals 6

Check

Look at the addition fact.
Write a subtraction fact.

1. 4 + 7 = 11
11 − 7 = 4

2. 8 + 3 = 11
11 − 3 = 8

3. 2 + 9 = 11
11 − 9 = 2

Macmillan/McGraw-Hill, MATHEMATICS IN ACTION
Grade 1, Chapter 9, Lesson 2, pages 265–266

RETEACHING-76

Name

PROBLEM SOLVING STRATEGY: USING SUBTRACTION TO COMPARE

Study

You can compare.
d d d d d
c c c c c [c c]
2 more chickens.

Jan saw 5 ducks.
She saw 7 chickens.
How many more ducks than chickens did she see?

You can subtract.
$7 - 5 = 2$
2 more chickens.

Jan saw 2 more chickens than ducks.

Check

Solve.

1. Bev found 9 white eggs.
   She found 6 brown eggs.
   How many more white eggs than brown eggs did she find?

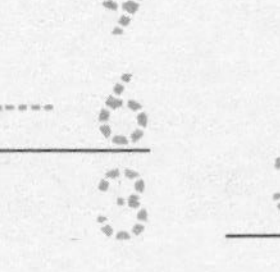

3 more

2. Jon saw 10 cows.
   He saw 5 horses.
   How many fewer horses than cows did he see? 5 fewer

3. Sonny picked 9 tomatoes.
   He picked 11 ears of corn.
   How many more ears of corn than tomatoes did he pick? 2 more

Macmillan/McGraw-Hill, MATHEMATICS IN ACTION
Grade 1, Chapter 9, Lesson 6, pages 273–274

RETEACHING-75

Name

PROBLEM SOLVING STRATEGY: CHOOSING THE OPERATION

Study

Subtract to find the part that is left.

Joe had 8 balloons.
He gave 3 balloons away.
How many does he have left?

$8 - 3 = 5$ 5 balloons

Add to combine two parts and find the whole.

Jill had 4 balloons.
She got 3 more from Joe.
How many does she have in all?

$4 + 3 = 7$ 7 balloons

Check

Ring the number sentence that solves the problem.

1. The team had 9 baseballs. They lost 3 baseballs. How many do they have left?
   $9 + 3 = 11$
   $9 - 3 = 6$ (ringed)
2. JoAnn had 8 beach balls. She gave 2 to Michael. How many does she have left?
   $8 + 2 = 10$
   $8 - 2 = 6$ (ringed)
3. Kevin had 7 tennis balls. He found 4 more balls. How many does he have in all?
   $7 + 4 = 11$ (ringed)
   $7 - 4 = 3$

Macmillan/McGraw-Hill, MATHEMATICS IN ACTION
Grade 1, Chapter 9, Lesson 4, pages 269–270

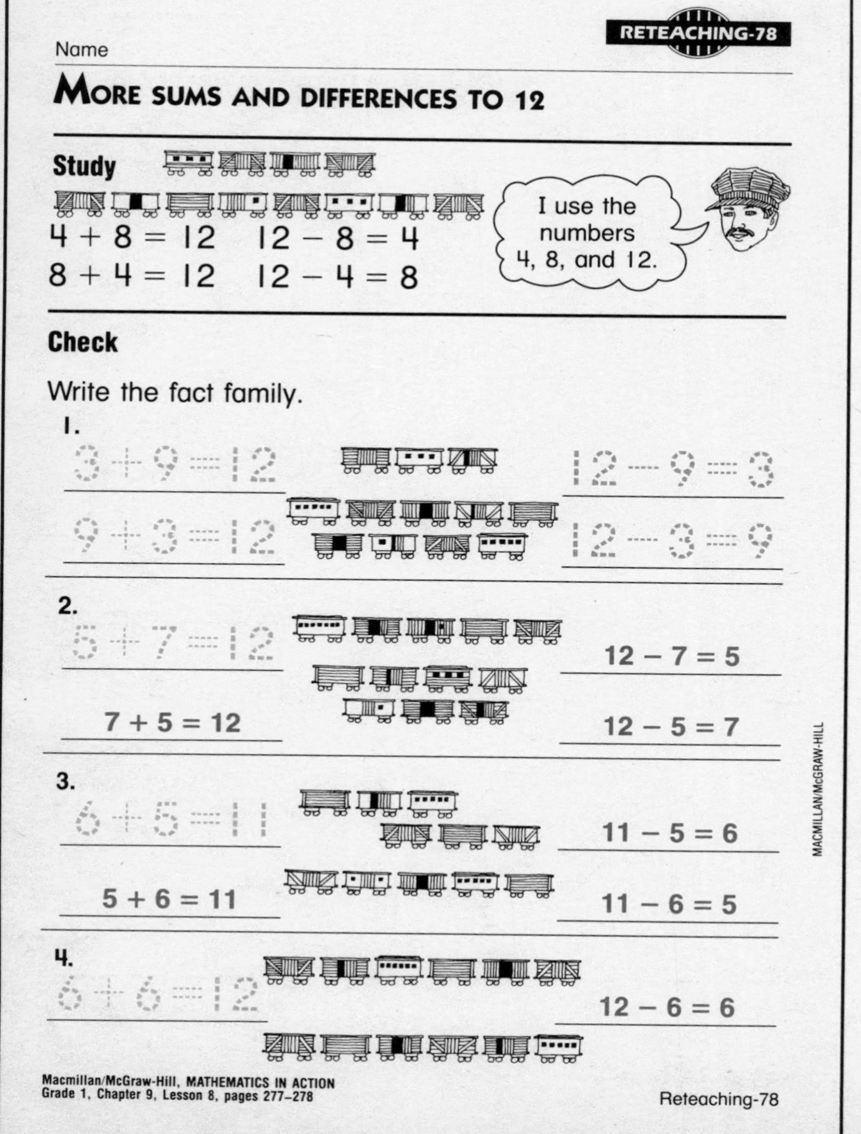

RETEACHING-78

Name

More Sums and Differences to 12

Study

4 + 8 = 12   12 − 8 = 4
8 + 4 = 12   12 − 4 = 8

Check

Write the fact family.

1. 3 + 9 = 12   12 − 9 = 3
   9 + 3 = 12   12 − 3 = 9

2. 5 + 7 = 12   12 − 7 = 5
   7 + 5 = 12   12 − 5 = 7

3. 6 + 5 = 11   11 − 5 = 6
   5 + 6 = 11   11 − 6 = 5

4. 6 + 6 = 12   12 − 6 = 6

Macmillan/McGraw-Hill, MATHEMATICS IN ACTION
Grade 1, Chapter 9, Lesson 8, pages 277–278

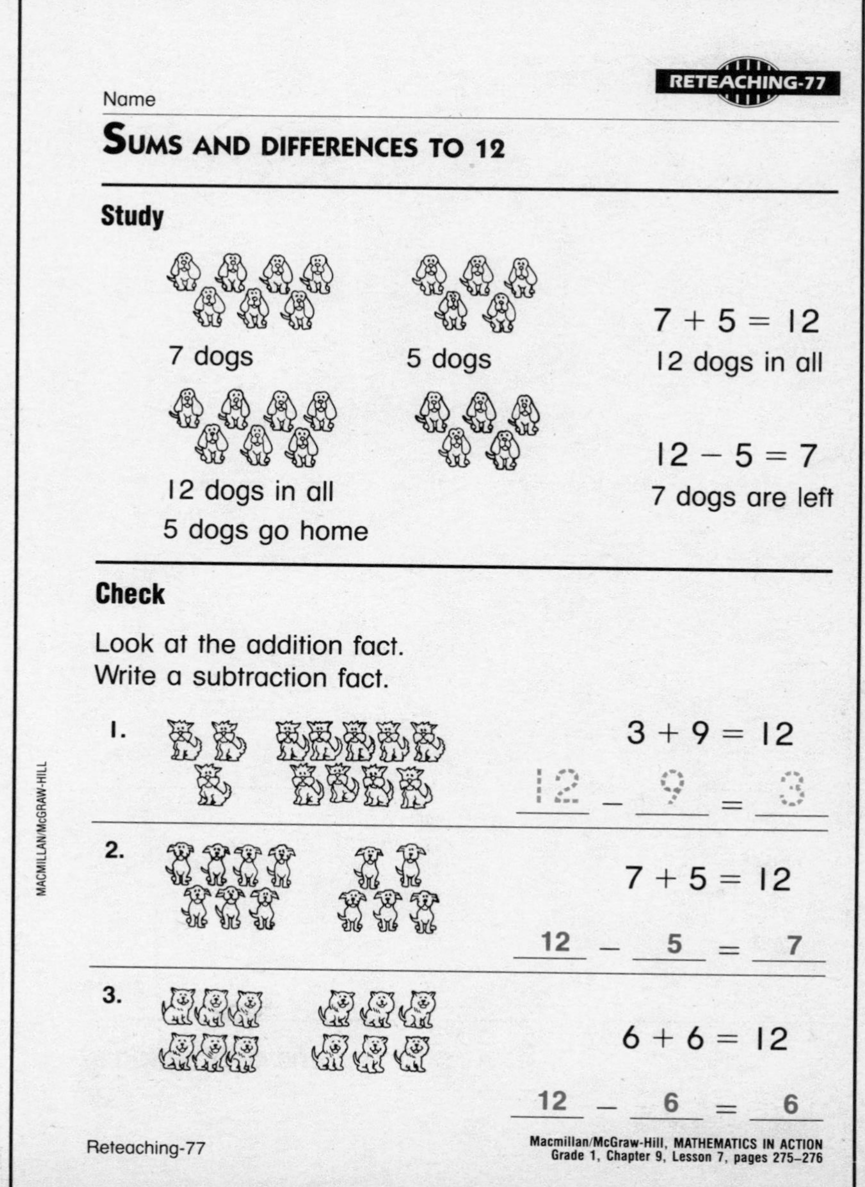

RETEACHING-77

Name

Sums and Differences to 12

Study

7 dogs   5 dogs   7 + 5 = 12
12 dogs in all

12 dogs in all
5 dogs go home   12 − 5 = 7
7 dogs are left

Check

Look at the addition fact.
Write a subtraction fact.

1. 3 + 9 = 12
   12 − 9 = 3

2. 7 + 5 = 12
   12 − 5 = 7

3. 6 + 6 = 12
   12 − 6 = 6

Macmillan/McGraw-Hill, MATHEMATICS IN ACTION
Grade 1, Chapter 9, Lesson 7, pages 275–276

RETEACHING-80

Name

THREE ADDENDS

Study

4 + 2 = 6

6 + 3 = 9

	4
	2
+	3

The sum is 9.

Check

Add. Use cubes to help.

1. 2 + 5 + 5 = 12 (2 + 5 = 7) 6 + 3 + 2 = 11 (6 + 3 = 9) 3 + 3 + 4 = 10 (3 + 3 = 6)

2. 5 + 2 + 3 = 10 8 + 1 + 3 = 12 1 + 2 + 7 = 10 3 + 4 + 3 = 10 4 + 2 + 5 = 11

3. 2 + 2 + 7 = 11 1 + 4 + 6 = 11 5 + 4 + 3 = 12 2 + 4 + 2 = 8 3 + 3 + 3 = 9

Macmillan/McGraw-Hill, MATHEMATICS IN ACTION
Grade 1, Chapter 9, Lesson 10, page 280

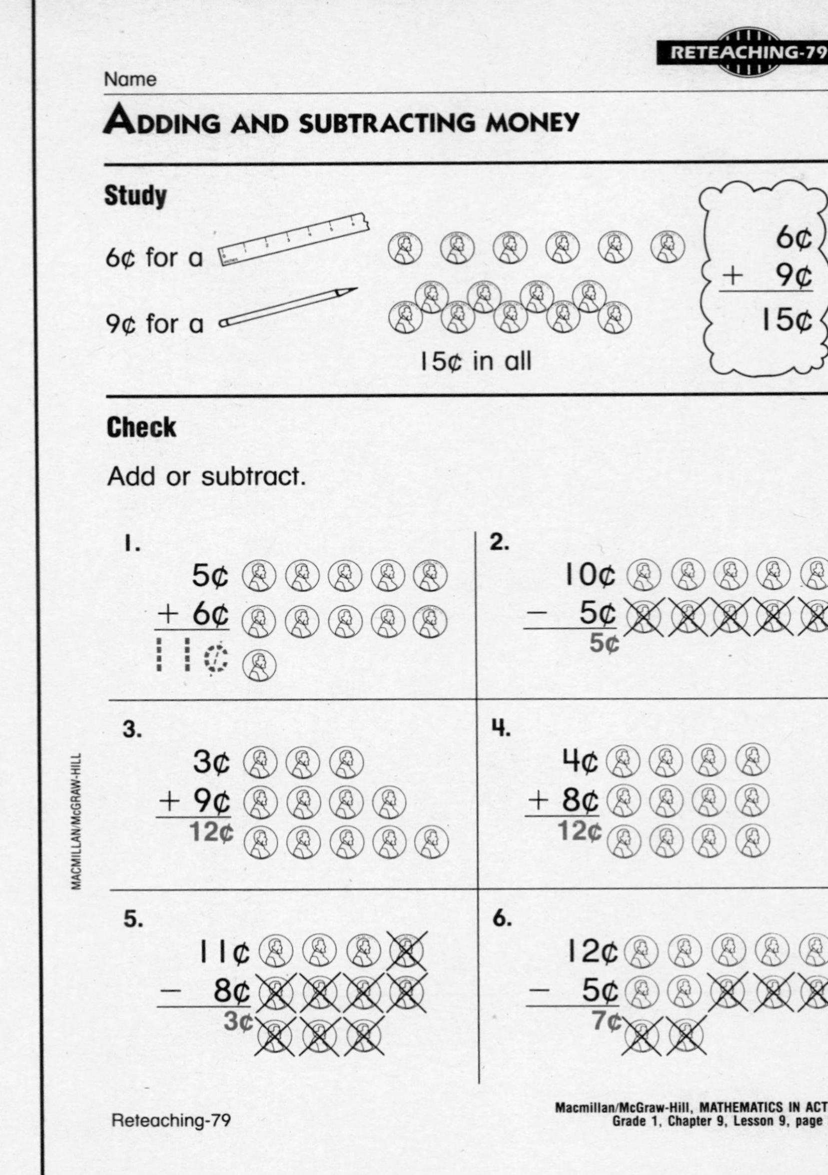

RETEACHING-79

Name

ADDING AND SUBTRACTING MONEY

Study

6¢ for a

9¢ for a

15¢ in all

6¢ + 9¢ = 15¢

Check

Add or subtract.

1. 5¢ + 6¢ = 11¢

2. 10¢ − 5¢ = 5¢

3. 3¢ + 9¢ = 12¢

4. 4¢ + 8¢ = 12¢

5. 11¢ − 8¢ = 3¢

6. 12¢ − 5¢ = 7¢

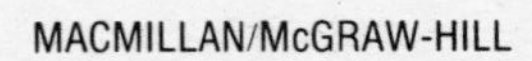

Macmillan/McGraw-Hill, MATHEMATICS IN ACTION
Grade 1, Chapter 9, Lesson 9, page 279

RETEACHING-82

Name

MORE ABOUT TIME TO THE HOUR

Study

hour hand — minute hand

4:00 or 4 o'clock

hour hand — minute hand

8:00 or 8 o'clock

Check

Ring the time.

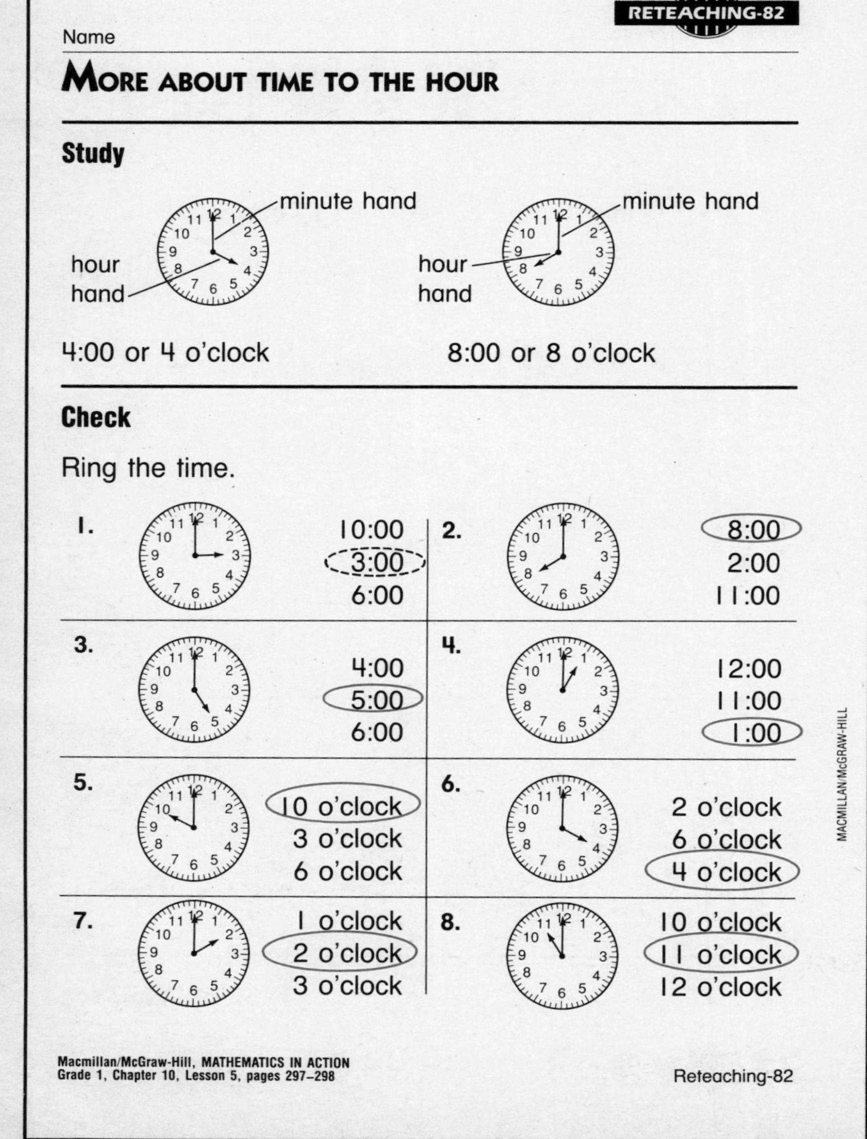

1. 10:00 / 3:00 / 6:00
2. 8:00 / 2:00 / 11:00
3. 4:00 / 5:00 / 6:00
4. 12:00 / 11:00 / 1:00
5. 10 o'clock / 3 o'clock / 6 o'clock
6. 2 o'clock / 6 o'clock / 4 o'clock
7. 1 o'clock / 2 o'clock / 3 o'clock
8. 10 o'clock / 11 o'clock / 12 o'clock

RETEACHING-81

Name

HOUR

Study

2:00 — 5:00

2 o'clock   2 o'clock   8 o'clock   5 o'clock

Check

Ring the clocks that show the same time.

1. 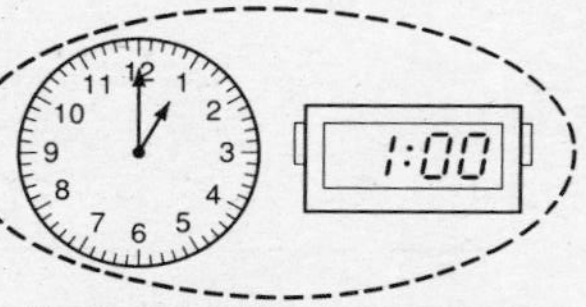 1:00
2.  3:00
3. 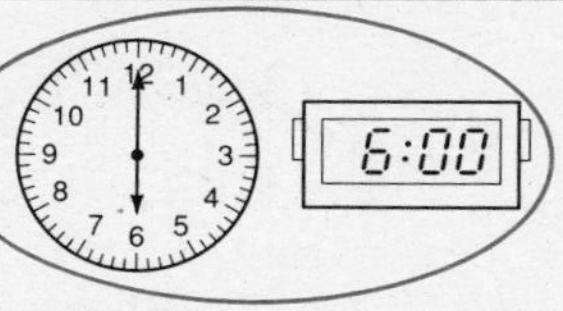 6:00
4.  9:00
5. 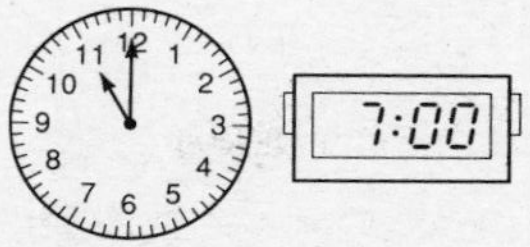 7:00
6. 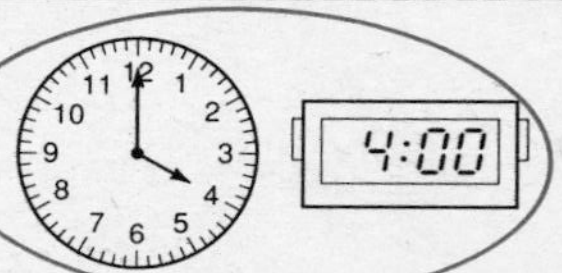 4:00

RETEACHING-84

Name

HALF HOUR

Study

An hour has 60 minutes.

It's 4 o'clock.

4:00

A half hour has 30 minutes.

It's 30 minutes after 4 o'clock.

4:30

Check

Ring the time.

(2:00) 2:30	8:00 (8:30)
10:00 (10:30)	7:00 (7:30)
(1 o'clock) 30 minutes after 1 o'clock	3 o'clock (30 minutes after 3 o'clock)
9 o'clock (30 minutes after 9 o'clock)	(5 o'clock) 30 minutes after 5 o'clock

Macmillan/McGraw-Hill, MATHEMATICS IN ACTION
Grade 1, Chapter 10, Lesson 8, pages 303–304

Reteaching-84

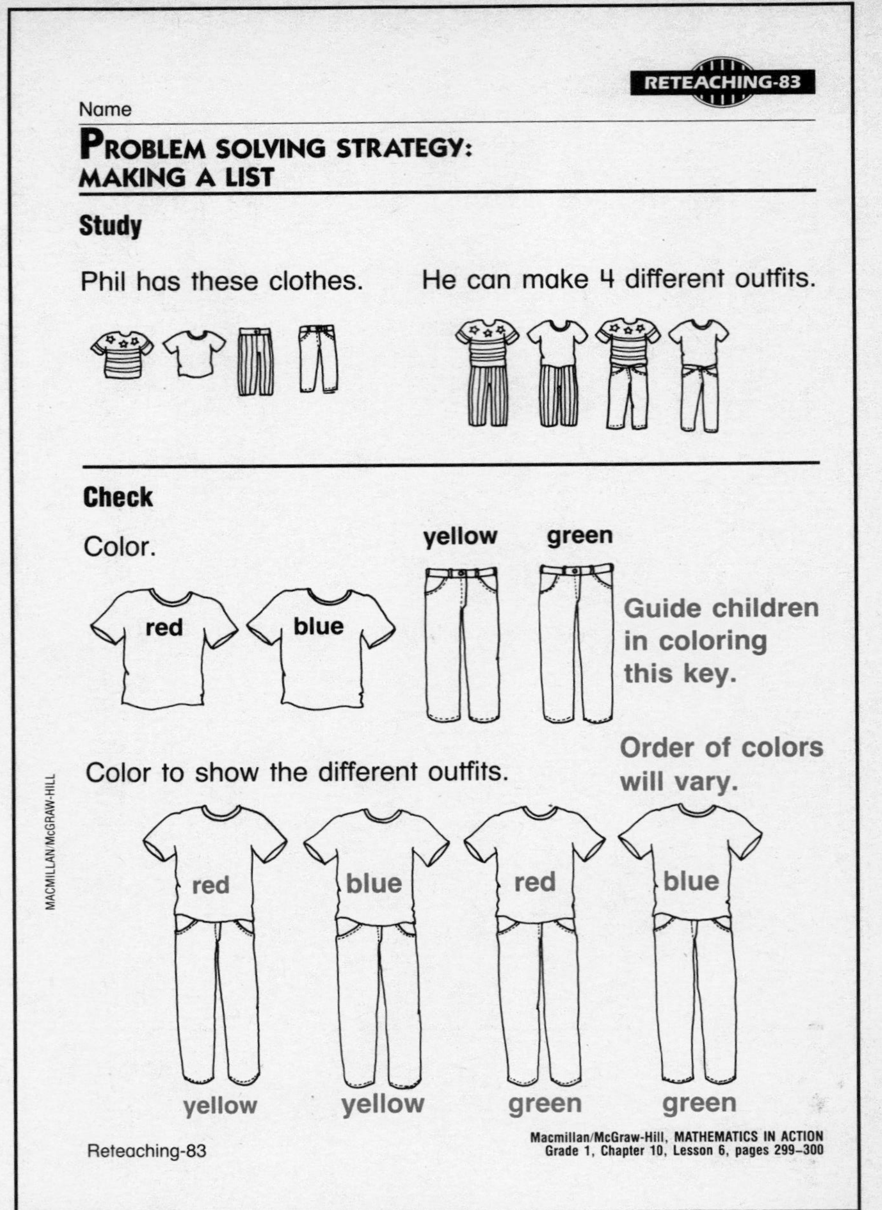
RETEACHING-83

Name

PROBLEM SOLVING STRATEGY: MAKING A LIST

Study

Phil has these clothes.

He can make 4 different outfits.

Check

Color.

red blue yellow green

Guide children in coloring this key.

Color to show the different outfits.

Order of colors will vary.

red yellow | blue yellow | red green | blue green

Reteaching-83

Macmillan/McGraw-Hill, MATHEMATICS IN ACTION
Grade 1, Chapter 10, Lesson 6, pages 299–300

RETEACHING-86

Name

DAYS OF THE WEEK

Study

MONTH	JUNE							
	Sunday	Monday	Tuesday	Wednesday	Thursday	Friday	Saturday	Days
					1	2	3	
1 week	4	5	6	7	8	9	10	
	11	12	13	14	15	16	17	
	18	19	20	21	22	23	24	
	25	26	27	28	29	30		

Check

1. Write the name of the month. June
2. Write the days of the week. Sunday

   Monday Tuesday Wednesday

   Thursday Friday Saturday
3. How many days are in a week? 7
4. How many days are in June? 30
5. How many Mondays? 4
6. How many Fridays? 5

Macmillan/McGraw-Hill, MATHEMATICS IN ACTION
Grade 1, Chapter 10, Lesson 10, pages 307–308

RETEACHING-85

Name

MORE ABOUT TIME TO THE HALF HOUR

Study

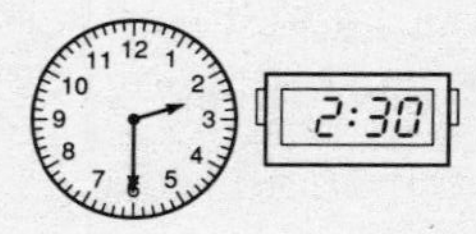

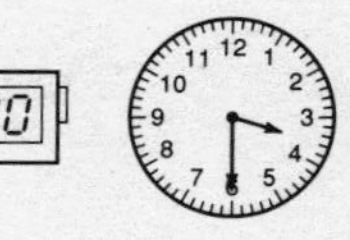

2:30 — 30 minutes after 2 o'clock

3:00 — 3 o'clock

3:30 — 30 minutes after 3 o'clock

Check

Write the time.

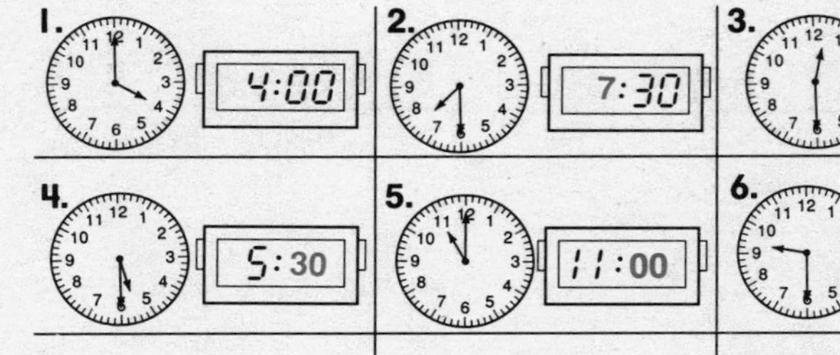

1. 4:00
2. 7:30
3. 12:30
4. 5:30
5. 11:00
6. 9:30
7. 1:30
8. 10:30
9. 4:30
10. 9:00
11. 7:00
12. 2:30

Macmillan/McGraw-Hill, MATHEMATICS IN ACTION
Grade 1, Chapter 10, Lesson 9, pages 305–306

RETEACHING-88

Name

Three-Dimensional Figures

Study

cube cone sphere cylinder box

Check

Draw lines to match.
Color to match.

Colors will vary.

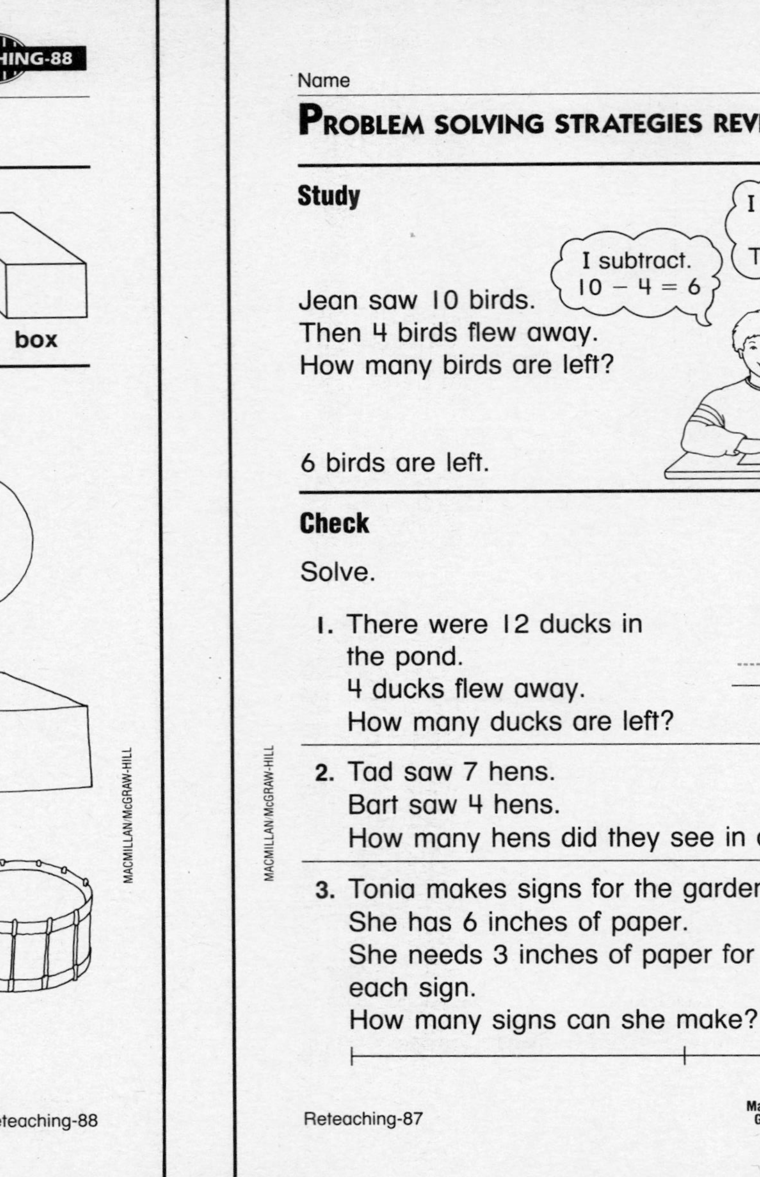

RETEACHING-87

Name

Problem Solving Strategies Review

Study

Jean saw 10 birds.
Then 4 birds flew away.
How many birds are left?

I subtract.
10 − 4 = 6

I use models.
Show 10.
Take away 4.

6 birds are left.

Check

Solve.

1. There were 12 ducks in the pond.
4 ducks flew away.
How many ducks are left?
12 − 4 = 8
8 ducks

2. Tad saw 7 hens.
Bart saw 4 hens.
How many hens did they see in all?
11 hens

3. Tonia makes signs for the garden.
She has 6 inches of paper.
She needs 3 inches of paper for each sign.
How many signs can she make?
2 signs

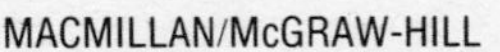

RETEACHING-90

Name

SYMMETRY

Study

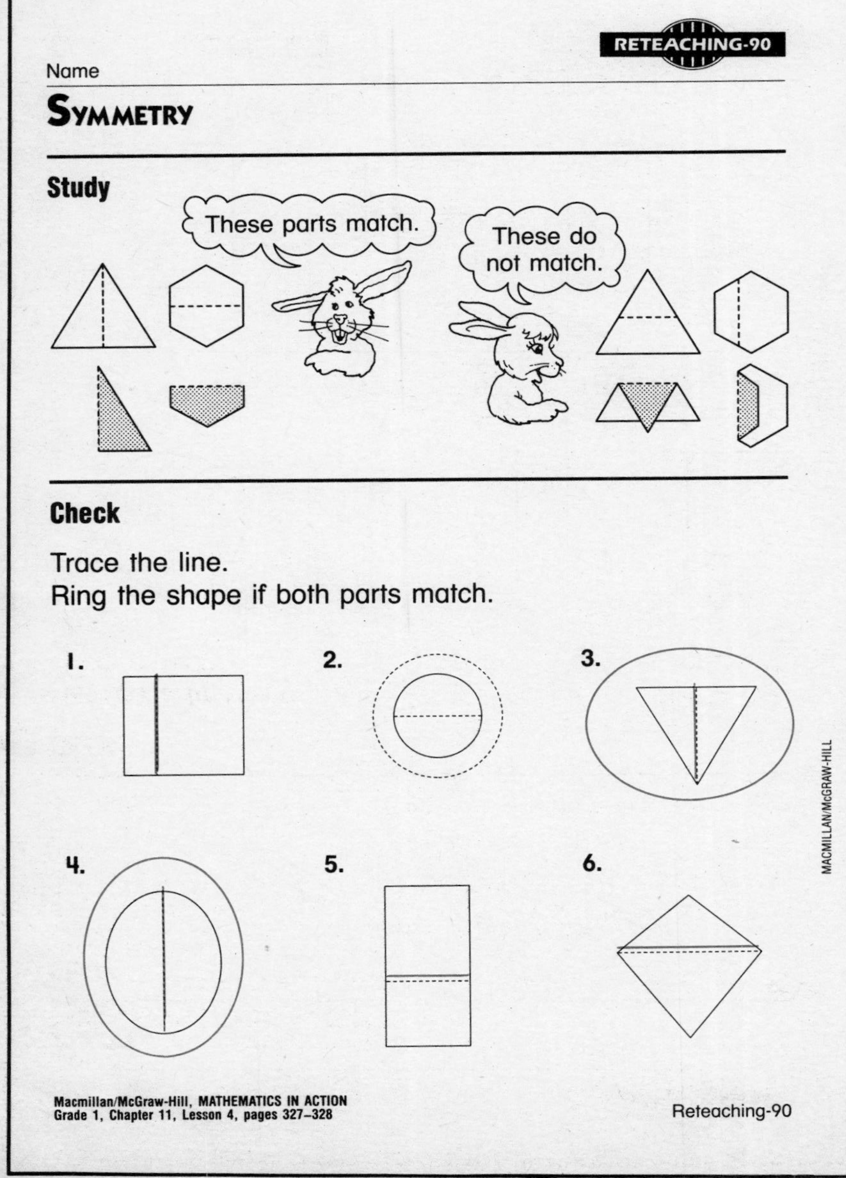

Check

Trace the line.
Ring the shape if both parts match.

1. 2. 3.

4. 5. 6.

Macmillan/McGraw-Hill, MATHEMATICS IN ACTION
Grade 1, Chapter 11, Lesson 4, pages 327–328

RETEACHING-89

Name

TWO-DIMENSIONAL FIGURES

Study

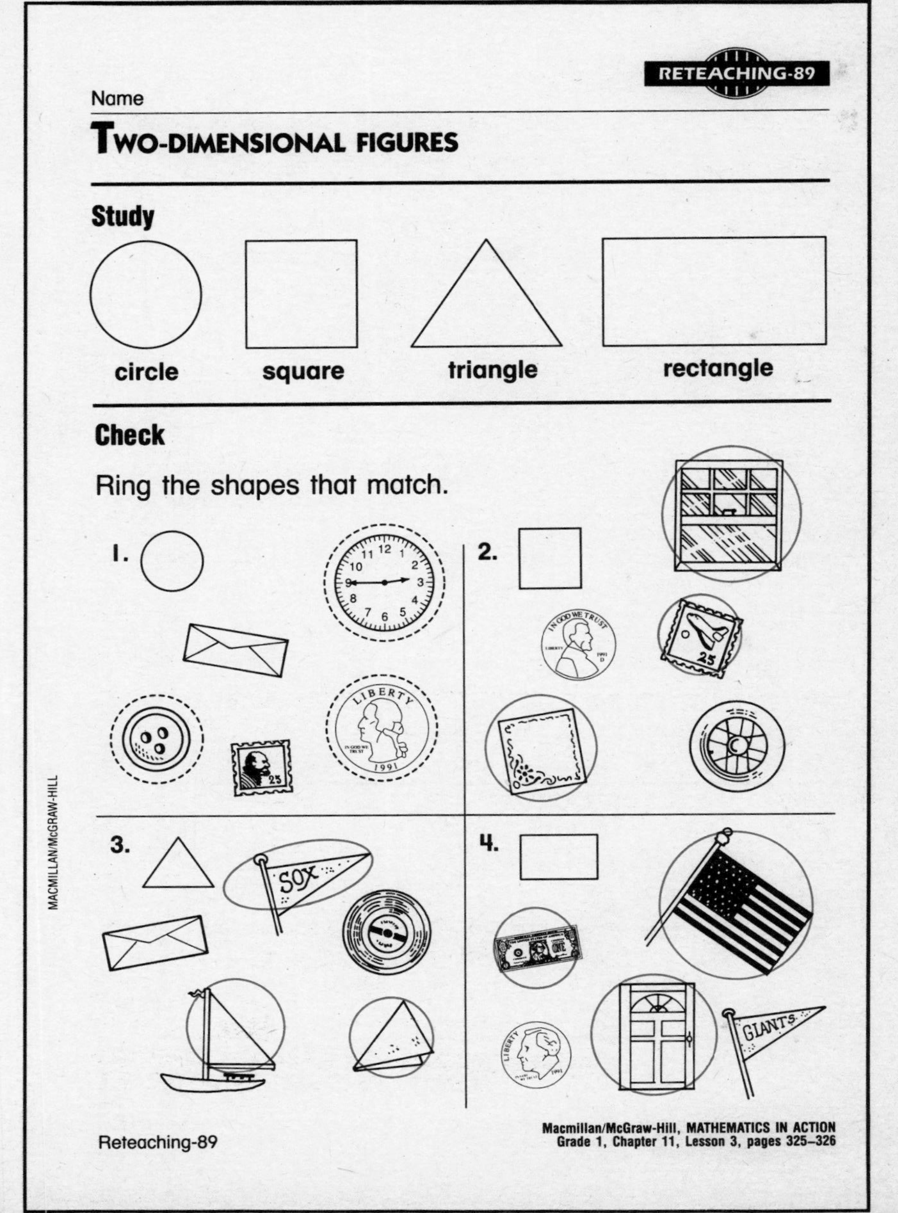

Check

Ring the shapes that match.

1. 2.

3. 4.

Macmillan/McGraw-Hill, MATHEMATICS IN ACTION
Grade 1, Chapter 11, Lesson 3, pages 325–326

RETEACHING-92

Name

Halves

Study

halves

not halves

Check

Halves? Ring *yes* or *no*.

1. (yes) no
2. yes (no)
3. (yes) no
4. (yes) no
5. (yes) no
6. yes (no)

Macmillan/McGraw-Hill, MATHEMATICS IN ACTION
Grade 1, Chapter 11, Lesson 7, pages 333–334

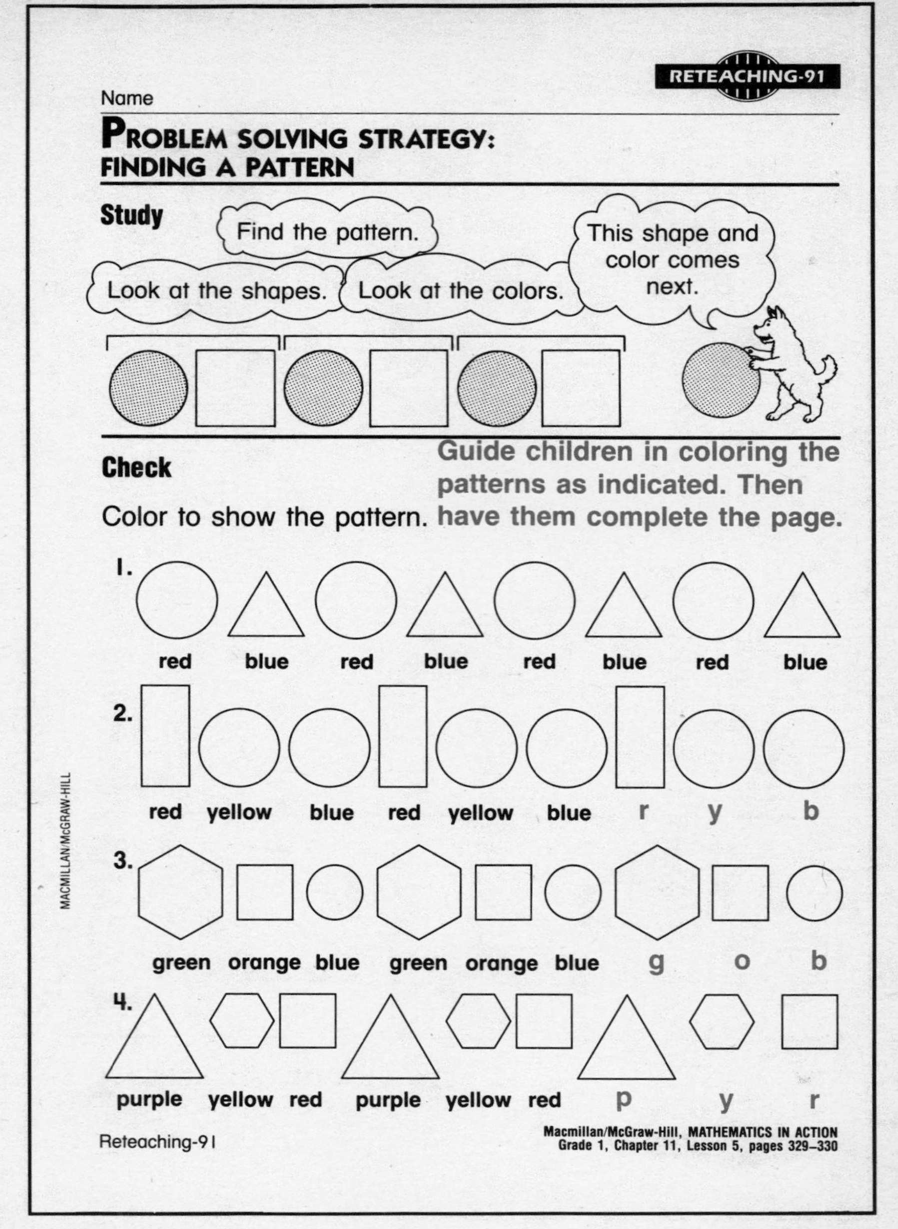

RETEACHING-91

Name

Problem Solving Strategy: Finding a Pattern

Study

Check

Color to show the pattern. **Guide children in coloring the patterns as indicated. Then have them complete the page.**

1. red blue red blue red blue red blue
2. red yellow blue red yellow blue r y b
3. green orange blue green orange blue g o b
4. purple yellow red purple yellow red p y r

Macmillan/McGraw-Hill, MATHEMATICS IN ACTION
Grade 1, Chapter 11, Lesson 5, pages 329–330

RETEACHING-94

Name

THIRDS

Study

one third

not one third

Check

Ring the shapes that show thirds.
Color $\frac{1}{3}$ of those shapes.

Coloring will vary.

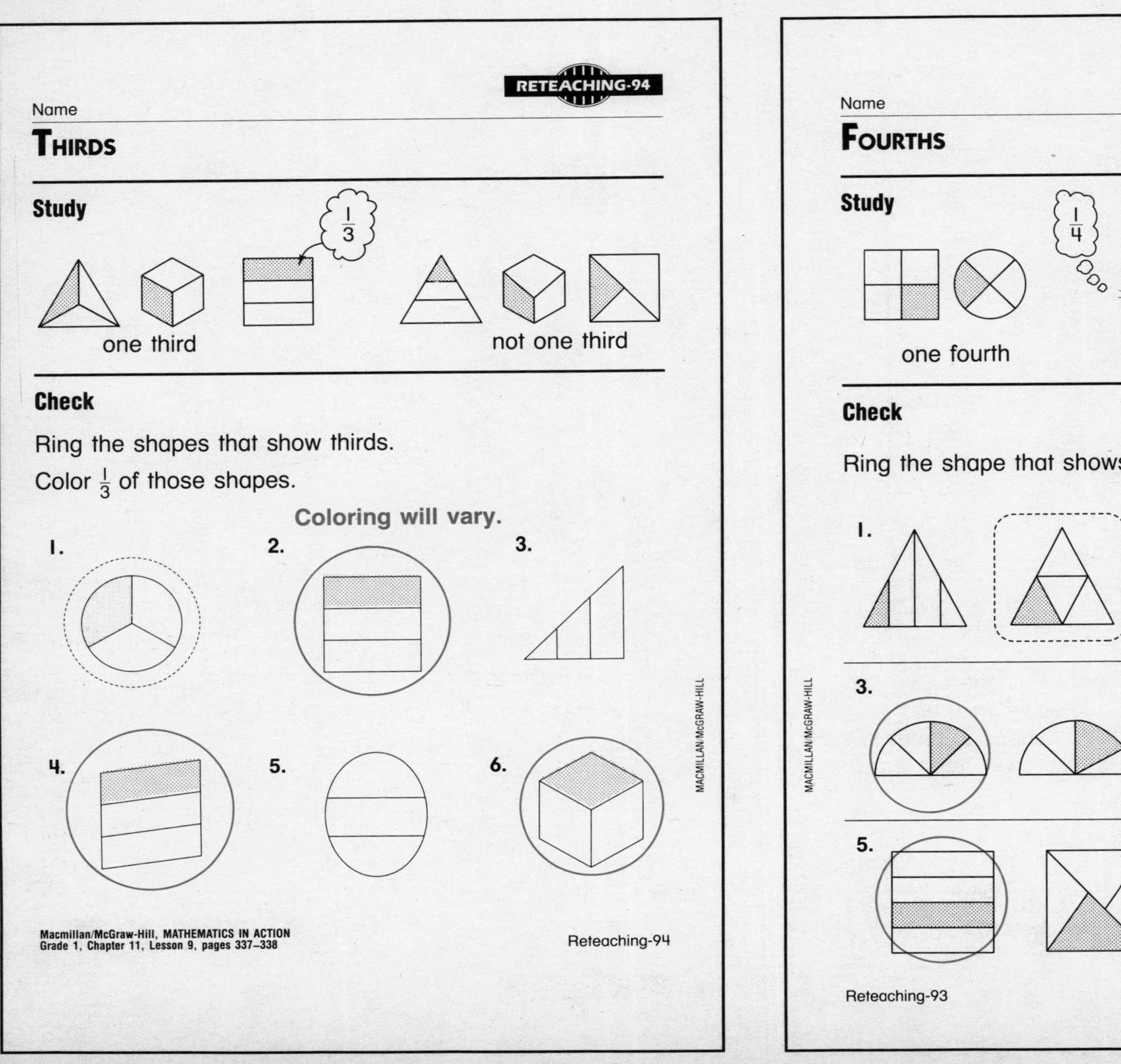

RETEACHING-93

Name

FOURTHS

Study

one fourth

not one fourth

Check

Ring the shape that shows $\frac{1}{4}$.

RETEACHING-96

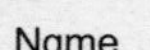

Name

SUMS AND DIFFERENCES TO 13

Study

Addition Sentence

$8 + 5 = 13$

Subtraction Sentence

$13 - 5 = 8$

Check

Complete the number sentences.

1. $6 + 7 =$ 13

2. $13 - 7 =$ 6

3. $4 + 9 =$ 13

4. $13 - 9 =$ 4

5. $5 + 8 =$ 13

6. $13 - 8 =$ 5

RETEACHING-95

Name

PROBLEM SOLVING STRATEGY: DRAWING A PICTURE

Study

The 4 children will share the sheet of paper.
How can they divide the paper into equal pieces?

Check

Draw a picture to show how the children share.

1. 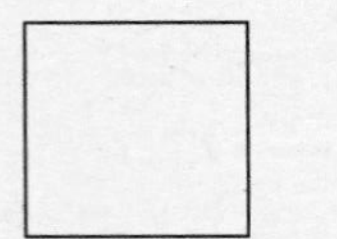 3 children share the paper.

2. 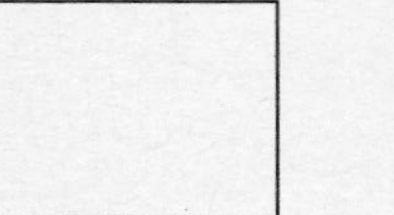 2 children share the paper.

3. 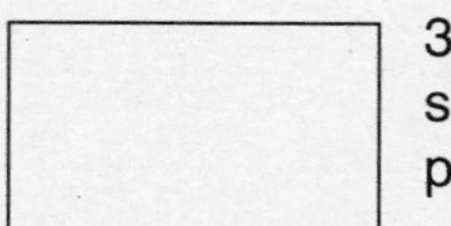 3 children share the paper.

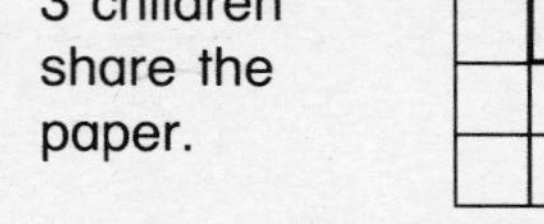

RETEACHING-98

Name

Sums and Differences to 14

Study

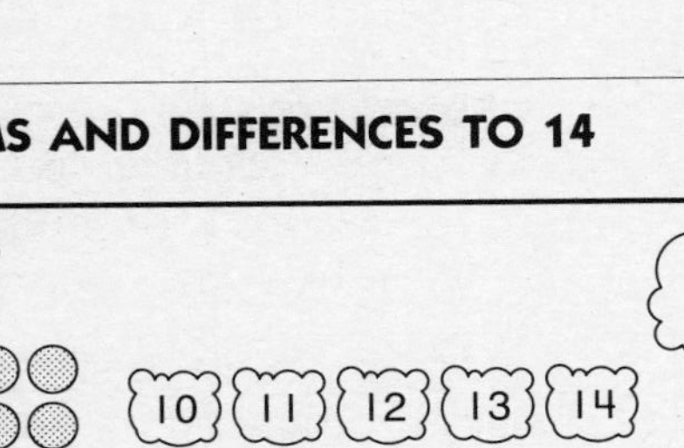

10 11 12 13 14

9 + 5 = 14

Check

Write an addition fact and a subtraction fact.

1. 8 + 6 = 14

14 − 6 = 8

2. 7 + 7 = 14

14 − 7 = 7

3. 5 + 9 = 14

14 − 9 = 5

RETEACHING-97

Name

More Sums and Differences to 13

Study

fact family

6 + 7 = 13

13 − 7 = 6

7 + 6 = 13

13 − 6 = 7

Check

Complete each fact family.

1. 5 + 8 = 13 13 − 8 = 5

8 + 5 = 13 13 − 5 = 8

2. 9 + 4 = 13 13 − 4 = 9

4 + 9 = 13 13 − 9 = 4

3. 7 + 5 = 12 12 − 5 = 7

5 + 7 = 12 12 − 7 = 5

RETEACHING-100

Name

PROBLEM SOLVING STRATEGY: CHOOSING THE OPERATION

Study

Carlos has 7 stickers.
He has 9 stamps.
How many fewer stickers than stamps does he have?

$9 - 7 = 2$ Carlos has 2 fewer stickers.

Check

Solve.

1. Anita has 8 toy bears. She has 6 toy cats. How many toy animals does Anita have? $6 + 8 = 14$ 14 toy animals
2. George has 4 toy trucks. He has 9 toy cars. How many more cars than trucks does he have? 5 more
3. Donny had 16 cookies. He gave 9 cookies to three friends. How many cookies does he have left? 7 cookies

RETEACHING-99

Name

MORE SUMS AND DIFFERENCES TO 14

Study

fact family

$5 + 9 = 14$ $9 + 5 = 14$

$14 - 9 = 5$ $14 - 5 = 9$

Check

Write the fact family.

1. $7 + 6 = 13$ $13 - 6 = 7$ $6 + 7 = 13$ $13 - 7 = 6$
2. $6 + 8 = 14$ $14 - 8 = 6$ $8 + 6 = 14$ $14 - 6 = 8$
3. $7 + 5 = 12$ $12 - 5 = 7$ $5 + 7 = 12$ $12 - 7 = 5$
4. $7 + 7 = 14$ $14 - 7 = 7$

RETEACHING-102

Name

SUMS AND DIFFERENCES TO 16, 17, AND 18

Study

9 + 7 = 16   16 − 7 = 9

9 + 8 = 17   17 − 8 = 9

9 + 9 = 18   18 − 9 = 9

Check

Add or subtract.

1. 8 + 8 = 16   16 − 8 = 8
2. 8 + 9 = 17   17 − 9 = 8
3. 16 − 9 = 7   17 − 8 = 9   16 − 8 = 8   18 − 9 = 9   16 − 7 = 9
4. 9 + 8 = 17   8 + 8 = 16   9 + 9 = 18   8 + 9 = 17   9 + 7 = 16
5. 17 − 9 = 8   7 + 9 = 16   16 − 9 = 7   9 + 8 = 17   18 − 9 = 9

RETEACHING-101

Name

SUMS AND DIFFERENCES TO 15

Study

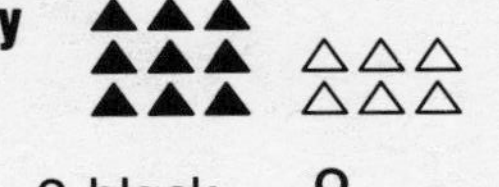

9 black   9 + 6 = 15   15 − 6 = 9
6 white

6 black   6 + 9 = 15   15 − 9 = 6
9 white

Check

Add or subtract.

1.  7 + 6 = 13   13 − 6 = 7
2. 7 + 7 = 14   14 − 7 = 7
3. 8 + 7 = 15   15 − 7 = 8
4. 4 + 9 = 13   13 − 9 = 4
5. 6 + 8 = 14   14 − 8 = 6
6. 7 + 8 = 15   15 − 8 = 7
7. 6 + 9 = 15   15 − 9 = 6
8. 9 + 5 = 14   14 − 5 = 9

Name

MONEY

Study

	7¢
+	7¢
	14¢

Check

Add or subtract.

1.

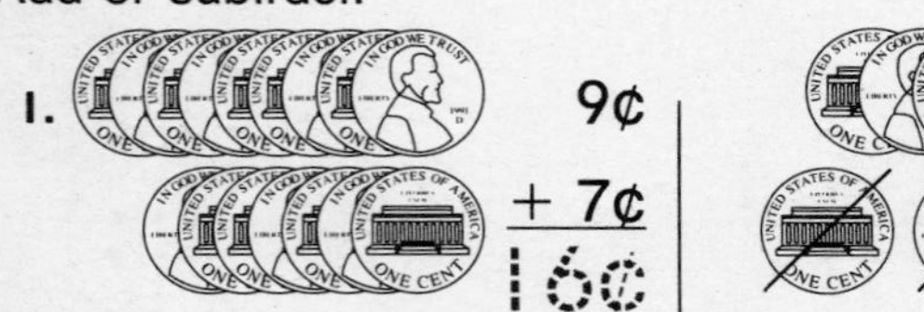

	9¢
+	7¢
	16¢

	9¢
−	3¢
	6¢

2.	8¢ + 6¢ = 14¢	5¢ + 9¢ = 14¢	6¢ + 4¢ = 10¢	9¢ + 8¢ = 17¢	8¢ + 5¢ = 13¢
3.	14¢ − 7¢ = 7¢	16¢ − 7¢ = 9¢	18¢ − 9¢ = 9¢	17¢ − 8¢ = 9¢	15¢ − 9¢ = 6¢
4.	8¢ + 7¢ = 15¢	7¢ + 6¢ = 13¢	17¢ − 9¢ = 8¢	15¢ − 8¢ = 7¢	9¢ + 4¢ = 13¢

Macmillan/McGraw-Hill, MATHEMATICS IN ACTION
Grade 1, Chapter 12, Lesson 11, page 373

RETEACHING-103

Name

ADDITION AND SUBTRACTION PATTERNS

Study

3	4	5	6	7	8	9 ← one more
+ 2	+ 2	+ 2	+ 2	+ 2	+ 2	+ 2 ← same
5	6	7	8	9	10	11 ← one more

Check

Add or subtract.

1.	13 − 9 = 4	13 − 8 = 5	13 − 7 = 6	13 − 6 = 7	13 − 5 = 8	13 − 4 = 9
2.	8 + 1 = 9	7 + 2 = 9	6 + 3 = 9	5 + 4 = 9	4 + 5 = 9	3 + 6 = 9
3.	12 − 4 = 8	12 − 5 = 7	12 − 6 = 6	12 − 7 = 5	12 − 8 = 4	12 − 9 = 3
4.	1 + 1 = 2	2 + 2 = 4	3 + 3 = 6	4 + 4 = 8	5 + 5 = 10	6 + 6 = 12

Macmillan/McGraw-Hill, MATHEMATICS IN ACTION
Grade 1, Chapter 12, Lesson 10, pages 371–372

RETEACHING-106

Name

PROBLEM SOLVING STRATEGIES REVIEW

Study

Choose a strategy.

add or subtract

15 horses are in the barn.
6 go out of the barn.
How many are left?

subtract: 15 − 6 = 9
9 horses left

Check

Solve.

1. Pam has 7 white hens.
   She has 8 red hens.
   How many hens does she have?
   15 hens
   add / subtract

2. 9 cows in the field.
   8 horses in the field.
   How many more cows than horses are there?
   1 more
   add / subtract

3. There are 6 ducks in the pond.
   There are 7 ducks in the grass.
   How many ducks in all?
   13 in all
   add / subtract

RETEACHING-105

Name

ADDING THREE NUMBERS

Study

2, 3, + 2 = 7 — Add the double first.

1, 7, + 8 = 16 — Add 1 first.

3, 3, + 7 = 13 — Add a 10 first.

Check.

Add the numbers in the arrow first.

1. 6 + 4 → 10; 6 + 4 + 2 = 12 | 4 + 3 → 6; 3 + 4 + 3 = 10 | 9 + 1 → 10; 9 + 1 + 5 = 15

2. 7 + 3 → 10; 6 + 7 + 3 = 16 | 4 + 4 → 8; 4 + 4 + 5 = 13 | 2 + 3 → 5; 7 + 2 + 3 = 12

3. 3 + 1 → 4; 8 + 3 + 1 = 12 | 5 + 5 → 10; 5 + 6 + 5 = 16 | 5 + 4 → 9; 9 + 5 + 4 = 18

RETEACHING-108

Name

MORE ADDING ONES AND TENS

Study

show the models

	tens	ones
	2	4
+	1	3

add ones

	tens	ones
	2	4
+	1	3
		7

add tens

	tens	ones
	2	4
+	1	3
	3	7

Check

Add.

1.

	tens	ones
	4	7
+	3	2
	7	9

	tens	ones
	2	2
+	1	0
	3	2

	tens	ones
	1	5
+	7	1
	8	6

	tens	ones
	3	5
+	1	1
	4	6

2.

	tens	ones
	1	8
+	2	1
	3	9

	tens	ones
	1	4
+	6	2
	7	6

	tens	ones
	3	6
+	4	3
	7	9

	tens	ones
	5	4
+	2	3
	7	7

3. 84 + 15 = 99   52 + 22 = 74   76 + 13 = 89   35 + 42 = 77   25 + 30 = 55

Macmillan/McGraw-Hill, MATHEMATICS IN ACTION
Grade 1, Chapter 13, Lesson 3, pages 391–392

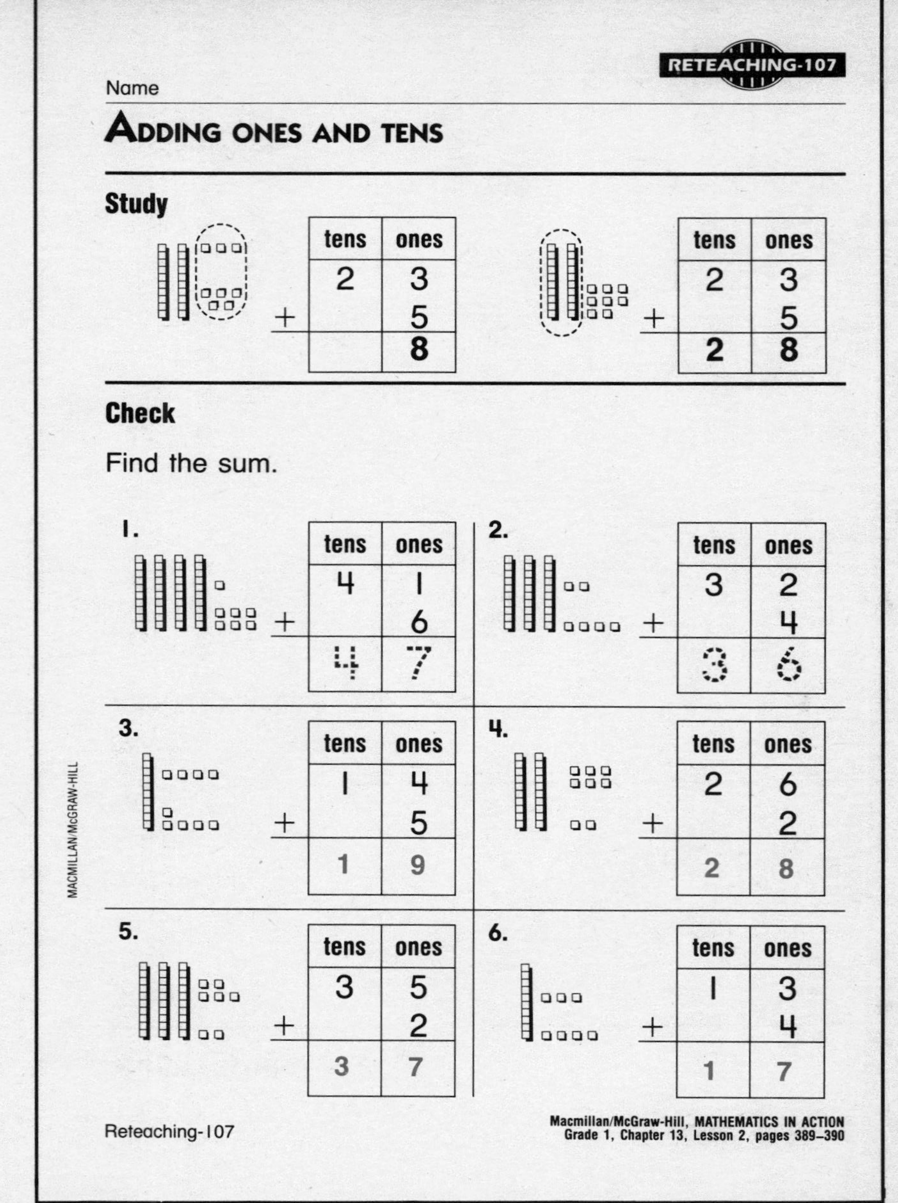

RETEACHING-107

Name

ADDING ONES AND TENS

Study

	tens	ones
	2	3
+		5
		8

	tens	ones
	2	3
+		5
	2	**8**

Check

Find the sum.

1.

	tens	ones
	4	1
+		6
	4	7

2.

	tens	ones
	3	2
+		4
	3	6

3.

	tens	ones
	1	4
+		5
	1	9

4.

	tens	ones
	2	6
+		2
	2	8

5.

	tens	ones
	3	5
+		2
	3	7

6.

	tens	ones
	1	3
+		4
	1	7

Macmillan/McGraw-Hill, MATHEMATICS IN ACTION
Grade 1, Chapter 13, Lesson 2, pages 389–390

RETEACHING-110

Name

SUBTRACTING ONES AND TENS

Study

	tens	ones
	3	8
−		5
		3

	tens	ones
	3	8
−		5
	3	3

Check

Find the difference.

1.

	tens	ones
	4	9
−		4
	4	5

2.

	tens	ones
	6	5
−		3
	6	2

3.

	tens	ones
	3	6
−		4
	3	2

4.

	tens	ones
	5	7
−		2
	5	5

5.

	tens	ones
	2	8
−		4
	2	4

6.

	tens	ones
	4	3
−		1
	4	2

Macmillan/McGraw-Hill, MATHEMATICS IN ACTION
Grade 1, Chapter 13, Lesson 6, pages 397–398

RETEACHING-109

Name

PROBLEM SOLVING STRATEGY: USING INFORMATION FROM A TABLE

Study

PLAYING GAMES

	Grade 1	Grade 2
jumping	25	21
skipping	14	23
hopping	21	16

25 grade 1 children.
21 grade 2 children.
46 children jumping.

Check

Write the numbers. Solve.

1. 14 grade 1 children skipping.

23 grade 2 children skipping.

How many children skipping? 37

2. 16 grade 2 children hopping.

23 grade 2 children skipping.

How many grade 2 children hopping and skipping? 39

3. 25 grade 1 children jumping.

21 grade 1 children hopping.

How many grade 1 children jumping and hopping? 46

Macmillan/McGraw-Hill, MATHEMATICS IN ACTION
Grade 1, Chapter 13, Lesson 4, pages 393–394

Name

RETEACHING-112

ADDING AND SUBTRACTING MONEY

Study

22¢ + 13¢ = 35¢

24¢ − 11¢ = 13¢

Check

Add or subtract.

1. 31¢ + 24¢ = 55¢

2. 35¢ − 4¢ = 31¢

3.	60¢ + 10¢ = 70¢	47¢ + 21¢ = 68¢	86¢ + 3¢ = 89¢	15¢ + 43¢ = 58¢	64¢ + 25¢ = 89¢
4.	25¢ − 11¢ = 14¢	50¢ − 20¢ = 30¢	48¢ − 32¢ = 16¢	27¢ − 5¢ = 22¢	53¢ − 41¢ = 12¢
5.	67¢ − 5¢ = 62¢	32¢ + 16¢ = 48¢	57¢ + 20¢ = 77¢	56¢ − 33¢ = 23¢	98¢ − 54¢ = 44¢

Macmillan/McGraw-Hill, MATHEMATICS IN ACTION
Grade 1, Chapter 13, Lesson 8, pages 401–402

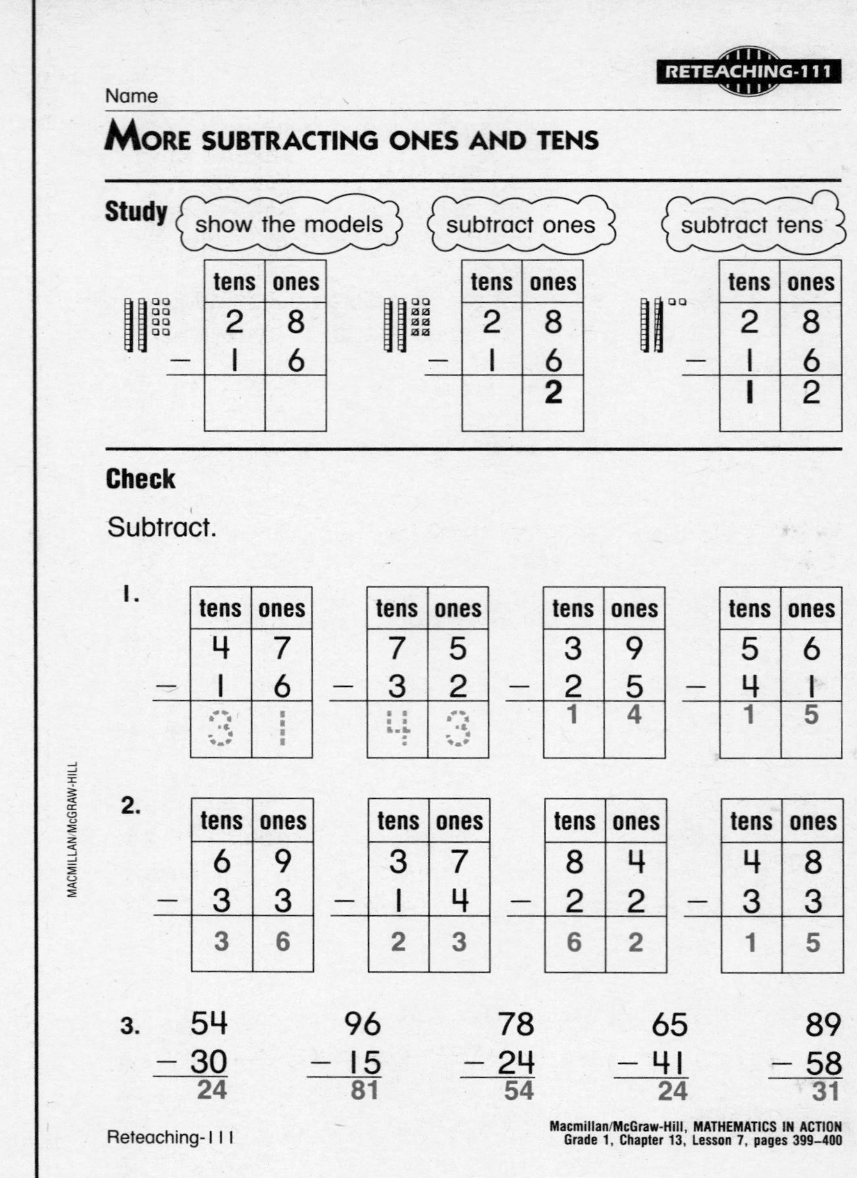

Name

RETEACHING-111

MORE SUBTRACTING ONES AND TENS

Study show the models — subtract ones — subtract tens

	tens	ones
	2	8
−	1	6
	1	2

Check

Subtract.

1. 47 − 16 = 31; 75 − 32 = 43; 39 − 25 = 14; 56 − 41 = 15

2. 69 − 33 = 36; 37 − 14 = 23; 84 − 22 = 62; 48 − 33 = 15

3. 54 − 30 = 24; 96 − 15 = 81; 78 − 24 = 54; 65 − 41 = 24; 89 − 58 = 31

Macmillan/McGraw-Hill, MATHEMATICS IN ACTION
Grade 1, Chapter 13, Lesson 7, pages 399–400

RETEACHING-113

Name

PROBLEM SOLVING STRATEGY: USING ESTIMATION

Study

About means you can estimate.

There are 31 red bicycles.
There are 28 blue bicycles.
About how many bicycles are there in all?

31 is about 30
28 is about 30
$30 + 30 = 60$

About 60 bicycles in all.

Check

Ring the closer estimate.

1. There were 12 children in the park. There were 7 adults. About how many people were in the park?
   - (20 people)
   - 30 people

2. 29 children ride the bus to school. 12 children ride the van. About how many children ride the bus and the van to school?
   - 30 children
   - (40 children)

3. 38 people saw the movie today. 19 people saw it yesterday. About how many people saw the movie during the two days?
   - 50 people
   - (60 people)

Macmillan/McGraw-Hill, MATHEMATICS IN ACTION
Grade 1, Chapter 13, Lesson 12, pages 409–410